PELICAN BOOKS
A728

A GEOGRAPHY OF THE U.S.S.R.

Born in Sydney, Australia, in 1928, John Cole has lived almost all his life in England. He was educated at Bromley Grammar School, Kent, and then read Geography at Nottingham University, where he is now a lecturer in the Geography Department. After graduating in 1950 he spent a year on a British Council Scholarship at Pavia University, Italy. During his National Service he was trained as a Russian-language interpreter at the Joint Services School for Linguists and became interested in Soviet geographical material.

His *Geography of World Affairs* is a Pelican and he has also written on the geography of Italy and Latin America. John Cole is married and has two sons.

JOHN COLE

A GEOGRAPHY OF THE U.S.S.R.

PENGUIN BOOKS
BALTIMORE · MARYLAND

Penguin Books Ltd, Harmondsworth, Middlesex, England
Penguin Books Inc., 3300 Clipper Mill Road, Baltimore 11, Md, U.S.A.
Penguin Books Australia Ltd, Ringwood, Victoria, Australia

—

First published 1967

—

Copyright © J. P. Cole, 1967

—

Made and printed in Great Britain
by Cox & Wyman Ltd,
London, Reading and Fakenham
Set in Monotype Times

To the memory of Jan Kowalewski, born
in Lodz 1892, died in London 1965

CONTENTS

Contents

Contents

Russia is often mentioned as being great, but let the House consider for a moment what Russia is. The emperor of Russia rules over an extent of territory in Europe greater than all the rest of Europe put together, and this was joined by a tract of country by dominions in Asia, three times as great as the possessions of Russia in Europe.

Lord Dudley Stuart, 19 February 1836 (from *History in Hansard, 1803–1900*, compiled by Stephen King-Hall and Ann Dewar, pp. 67–8)

A French journalist . . . who has recently been in Siberia wrote . . . : 'Siberia already exerts pressure on the fate of the world with its production of steel and coal. In 30–40 years, at the beginning of the twenty-first century, with a huge effort, it could top the list of world producers . . . Anyone who does not know about Siberia does not know about the future of our planet . . .' We can say with certainty that the things the author is writing about will happen much sooner than he says.

Pravda, 6 October 1963

What is the character of the population over which Russia rules? It is a population completely devoted to the Sovereign who sways the sceptre, whom they view and reverence as the chief of their race and the head of their Church, and to whom they are bound by the triple tie of race, language, and fate. No property is held in Russia that is not subject to the disposition of the autocrat. So supreme is his power that one stroke of his pen can banish to distant countries any of his subjects, no matter what the rank, birth or property of that subject might be. There is no career open to any man but one connected with the state. No matter what his riches, if he is not in the service of the state he is as nothing. The very clergy are known to wear military orders. That organization disposed them to look for acquisitions and aggrandizement. But one enthusiasm pervades the entire population – that of advancing the pre-eminence of their country and its superior power over the rest of the world . . . .

Lord Dudley Stuart, 19 February 1836

History gave a great responsibility to our Party and to the Soviet people. We are resolving tasks of enormous magnitude. For almost half of a century our country has been setting new courses of social development. Each success of ours in constructing Communism is a contribution of the Soviet people to the general revolutionary struggle of the workers of every country for peace, freedom and a happy future for humanity.

Pravda, 7 November 1964

PREFACE

THIS book is about regional geography, since it is concerned with a given part of the Earth's surface rather than about a specific topic, such as climate or the distribution of industry. In its simplest form, regional geography has tended to be an inventory of information about places, a list of things such as prominent physical features, 'capes and bays', or towns. Much importance was often attached to learning their names as an exercise for its own sake. From this there has been a move in regional geography towards the study of relationships between different distributions on chosen parts of the Earth's surface. For example, it is obvious to anyone that much of the best arable land in the U.S.S.R. is found in the relatively limited belt of blackearth or associated soils. Often, however, one can detect, or one suspects, a more complicated correlation in a given area than the pairwise one suggested above. For example, the distribution of arable land is related only partly to the distribution of good soil, for it is also affected by the length of growing season and by the amount of precipitation. Further, the distribution of arable land also depends on whether or not people have needed to use potential farm land in a given area in the past.

Such correlations may be detected intuitively through ideas based on what has been observed in the field or on what ought to happen. They may also be detected from a visual impression conveyed by information suitably displayed on maps. If, however, one has a great deal of information and is looking for the relationship between many different distributions in area, then it is possible, using relatively simple techniques derived from mathematics and statistics, to sort out the pairwise relationships. It is even possible, using more complicated techniques, to have a fairly precise assessment of multiple relationships. In the long run these techniques, while involving a large amount of calculation, are superior to the intuitive and/or visual approach to regional geography because, if one depends on one's own visual impressions, then it may be easy to see strong correlations, but one may miss seeing less obvious correlations and at the same time one may 'invent' relationships that do not really exist, simply because they are

expected. Part of Chapter 12 is devoted to a brief study of the
results of one of the more simple statistical correlation procedures.
It should be pointed out, of course, that the more sophisticated
statistical techniques also have drawbacks and that factor analysis,
one of the most promising new tools of the geographer, is both
complicated and mathematically suspect. Nevertheless, in any
given region of more than very small extent, complex relationships
do exist in the real world. At the moment, regional geography
either tends to make superficial comments about relationships in
area or, in using new methods, tends to come to very complex
conclusions.

It is obviously important, however, that both geographers and
non-geographers should be informed about the geography of the
U.S.S.R., given the great importance of this country in the world
today. Most of this book, therefore, has been made reasonably
straightforward and conventional. Before embarking on the
subject the reader is asked to think in somewhat more abstract
terms than usual, along the following lines. In reality, the U.S.S.R.
is something like a fragment of the shell of a very large round egg
(see Figure 1a). Given that the effective space occupied by the
U.S.S.R. extends a great distance across the Earth's surface, yet
extends only a few miles above and below, if we exclude the outer
space in which satellites operate, then it has a great extent in two
directions but only a negligible extent in the third, the vertical.
Although part of the surface of a sphere (and this should never be
forgotten), the U.S.S.R. can be forced on to a flat surface and
represented as a conventional map without excessive loss of
accuracy during the operation of projecting it (see Figures 1b, 1c).

The space occupied by the U.S.S.R. on the Earth's surface,
whether represented on a globe or as a flat map, may be considered
to be an infinite *set* of points, an arena, as it were, on which an
enormous number of objects of various shapes and sizes are
distributed. Some of the objects are physical (mountains, rivers,
trees), some are human or man-made (railways, factories, human
beings themselves). Some of the objects are fixed or move over the
surface gradually. Others move constantly or from time to time.
Although these objects are really three-dimensional themselves,
they are often considered conventionally by geographers to be
sets of surfaces (areas), lines or points occupying various portions

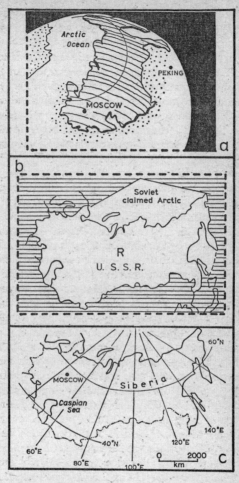

1. Ways of looking at the U.S.S.R. a. The U.S.S.R. as it actually looks from about 4,000 miles vertically above Moscow. b. and c. 'Noise' in the form of indicators of location, scale and orientation often interferes with the visual interpretation of symbols representing objects actually in the space concerned.

of the whole surface, the U.S.S.R. itself. Examples are given in Figure 2.

It is the relationship of these various sets of surfaces, lines and points to the total area of the U.S.S.R. and to one another that is of particular interest in regional geography. Out of apparent chaos, causal relationships can be established, and it may even be possible to predict with some confidence, though not of course with complete certainty, what relationships may be expected in the future. In general, the direction of influence is from physical to human, but man, especially since the Industrial Revolution, has made an enormous impact on some parts of the physical world, particularly soils and vegetation.

In preparing a regional geography of the U.S.S.R., or any other large region, one would, ideally, array one at a time something like thirty distinct distributions. Each would show a relevant distribution (or variable) such as altitude, annual rainfall, annual temperature, soil types, population, sources of energy, railways. These distribution maps would then be combined and examined in stages, two at a time, then three at a time, four at a time and so on up to thirty. Unfortunately, this would involve an impossibly large amount of work, since there are 2^{30}, or about 1,000,000,000, possible ways that thirty different distribution maps of the U.S.S.R. could be combined. One is therefore forced to produce, for a regional geography, a pathetic compromise, a selection of maps combining in a somewhat arbitrary way several different sets of dots, lines and/or areas. The visual picture achieved is further distorted by 'noise' (see Figure 1 c) in the form of place-names and other distractions such as parallels and meridians needed to locate places.

The purpose of this book is first of all to describe where some of the main distributions are on the surface of the U.S.S.R. Secondly, some obvious relationships will be suggested in an intuitive, subjective way. Thirdly, an example will be given (in Chapter 12) of a probe, limited in scope by, among other things, the inadequacy of Soviet data, aimed at detecting relationships statistically.

During the Communist period in the U.S.S.R. much of the work of Soviet geographers has been directed towards collecting and

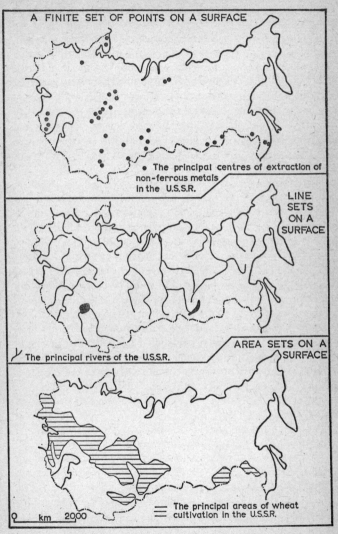

A FINITE SET OF POINTS ON A SURFACE

● The principal centres of extraction of non-ferrous metals in the U.S.S.R.

LINE SETS ON A SURFACE

The principal rivers of the U.S.S.R.

AREA SETS ON A SURFACE

≡ The principal areas of wheat cultivation in the U.S.S.R.

0   km   2000

2. Points, lines and surfaces on the U.S.S.R.

recording data about different parts of the country, and work in the field has obviously played a prominent part. Throughout the Communist period, but more particularly in the last decade or so, Soviet geographers have also assisted in planning, by deciding which resources should be exploited, what use should be made of the land, and what set of regions would be the best as a spatial framework for planning. In this respect the role of the geographer is a practical one and, in a small way so far, geographers are beginning to make the geography of the future. In the view of the author, however, Soviet geographers have not as yet come up with any brilliant or sophisticated ideas about the spatial location of economic activities.

At the moment, the nature and scope of geography is being widely debated in the U.S.S.R. Up to now there has been a tendency for Soviet geographers to recognize a fundamental division between physical and human geography, physical geography being amenable to explanation in terms of physical laws, human activities in terms of the Marxist–Leninist interpretation of history. References to this controversy are given in the Bibliography.

For a brief general geography of the U.S.S.R. such as this, there are at least three possible approaches that could lead to a reasonably complete study: an approach through the physical background, one through the historical background or one through economic planning. In this book the latter approach has been adopted. The reason for this emphasis is that for almost fifty years now, the U.S.S.R. has been using centralized planning as a means of finding the most sensible ways of locating productive activities. This makes it different from any other country in the world. In contrast, the same physical laws obviously affect the physical background here as anywhere else, while an approach through history tends to introduce many interesting if controversial themes of little or no relevance to present features and problems.

This book is intended mainly for non-geographers, for whom it should provide an ample geographical background to the U.S.S.R. Additional reading material has been suggested at appropriate stages. It is hoped that the book will also serve as a useful introduction to the geography of the U.S.S.R. for geographers. The order in which the topics have been arranged is one of many possible ones.[1] It is not meant to be rigid and the reader interested only in certain aspects may follow these in an appropriate sequence.

A great deal of material is now available on the geography of the U.S.S.R. There were some useful publications in the 1930s, one of them the magnificent *Bol'shoy sovetskiy atlas mira*. A considerable amount of quantitative data was made available in this period. During the Second World War and up to the early 1950s some atlases and mediocre textbooks were produced, but very little quantitative data. Since 1955, statistical publications have come out fairly regularly and although it is tantalizing to find the omission of some key sets of figures, such as data for non-ferrous metals, much material of use to the geographer can now be obtained. A growing number of textbooks and atlases have also been appearing recently. The textbooks on economic geography, unfortunately, are largely inventories of places and products. Soviet geographers themselves are clearly reluctant to go too deeply into spatial relationships by using quantitative data and methods. In addition, there are now many books in English on the geography of the U.S.S.R., while from 1960 it has been possible, using the excellent service provided by *Soviet Geography*, *Review and Translation*, to have in English, translated in full, many important Soviet journal papers. In short, there is much less excuse now than in the early 1950s to claim ignorance of the geography of the U.S.S.R. on the grounds that there is nothing on it available here.

In this book reference has been made in particular to a recent Soviet atlas, a textbook on the geography of the U.S.S.R., and a 1963 Statistical Year Book, while *Pravda* has been followed up to the time of completion for the latest developments. These and other sources are noted in the Bibliography at the end of the book. The idea of using Soviet statistical material still causes considerable apprehension in many people in the West interested in the U.S.S.R., and certainly the indiscriminate use of Soviet quantitative data is not to be recommended. It is pointless to discuss this controversial matter here, but it may be noted that while some sets of figures showing the relative rate of growth of the economy are quite absurd, many of those that show actual quantities of people, of commodities produced, of goods carried on the railways

1. It is possible to arrange no more than ten topics in over three million different ways (10 factorial or 10 (!)).

and so on, are reasonably correct. If they were not, it would be extremely inconvenient for people in the U.S.S.R. compiling and using the various statistical publications. Even the figures for agriculture, which have come in for criticism not only in the West, but also in the U.S.S.R. itself, may be expected to show general year-to-year fluctuations in output and yields. Soviet publications include, for example, very unflattering figures for livestock numbers in the 1930s and early 1950s, and for the depressingly bad grain harvest of 1963. Where for security reasons figures are considered secret, they are simply not published. Using Soviet quantitative data still has many pitfalls, however, because definitions are often being changed and regional boundaries altered.[1] In this book, where possible, figures for 1963 have been used, and sometimes for 1964 or 1965, but at times it has been necessary to draw on earlier figures giving a more complete picture.

Throughout this book metric measures have been used. Conversions will be found at the beginning of the book. A standard system of transliteration has been used for place-names (see Appendix 1) but the English version of certain commonly used names (such as Moscow instead of Moskva) has been used. The soft sign has been used in place-names but can be ignored by the reader. Many place-names were changed in Russia after the Communists came to power in 1917. The pre-Communist names of these have not usually been noted. On the other hand an attempt has been made to be up to date with names that have been changed back (or in some cases given a third name) since the late 1950s. These are listed in Appendix 2.

The author wishes to thank Mr D. M. Shapiro, of the University of Essex, for his useful advice and helpful cooperation as editor of the Penguin series on the U.S.S.R. He is grateful, also, to Col J. Kowalewski for assistance in obtaining material on certain topics, and to Prof. C. W. J. Granger, of the Department of Mathematics, Nottingham University, for compiling the computer programme used to process data in Chapter 12 and for advice on statistical matters in general. The maps were drawn by Miss Glenda Scholtz and Miss Carol Chambers.

1. See A. Nove, *The Soviet Economy*, Allen and Unwin, 1961, pp. 307–14, for a discussion.

CONVERSIONS

DISTANCE		
	1 cm. = 0·4 ins.	1 in. = 2·54 cm.
	1 m. = 3·3 ft	1 ft = 0·3 m.
	1 km. = 0·62 miles	1 mile = 1·61 km.

AREA

1 hectare = 2·47 acres
1 sq. km. = 0·386 sq. miles
1 acre = 0·4 hectares
1 sq. mile = 2·59 sq. km.

WEIGHT

1 kilogram = 2·2 lbs.
1 long (English) ton = 1,016 kilograms
1 metric ton = 1,000 kilograms
1 short (U.S.) ton = 907 kilograms
1 long ton = 2,240 lbs.
1 metric ton = 2,205 lbs.
1 short ton = 2,000 lbs.

TEMPERATURE

0° C = 32°F
10°C = 50°F
20°C = 68°F
30°C = 86°F

Conversion to the nearest degree Fahrenheit

°C	°F	°C	°F	°C	°F	°C	°F	°C	°F
0	32	7	45	14	57	21	70	28	82
1	34	8	46	15	59	22	72	29	84
2	36	9	48	16	61	23	73	30	86
3	37	10	50	17	63	24	75		
4	39	11	52	18	64	25	77		
5	41	12	54	19	66	26	79		
6	43	13	55	20	68	27	81		

PRECIPITATION *Centimetres to the nearest half-inch*

cm.	ins.	cm.	ins.	cm.	ins.	cm.	ins.
250	98½	160	63	85	33½	45	17¼
240	94½	150	59	80	31½	40	16
230	90½	140	55	75	29½	35	14
220	86½	130	51	70	27½	30	12
210	82½	120	47	65	25½	25	10
200	79	110	43½	60	23½	20	8
190	75	100	39½	55	21½	15	6
180	71	95	37½	50	19½	10	4
170	67	90	35½				

ELECTRICITY MEASURES

The capacity of an electric power station is measured either in kilowatts (kw.) or in horse-power, the *output* in kilowatt hours (kwh.). If a power station worked a year at full capacity all the time the output that year in kwh. would be the capacity multiplied by the number of hours in a year. In reality stations for various reasons never do work to full capacity. 1 kilowatt capacity is equal to 1·34 h.p. capacity.

ABBREVIATIONS

A.S.S.R.	Autonomous Soviet Socialist Republic
E.	east
kg.	kilogram(s)
km.	kilometre(s)
K.p.h.	kilometres per hour
kw.	kilowatt(s)
Kwh.	kilowatt-hours
m.	million(s), metre(s)
N.	north
R.S.F.S.R.	Russian Soviet Federal Socialist Republic
S.	south
S.S.R.	Soviet Socialist Republic (of which the R.S.F.S.R. is one)
S.S.S.R.	Soviet initials for U.S.S.R.
sq.km.	square kilometre(s)
U.S.S.R.	Union of Soviet Socialist Republics (= Soviet Union)
W.	west

The points of the compass have been written North, South, East, West, when referring to official regions (e.g. North Caucasus for *Severnyy Kavkaz*), northern, southern, eastern, western, when referring to less precisely defined areas (e.g. northern Kazakhstan)

ABBREVIATED TITLES

The following Soviet publications have been referred to frequently in the text. For convenience the abbreviated title shown has been used:

Vedishchev, A. I., *Problemy razmeshcheniya proizvoditel'nykh sil SSSR*, Moscow, 1963	*Vedishchev*
Narodnoye khozyaystvo SSSR v 1963 godu, Moscow, 1963 (Soviet Statistical Yearbook)	*Nkh SSSR 1963*
Similarly for R.S.F.S.R. Yearbook	*Nkh RSFSR 1963*
Similarly for 1961	*Nkh SSSR 1961*
Atlas SSSR, Glavnoye upravleniye geodezii i kartografii, Ministerstva geologii i okhrany nedr SSSR, Moscow, 1962	*Atlas SSSR*

Chapter 1

INTRODUCTION

I. GENERAL FEATURES

PERHAPS the most outstanding feature of the human geography of the U.S.S.R., a feature not usually obvious from conventional atlas maps, is the fact that about three quarters of the total population is still to be found in the European part on about one quarter of the total land surface, whereas many of the best natural resources lie in the eastern regions of the country. The disparity between the deployment of the resources of the country and of the people using them will be a theme that recurs frequently in this book. Soviet geographers have in recent years been stressing the magnitude of this problem and recommending ways of using resources as effectively as possible. The problem is not however the monopoly of geographers, for it has also attracted recommendations from economists. If the vast size of the country is a disadvantage in some respects, it is a blessing in one way, for, in contrast to many other parts of the world, there is with a few exceptions no question of any deficiency of resources. The question is rather to decide which resources to exploit next.

The U.S.S.R. is the third country in the world in population. In January 1965 it had 229 million people, and its population is growing at the rate of about 3 million a year. In area, the U.S.S.R. is the largest country in the world, being two or three times as extensive as the next five, China, Canada, the U.S.A., Brazil and Australia. It is remarkable for its great east–west extent, for it stretches almost half-way round the northern hemisphere, and is divided into eleven time-zones. Equally striking is the high latitude of the country, about nine tenths of the total land area lying nearer to the Pole than to the Equator. Low temperatures for much of the year in many areas are a consequence of high latitude, and have a particularly adverse effect on agricultural possibilities.

The U.S.S.R. is about a hundred times as large as the United Kingdom, and is characterized by very long hauls of goods by land transport. The great size is not however such a serious drawback as it may at first seem since the country is only about ten

times as far across, along its longest axis, as the United Kingdom.
The reason for this is that the distance across an area varies only
according to the square root of the area. Furthermore, people are
very unevenly spread in the U.S.S.R., and most of the journeys
are in fact made between places within the main western concentration of population already mentioned. Nevertheless, the great
size of the country should always be borne in mind, particularly

3. Comparative sizes of the U.S.S.R. and other selected countries.

when there is a question of opening up new resources in remote
areas. In Figure 3 the U.S.S.R. is compared in size with the U.S.A.,
the United Kingdom and other selected areas. On the whole, the
U.S.S.R. is reasonably compact, at least compared with an

elongated country like Chile, or a split one like Pakistan. Its compactness is even more marked if one considers only European U.S.S.R., the part in which, to this day, most of the population and production are still to be found.

4. The position of the U.S.S.R. in the world. The projection is not an oblique zenithal and distances are not therefore correct outward from any point in the U.S.S.R. The scale is approximate.

The U.S.S.R. occupies a hemisphere of which a considerable part is land. Within the hemisphere centring on Novosibirsk are found all the countries of Asia and Europe, and many of those of Africa, containing, with the U.S.S.R. itself, about five sixths of the world's population. The three largest concentrations of population in the world, Europe, India and China, adjoin the U.S.S.R. or lie close to it. These features are illustrated in Figure 4. Movement into and out of the U.S.S.R. is however difficult at most places along its land boundaries, and except in East Europe contact with its many neighbours (see Figure 5) is not on the whole

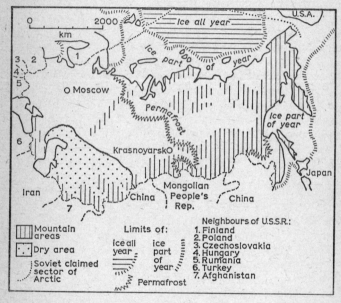

5. Outstanding physical features of the U.S.S.R. and its neighbours.

easy. Most of the coasts of the U.S.S.R. are frozen for anything between a few weeks and nine or ten months each year. Since the building of new roads and railways, the construction of modern ice-breakers, and particularly the establishment of international air services, these physical barriers around the Soviet Union have come to exert less influence than previously.

The geography of the U.S.S.R. cannot be fully appreciated without reference to certain neighbouring countries, those now forming with the U.S.S.R. the economic union called COMECON. Since the Second World War the Soviet Union has exerted varying degrees of economic dominance over a number of countries in Central Europe, the area now commonly referred to as East Europe. Although small in extent and possessing only a mediocre population/resource balance, these countries[1] have together almost half as many people as the U.S.S.R. East Europe has been industrializing rapidly since the Second World War, and is needing growing quantities of energy and raw materials. The question of whether East Europe, like West Europe, should obtain these from all over the world, or whether it should receive most of them from the U.S.S.R., has not yet been fully decided, but at all events it seems inevitable that a considerable part will come from the U.S.S.R. This naturally aggravates the disparity already noted between population at the western end of the U.S.S.R. and resources in the east, by adding a large new concentration of people even further west than European U.S.S.R.

II. LEVEL OF ECONOMIC AND SOCIAL DEVELOPMENT

What level of achievement in its economic and social life has the U.S.S.R. reached after half a century of Communism? The data in the table on the next page show roughly its position among selected countries of the world, using amounts *per caput* to eliminate the (direct) influence of the size of countries on absolute totals.

It is of course difficult to compare the economic level of any two countries on account of different methods of collecting data and of assessing the relative importance of different branches of the economy. Any comparison between the U.S.S.R. and other countries is particularly difficult since Western economists tend to assume that Soviet assessments of its own achievements are greatly inflated and growth figures bogus, while Soviet statisticians accuse Western capitalist countries of double counting in assessing their national incomes. Furthermore, industrial countries tend to have different priorities and different indicators of success. The private car, which holds such a prominent place in the U.S.A., hardly exists in the U.S.S.R. Housing in the United Kingdom is greatly superior to that in the U.S.S.R. In the Soviet Union, the

1. East Germany, Poland, Czechoslovakia, Hungary, Rumania, Bulgaria.

production of such items as electricity, steel and chemicals are key measures of development and of success.

In spite of these drawbacks it is clear from the data that the Soviet Union is some way behind the most highly industrialized

	I Energy	II Steel	III Physicians	IV National income	V Industrial origin of gross domestic product
U.S.S.R.	3,234	344	198	836	22
U.S.A.	8,507	540	119	1,828	4
Australia	4,213	389	112	1,068	13
United Kingdom	5,090	368	89	910	4
Italy	1,570	277	161	547	16
Japan	1,532	258	110	401	13
Brazil	377	44	35	150	28
India	170	16	17	59	45
Nigeria	31	4	2	74	62

SOURCES: (1) *United Nations Statistical Yearbook 1964*, New York, United Nations, 1965; (2) *Nkh SSSR 1963*.

KEY:

I *Per caput* consumption of all sources of energy in 1963 in kilograms of coal equivalent. Source 1, pp. 330–33.

II *Per caput* consumption of steel in 1963 in kilograms per inhabitant. Source 1, pp. 379–80.

III Physicians per 100,000 inhabitants in 1963 or nearest year. Source 1, pp. 648–50.

IV National income in dollars per inhabitant in 1963 or nearest year. Source 2, pp. 71–2.

V Industrial origin of gross domestic product in early 1960s. Percentage of total gross domestic product contributed by agriculture, forestry and fishing. Source 1, pp. 536–41.

NOTES:

(a) The figures are only comparable down columns, not across rows.

(b) Column IV contains Soviet data which claim to remove double counting in the national incomes of the more advanced industrial countries and therefore place the U.S.S.R. index closer to these than it is in Western and United Nations sources.

countries of the world, but far ahead of any under-developed countries. It began to industrialize on modern lines roughly at the same time as Japan and Italy, and although differences in size, resources and political background make precise comparison dubious, it has been noted more than once how close many economic indices (in *per caput* terms) for the three countries have been during the present century.

From the point of view of the most advanced industrial countries the achievements of the U.S.S.R. do not seem all that impressive, and in total the U.S.S.R., with rather more people than the U.S.A., still only produces about two fifths as many goods and services as its rival. On the other hand, the level of industrialization achieved by the U.S.S.R., and built up largely during the Communist period, obviously seems impressive to less developed countries. In recent years indeed it has been stressed in Soviet statistical publications that the U.S.S.R. has now overtaken the U.S.A. in sheer volume of production of many items. On the other hand, this is not necessarily advantageous. For example, the U.S.S.R. has been producing more coal than the U.S.A. for some time now, but this is because the production of coal has dropped in the U.S.A. as consumption of oil and gas, cheaper sources of energy, has risen. Likewise, the U.S.S.R. now produces more iron ore than the U.S.A., but this is because the U.S.A., rightly or wrongly, is importing large quantities of high grade ore and saving its home reserves. More goods are now handled on the Soviet railways than on those of the U.S.A., but again there is no merit in this.

Other ways of assessing the level of development of the U.S.S.R. include a consideration of employment structure, of the percentage of gross national product accounted for by agriculture, and of the degree of urbanization. Agriculture still employs a much larger proportion of the total labour force in the U.S.S.R. than in the most advanced industrial countries, about 30 per cent in 1965 (a figure roughly similar to that for Italy), compared with only about 5 per cent in the U.S.A. and 4 per cent in the United Kingdom. But the proportion of people engaged in agriculture is not only declining relatively but even absolutely. In the U.S.S.R. the total value of industrial production is now about four times as large as that of agricultural production, but in the United Kingdom and the United States it is about ten times as large.

As the importance of agriculture has declined and people have been leaving the land, the proportion of urban dwellers to total population has been rising impressively, and by the early 1960s 50 per cent of the population of the Soviet Union was defined as urban, a proportion expected to reach two thirds by 1980. In the

U.S.A. about two thirds of the population is already defined as urban, however, and in the United Kingdom over 80 per cent. The definition of urban varies among countries, but if it means communities in which the amenities expected in an urbanized society are available, then the degree of urbanization in the United Kingdom and the United States is even greater than their percentage figures suggest. Eventually it would be possible, and has even been considered desirable, virtually to urbanize completely the population of the U.S.S.R., by moving collective farmers into agricultural towns (*agrogorods*), but at the moment almost half of the population of the U.S.S.R. still lives in deeply rural conditions.

III. THE RÉGIME

From whatever angle one approaches the study of the U.S.S.R. it is virtually impossible to ignore the presence of the Communist Party and the idea of Communism. Even biological science has become involved in Marxist–Leninist ideas. Economics and economic geography are incomprehensible without reference to these ideas. It is essential for the reader to have a clear idea about the distinction between the Communist Party of the Soviet Union (C.P.S.U.), and Communism. Communism is a vague concept with economic, social, political and territorial connotations, whereas the Communist Party of the Soviet Union is a clearly defined set of individual members. Communism has about as many different versions as there are people who have tried to define it. The full members of the C.P.S.U., on the other hand, are kept in close check with a tally in the form of a membership card. In 1964 there were over eleven and a half million full Party members, not counting Young Communists (*Komsomol*). This means that there is about one full party member for every twenty ordinary or 'non-party' citizens.

The C.P.S.U. runs the U.S.S.R. The establishment of Communism is its aim and the supposed reason for its existence. In the early 1960s it was being forecast that the transition from socialism to Communism would be completed by about 1980. The Communist Party is a hierarchy of individuals dispersed throughout the community, watching the life of the whole population and making many of the major decisions at all levels. Membership of the party is a serious matter and the members form a kind of élite, *the* establishment. Enterprising and inventive individuals are encouraged to join, but if full Party membership were allowed to spread to the whole population, the position and purpose (if any) of the Party would be quite different from what it is now. In passing it may be noted that non-Russians, who make up almost a half of the total population of the Soviet Union, are well represented in the Party, but may not often make big decisions.[1]

The general concept of Communism in the U.S.S.R. can best briefly be summarized by a few recent references to the Soviet press. Very broadly there are two main aspects. The first is the creation of a situation in which enormous material production ensures a very high standard of living. The second is the question of educating people to a way of life superior to that known as yet in any other part of the world. The first aspect was summarized by Lenin in the early 1920s when he said that Communism is Soviet power plus electrification of the whole country. Much more recently the slogan has been extended to: 'Communism is Soviet power plus the electrification of the whole country plus the chemicalization (*khimizatsiya*) of the national economy.' So that people will not think that the great expansion of material production is being encouraged for its own sake, it is frequently stressed that in the end production is really for the sake of human beings, and that this is the goal of Communist construction.

The second aspect of Communism is perhaps adequately summarized in the following quotation (*Pravda*, 7 November 1963): 'Communism is a society with material abundance and a high degree of organization, a classless society with people developed and highly perceptive in every way. The deciding factor in the creation of such a society will be the achievement of a high level of development of productive forces.' The end-product of all this will be well-fed, contented citizens with all possible material needs but living unselfishly and decently; in short the creation of the most cultured and enlightened society in the world. Whether this will come about or not remains to be seen.

To achieve its aims, the Communist Party has undertaken two

1. See S. Bialer, 'How Russians Rule Russia', *Problems of Communism*, September–October 1964, p. 45.

not entirely mutually exclusive tasks: to build up a high level of industrial production, based on heavy industry and depending almost entirely on home produced materials, and to encourage the spread of socialism or Communism elsewhere in the world. Behind this is the idea that, at some time in the future, the whole world will become Communist.[1] The world economy would then be organized on a world basis. The need to achieve this by peaceful means has however frequently been stressed recently in the Soviet press (e.g. *Pravda*, 1 November 1964, p. 2).

It has been noted both by the Chinese Communists and in the West that both in the internal organization of its economy and in its relations with foreign countries the Soviet Union has changed considerably since the death of Stalin. The idea that socialism (or Soviet Communism) and capitalism are becoming more similar is however strongly denied in the Soviet press (e.g. *Pravda*, 10 July 1964, p. 2). This has not prevented the Soviet Union from borrowing new techniques from more advanced countries, a process, of course, that was occurring long before the Revolution in 1917. Even in the inter-war period, United States experts were brought in to help in the establishment of certain industries. In recent years the development of cybernetics in North America and West Europe has been closely watched, while since the bad grain harvest in 1963, the Soviet Ministry of Agriculture has been studying the use of fertilizers in these countries (*Pravda*, 11 February 1964). More sinister as far as the Soviet Communist Party is concerned have been the suggestions that some ideas of a (free) market economy might usefully be adopted in the U.S.S.R. However, since Communism has not yet been created in the U.S.S.R. such inconsistencies as these have to be tolerated.

1. e.g. 'Our general aim is to build a world socialist economy as one single complex'. N. S. Khrushchev, *Kommunist*, No.12, 1962, p. 12.

Chapter 2

THE PHYSICAL BACKGROUND[1]

PHYSICAL geography is studied both in its own right, to increase understanding of spatial aspects of physical phenomena, and from a practical point of view, to help geologists and others in the exploration of economic minerals, to help farmers to decide what best to grow on their land, and so on. Books on regional geography usually start with a study of the physical background, it would seem, for two main reasons. Firstly, it tends to change more slowly over time than human geography does and often in the context of a short period such as the last few decades, or even centuries, may be considered fixed. Secondly, it influences man and his activities more than man influences it. In practice, some features, such as the underlying structure of the land surface, and relief features, change very gradually, whereas marked climatic changes (not of course seasonal ones but long-term ones) may occur during a few centuries, while soil and vegetation can change or be changed even more rapidly.

Turning to the influence of the environment on man, there have been several views held as to this relationship. It is generally accepted and obvious that as technology improves, man becomes better and better equipped to make use of his environment. Nevertheless the view has been held, and still remains, that there is a deterministic relationship between the underlying physical patterns and influences on the one hand, and man and his activities on the other. This view has largely been rejected in Western countries, or replaced by a more flexible view, possibilism. In passing it may be suggested that this is being superseded by a probabilistic view in the West. In the Communist world, determinism in relation to the physical environment has been strongly denied. Man's ability to dominate the environment has been stressed. During the Soviet period the environment has, indeed, been accepted as a challenge in the Soviet Union, but this is no monopoly of the Communists, for one might say that the Canadians and Brazilians, for example, have adopted a similar attitude.

1. When reading this chapter reference should be made to appropriate maps in Chapter 5 as well as to maps accompanying the text here.

Whatever the attitude of the Soviet Communists, the fact must be faced that they have inherited some of the coldest lands in the world and also some of the driest and most rugged.

This section consists of a brief description of some aspects of the physical background of the U.S.S.R., particularly those most closely influencing human activities. Thus the emphasis is put on relief and drainage, climate, soil and vegetation. Other aspects of the physical background, all of which influence in some way the aspects already mentioned, and ultimately, also, human activities, are geology, including age and type of rocks on and beneath the Earth's surface, structure (tectonic features), earthquakes and volcanoes, and geomorphology (land forms). In this section the emphasis is mainly on describing the physical background rather than pointing out in what ways it is useful or otherwise to man; this will be done in Chapter 5.

I. RELIEF

For a simple initial appreciation of the distribution of relief features, the Soviet Union may conveniently be divided first of all into two main parts, roughly equal in extent, an area consisting mainly of lowland or hill country to the west of the River Yenisey (see Figure 6) and an area consisting mainly of high mountain ranges and plateaux east of it. Each of these may be further subdivided. The U.S.S.R. west of the Yenisey is cut in half by the Ural Range, leaving European U.S.S.R. with its broad lowlands, widespread hill country and mountain fringes to the west, and the great West Siberian Lowland, drained mainly by the Ob' and Irtysh to the east. This enormous plain of *quaternary*[1] deposits slopes imperceptibly towards the Arctic and is only broken by minor relief features. The half (almost) of the U.S.S.R. lying east of the Yenisey consists of the Mid-Siberian Plateau in the west, an area with its surface mainly between about 300 and 1,000 metres above sea-level, but dissected by many large rivers, and, east and south of the River Lena, very high mountain ranges and limited lowlands. Some of the ranges here rise precipitously behind the

1. In Geology, quaternary refers to material deposited roughly in the last million years or so and therefore of relatively recent origin compared with other rocks.

6. Prominent physical features of relief and drainage in the U.S.S.R. Note that the upper map is on a larger scale than the lower one.

Pacific coast. This fourfold scheme of relief features of the U.S.S.R. must be completed by adding three important elements not readily fitting in, the Kazakh Plateau to the south of the West Siberian Lowland, the lowlands around the Aral Sea and to the north of the Caspian Sea, and the very high mountains of relatively recent origin (geologically speaking) in Central Asia (Tyan'-Shan', Alau, Pamir) and the Caucasus.

Some essential relief features of the U.S.S.R. can be seen in Figure 6, but the reader is advised to consult an atlas for greater detail. Since European U.S.S.R. is relatively of greater importance than the rest of the country some further features of it should be noted. Most of the area consists of broad river valleys, such as those of the Dnepr and the upper Volga, but the intervening hill areas, with surfaces generally between about 100 and 300 metres above sea-level, can be greatly dissected, as in both the Podol'sk Uplands of the Ukraine and the Mid-Russian Upland south of Moscow. Some of the hill country, including the Smolensk–Moscow Upland north-west of Moscow, is composed of material left by glaciers in the Ice Age. The north-western part of European U.S.S.R., both the hill country and the plains, tends to be ill-drained, since drainage has been impeded by glacial material. Only in the lowland area north of the Caspian Sea is the land almost dead flat. In places, European U.S.S.R. is fringed by mountains, including small relics of a former mountain area in the Kola Peninsula, part of the Carpathian Range, which curves through Central Europe, the limited but steep sided mountains of the Crimea, and the more extensive and impressive Greater Caucasus and Lesser Caucasus between the Black and Caspian Seas. The north–south Ural Range is the traditional eastern limit of European U.S.S.R. It is narrow but high for much of its length in the north, but widens and becomes lower in the south.

If the Ice Age left effects of one sort or another – whether lake-filled basins, hills, or fine material, loess, derived from glacial deposits – over much of European U.S.S.R., Siberia was less affected by glaciation in spite of being in general much colder. A legacy of the Ice Age here, however, is the widespread permafrost, a condition in which the moisture in the ground is permanently frozen to depths ranging from one or two metres to several hundred metres, and thaws at the surface each year during the spring and summer, causing widespread flooding. The area entirely or partially affected by permafrost is shown in Figure 5.

Much of the U.S.S.R. is characterized by large rivers with very gentle gradients. Three of the largest basins, those of the Ob', Yenisey and Lena, drain to the Arctic Ocean; some of the tributaries of the first two originate in the heart of Asia, south of the U.S.S.R. The Amur, part of whose basin is in China, has its outlet in the Pacific. In European U.S.S.R., the Volga, the upper part of whose basin coincides with the area around Moscow, in which modern Russia has its origins, flows to the Caspian, an interior sea, the surface of which is 28 metres below sea-level, but the Don and Dnepr reach the Black Sea. Another area of interior drainage, that of the Aral Sea, lies east of the Caspian, and is crossed by two large rivers, the Amu-Dar'ya and Syr-Dar'ya.

The various rivers mentioned differ greatly in length, volume of water carried, régime (occurrence of periods of maximum and minimum flow) and duration, if any, of freezing. Their courses, too, are characterized in some places by precipitous valleys, gorges and great rapids, especially in the mountains of Central Asia and on the Mid-Siberian Plateau, but in other places by wide almost flat valley floors, and even, as in the lower Ob', wide flood plains that are periodically inundated. Figure 7a, showing the duration of snow cover each year, is a rough guide to the parts of the U.S.S.R. in which the rivers are affected by freezing, but the correlation is not exact. One feature of Russian rivers that has attracted attention and may be mentioned but not commented on here is their widespread tendency to have higher right banks than 1 ft banks.

II. CLIMATE

For the purposes of this book, certain individual features of climate have been picked out and are mapped in Figures 7, 16a and 18a. Maps 7b and c show January and July mean temperatures, but Figure 7a, showing the duration of snow cover, brings home more impressively the implications of the cold conditions that prevail in much of the U.S.S.R.; around Moscow, snow lies on the ground almost without interruption for about five months in the year. People working in the more remote parts of the Arctic are faced with eight or nine months of snow.

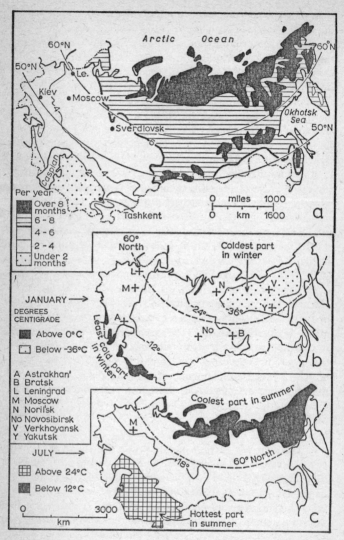

7. Features of temperature. a. Mean duration of snow cover. b, c. Mean air temperatures of January (d) and July (c).

In winter in general (see Figure 7b for January), conditions are not coldest in the extreme north of the U.S.S.R. along the Arctic coast, but in the interior of north-east Siberia. Here the mean temperature for January is as low as $-50°C$ in certain places and temperatures much lower than this have been recorded on occasions. At the other extreme a few areas near the Black Sea and Caspian and in Central Asia have a mean January temperature above $0°C$, though this is still very cold and does not of course rule out the occurrence of frosts. Except in the extreme east of the U.S.S.R., winter temperatures diminish in a north-easterly direction rather than northwards, and one can expect to find places in Siberia much colder than places at the same latitude in European U.S.S.R.; contrast the Moscow area in January, about $-8°C$, with Novosibirsk, about $-18°C$. In their turn these places are much colder than places at the same latitude in western Europe (e.g. Edinburgh about $+5°C$). Similarly, places in the extreme north-west of European U.S.S.R. are no colder than places much further south in the interior; for example Leningrad and Astrakhan' have roughly the same January temperatures but Astrakhan' is 1500 km. further south from the North Pole than Leningrad.

In summer (see July temperatures, Figure 7c) conditions become progressively cooler in a northerly direction, with of course local anomalies, and variations in the rate of change. The hottest part of the U.S.S.R., with mean July temperatures of over $30°C$ in a few places, is Central Asia and southern Kazakhstan. Coldest of all, apart from high mountain areas throughout the country, are the shores of the Arctic Ocean. In some of the islands off the coast, mean temperature never rises above $0°C$. Summer heat is sufficient only to melt the ice along much of the Arctic Coast for a mere two or three months.

Much of the Soviet Union is characterized by a very great range between winter and summer temperatures. These conditions are very 'continental' by West European standards. They occur even in the Ukraine where, for example, the central Ukraine has a mean January temperature around $-5°C$, a corresponding July temperature of $+20°C$, and altogether, therefore, a mean annual range of $25°C$ which is nearly twice as great as that in London. Around Moscow the range is about $28°C$ and in Novosibirsk more than $35°C$.

Cold conditions are among the first features that come to mind when foreigners consider the U.S.S.R., and although there is not space here to enlarge on their enormous influence on life in most of the country and their part in many of the works of Russian literature, a few aspects may briefly be noted. Early in Russian history, Alexander Nevsky defeated the Teutonic Knights in 1242 in a battle on the ice of Lake Pskov. During the Second World War Leningrad, which held out against the Germans in spite of being almost completely encircled, was supplied in winter across the ice-covered surface of Lake Ladoga. At times in the present century a short-cut has been made for the Trans-Siberian Railway in winter by placing rails on the surface of Lake Baykal. Most daring, perhaps, have been the achievements of Soviet airmen in landing on ice-floes in the Arctic and establishing floating scientific stations on these, both before and since the Second World War. For varying lengths of time each year, ice prevents navigation on many Soviet waterways, and access to most of the ports. The U.S.S.R. has constructed the first atomic ice breaker in the world, the *Lenin*. In the economic life of the country, cold conditions make it impossible and useless to do any agricultural work for much of the year, and it was estimated in the early 1960s that ten to twelve million collective farm workers are still unable to make any useful contribution to the economy during the winter. Much of the U.S.S.R. is in fact too cold for any agriculture at all, and if vegetables are grown in hothouses well within the Arctic circle, this gesture of defiance merely underlines the true problem.

In transportation and construction, special difficulties and increased costs are caused by the cold. Snow-drifts block roads and railways and these have to be protected by shelters. Frost cracks rails, prevents points from working and freezes water needed for steam locomotives, and even lubricating oil. Heaving ground caused by thawing can damage railbeds. In many towns of the U.S.S.R., walls of houses have to be very thick and windows generally small, to retain heat. Such drawbacks as these have not prevented the Soviet Union from exploiting resources even in the coldest parts, often at great expense and inconvenience. But to this day the coldest half of the country, roughly that part having a January temperature below $-24°C$ (see Figure 7b), while occupying almost 50 per cent of the total national area, has less than 2 per cent of the total population.

Rainfall, which, in a Soviet context should strictly be referred to as precipitation in view of the large proportion of it occurring in the form of snow, is in some parts of the U.S.S.R. more of an obstacle to development than low temperatures. Mean annual precipitation, which is mapped in Figure 18a, is a useful initial summary of the amount of water available in different parts of the country, but the usefulness or effectiveness of this diminishes as temperature increases; moreover completely arid areas can in fact be made useful by drawing on water in rivers passing through them. These practical aspects of precipitation will be dealt with in Chapter 5.

Disregarding its actual effectiveness, the distribution of mean annual precipitation in the U.S.S.R. can be summarized by picking out two general areas of low precipitation, firstly (see Figure 18a) the area lying east of and immediately north of the Caspian Sea (less than 10 cm. in the driest part), and secondly much of north-east U.S.S.R., particularly the Lena lowlands and the Arctic coast (less than 20 cm. in places). The parts receiving most precipitation are the high mountain areas of the southern fringe and Pacific coast (some places receive over 80 cm.) but, given the relatively high latitude and consequent limited evaporation, the 50–65 cm. falling over most of European U.S.S.R. and the West Siberian Lowland is considerable.

It is customary in regional textbooks and atlases to have maps of climatic regions. Recently the concept of climatic regions has been criticized by some geographers. Different parts of the world obviously have different climates, but to divide the world or parts of it into compartments each apparently having a precisely defined type of climate gives the impression, at least to those without much experience in the problem of defining regions, that at the limit of each climatic region a rapid change occurs as one steps, as it were, from one into the next. Such a change would be expected, to take a Soviet example, between the humid sub-tropical climate of western Transcaucasia and the dry sub-tropical climate of eastern Transcaucasia. In reality, except where appreciable changes in altitude occur over limited horizontal distances, climatic features, such as mean annual temperature, precipitation or snow cover, tend to change gradually over area. We are really dealing with a continuum and a gradual transition, rather than a number of clearly distinguishable areas. Notwithstanding these drawbacks, a recent Soviet Atlas[1] divides the U.S.S.R. into four main climatic belts, twenty-four sub-regions, and about twice as many subsidiary areas in these. It is something of a shock to find that one of the four major climatic belts in this map, the temperate (*umerennyy*) belt, extends to the Arctic circle and includes places in the Lena valley that in January regularly have temperatures as low as −40°C. Surprisingly, too, the *sub-tropical* belt in Transcaucasia lies almost as near to the Pole as to the equator, and that in Central Asia has a snow cover lasting on average three weeks each winter.

III. SOILS AND VEGETATION

Two other features of the physical background, soil and vegetation, are of particular interest and are an essential part of the resource background of the U.S.S.R. Indeed Russian scientists were among the pioneers in the study of the distribution of different types of soil, and maps in modern Soviet atlases give an idea of the enormous amount of data that must have been collected in the Communist period. Soils are usually derived by weathering from the rocks on which they lie. This action is dependent partly on the climate of the area and partly on its vegetation. Like soil, vegetation is also of course affected by climate.

Often particular soil conditions are associated with certain plant communities, though in the Soviet Union now much of the vegetation that existed before human interference has either been completely removed or at least modified by cultivation, grazing, timber felling, peat cutting and so on. Thus for example there is a broad correspondence between the belt of blackearth soils (*cherno-zems*) that extend through the Ukraine, across the Volga and Ural region and into Siberia, and the grassland vegetation known as steppe. If precipitation were higher than it is in the *chernozem* belt, there is of course no reason why it should not have a tree vege-tation, but the higher precipitation would in time contribute to modify the *chernozem* soil itself.

Like climatic regions, and for broadly the same reasons, vege-

1. *Atlas SSSR*, Moscow, 1962, p.78.

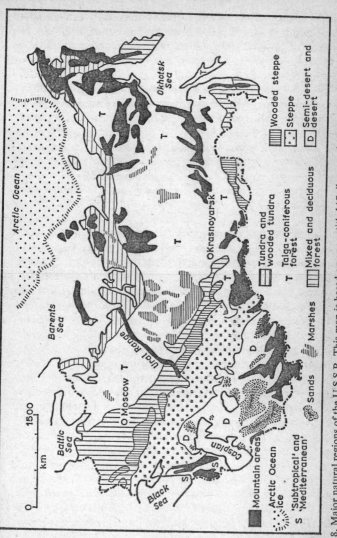

8. Major natural regions of the U.S.S.R. This map is based on one entitled 'Soil-vegetation zones' in *Atlas SSSR dlya sredney shkoly*, Moscow, 1960, and is greatly simplified.

Legend:

- Tundra and wooded tundra
- Taiga-coniferous forest
- Mixed and deciduous forest
- Wooded steppe
- Steppe
- Semi-desert and desert
- Sands
- Marshes
- Mountain areas
- Arctic Ocean ice
- 'Subtropical' and 'Mediterranean'

Labels on map: Arctic Ocean, Barents Sea, Okhotsk Sea, Ural Range, Moscow, Krasnoyarsk, Baltic Sea, Black Sea, Caspian, km, 0, 1500 tation and soil regions are difficult to define, but it is nevertheless convenient to work out and map regions. In more elementary Soviet geographical texts, soil and vegetation zones are sometimes combined on one map,[1] but more discriminating publications keep the two separate.[2]

Figure 8, showing natural regions of the U.S.S.R., reduces to about as simple a form as possible the distribution of the main vegetation types. Figure 16b shows soil types only in the western part of the U.S.S.R., the part, however, in which about 95 per cent of the arable land is found. The continuity of transition from one general type of soil and of vegetation to another that occurs widely in the U.S.S.R. in a north–south direction is interrupted by high mountain and plateau areas and to a lesser extent by river flood plains. To the east of the Yenisey, mountain areas, with their low temperatures, bring the soil and vegetation conditions associated with the Arctic far to the south. Here, owing to the confused arrangement of mountain ranges, it is difficult to pick out east–west belts of different types of soil and vegetation. West of the Yenisey it is easier to do this. Here, in very general terms, soils change from an environment with super-abundant moisture and leached soils, through a zone of moisture balance, roughly the forest-steppe zone, to one of increasing evaporation and moisture deficiency in which there is a tendency for alkaline soils to form.

The northern belts are associated either with the very cold conditions of the Arctic tundra or with the *podzol* soils of the coniferous and/or deciduous forest. Considerable areas here are in fact waterlogged and may have only a sparse forest cover, but vast areas are covered, or have been covered before their exploitation, by pine (*Pinus* species), fir (*Abies* species) and spruce (*Picea* species). Larch (*Larix* species) are also found but are particularly widespread east of the Yenisey. The general term for the coniferous forest zone is *taiga*. Areas with predominantly coniferous species are found alongside ones with mainly broadleaf species such as the birch and oak, while in European U.S.S.R., broadleaf forest predominates in places.

The forest vegetation thins out along its southern margin in a

1. e.g. *Atlas dlya sredney shkoly*, Moscow, 1960, pp.17 and 29.
2. e.g. *Atlas SSSR*, Moscow, 1962, pp. 84–5 and 88–9.

zone widely referred to in Soviet publications as the wooded steppe (see Figure 8). Here drier conditions prevail, leaching of the soil diminishes and one passes southwards through areas of leached and podzolized blackearths and then typical deep blackearth soils, rich in humus, to the drier fringes, with brown and chestnut soils and traces of saline conditions. Associated with this middle belt of soils is the typical steppe vegetation with its many grass species.

Beyond the drier southern margins of the belt of black, brown and chestnut soils and of steppe vegetation, extends the zone of light chestnut and grey-brown soils which merges into semi-desert and desert lands. Much of the surface of the most arid part of the Kazakhstan and Central Asia is covered with shifting or only semi-fixed sands in which proper soil has not formed. In places in the arid zone, dried salt lakes (*takyrs*) are found, while a distinction is made in Russia between three types of saline soils that occur widely, *solodi*, *solontsy* and *solonchaki*. Vegetation is scanty or virtually non-existent. Xerophytic species often predominate, while ephemeral plants grow quickly and enjoy a brief life following the occasional periods of rain.

High mountain areas are characterized by very varied soil and vegetation conditions. These tend to be arranged in bands at certain altitude levels. In theory one may expect to encounter in a traverse up a mountain-side from sea-level to say 5,000 metres all the soil and vegetation types to be expected on a traverse from the area in which the mountain is located to the Arctic itself. In practice this does not happen perfectly, but in the Greater Caucasus, for example, one may ascend from steppe through broadleaf and coniferous forest to the equivalent of tundra and finally to small snowfields and glaciers, a replica of the Arctic, if only in miniature. In many high mountain areas the soil cover is very thin and soil is easily washed away on steep slopes. In Central Asia, the mountains are so dry in places that grassland or semi-desert is found at altitudes at which forest would be expected.

Soviet Communists have introduced an element of drama into the relationship between man and his physical environment by asserting that under Communism man need no longer be at the mercy of physical conditions. Their attitude has been that money is no object, that new plants can be found to grow in areas hitherto considered impossible for cultivation, and even that nature can be transformed. Human beings have in fact been changing nature for many millennia now by removing natural vegetation, diverting water to irrigate fields and so on. Vegetation and soil can be interfered with fairly easily by man, though often with unfavourable results. Soviet plans for changing nature by forming large reservoirs, diverting rivers and planting extensive tree belts, have perhaps been more ambitious than any devised previously, while recently Soviet farmers have apparently been no less successful than United States farmers around 1930 in transforming nature by over-ploughing in dry areas and causing soil erosion. But the creation of reservoirs may cause unexpected evaporation, and trees planted in belts in semi-desert areas may simply refuse to grow. As will be suggested in Chapter 5, when Soviet resources are outlined, climate and relief are changing only very slowly, and Soviet planners are not likely to be any more successful than their capitalist rivals in modifying these, at least with present-day capital resources and technology.

Chapter 3

HISTORICAL GROWTH OF RUSSIA

In 1917 the Soviet Communists attempted to make a fresh start by forgetting the past and transforming the life of Russia. But they are indebted to the work of their predecessors, who acquired over the previous four centuries a very large territory and magnificent natural resources on which the 'first socialist state' could be built virtually without depending on any other part of the world. While it is not possible in a geography book to go over the history of Russia in detail the reader with no background in this subject will benefit from a brief account of the way the Russian empire was formed. The peoples, languages and religions, as well as the varying economic activities and differing levels of development and prosperity, often reflect patterns that originated many centuries ago.

I. TERRITORIAL GROWTH OF THE RUSSIAN EMPIRE

The Russian Empire was built up in a difficult physical environment. Until the nineteenth century the Russians were largely acquiring lands in the cold coniferous forest zone and even in the Arctic tundra. In the nineteenth century they turned their attention to desert and high mountain areas in the heart of Asia. Siberia, which was largely overrun by the Russians in the seventeenth century, has particularly long winters, and for much of the year movement had to take place over snow-covered ground or along frozen rivers. Food must often have been short and food supply insecure. Until the second part of the nineteenth century, the movement of goods over any but the shortest distances was largely by waterway.

One interpretation of Russian history has been that from their interior homeland the Russians have constantly been seeking outlets, preferably ice-free, on the coast. Whether or not there has been a conscious drive to achieve this, it may be noted before proceeding that in the sixteenth century the Russians reached the Arctic coast, in the seventeenth century the Pacific and in the eighteenth century the Baltic and Black Seas. It must be admitted, however, that until the 1950s they have never made much use of their opportunities to trade directly with other parts of the world. The following account of the growth of Russia merely describes the way in which new areas were acquired and the main peoples involved in Russian conquest.

By the eighth century A.D. a considerable part of Central and Eastern Europe was occupied by three groups of Slavs, the West Slavs roughly in what is now Poland and Czechoslovakia, the South Slavs in Yugoslavia and Bulgaria, and the East Slavs in what is now the western Ukraine, Belorussia and part of the north-west of the U.S.S.R. The East Slavs were divided into many tribes, but by about A.D. 850 these were organized loosely in the State of Kiev, known as Rus. This unit lay along the route between the Baltic and the Black Sea, following here the course of the Dnepr, a trade route between Scandinavia and the Byzantine Empire. By the eleventh century the Rus of Kiev had broken up into a number of principalities, the centres of which are among the oldest towns in Russia (e.g. Chernigov, Smolensk, Novgorod and Vladimir). Most of these units were quickly overrun early in the thirteenth century by Mongol and Tatar invaders. These Asiatic peoples first penetrated Russia in 1223, coming from arid and semi-arid lands in Asia, across the open steppe country of what is now the southern Ukraine. Various waves of invaders settled in Russia and for a time controlled much of it, although Pskov and Novgorod, lying far north in the forest, remained untouched. During the same period Swedes, Lithuanians and the Teutonic Order were attacking Russia from the west.

It was around Novgorod, which in the fourteenth century formed a great principality in the northern part of European Russia, that the revival of Russia's fortunes began, but in due course the principality of Moscow (the town was founded in 1143), only of modest size in 1300 (about 150 × 80 km.), took over. By 1450 Moscow had extended its control eastwards along the Volga, south to the River Oka, and in a northerly direction as well. After 1480 Moscow no longer paid tribute to the khanate of Kazan', and thereby symbolically the independence of Russia was reachieved. Under Ivan III (reigned 1462–1533) a centralized Russian state was formed.

By 1533, Russia extended from near Kiev in the south to the Arctic coast in the north (see Figure 9). It had already absorbed

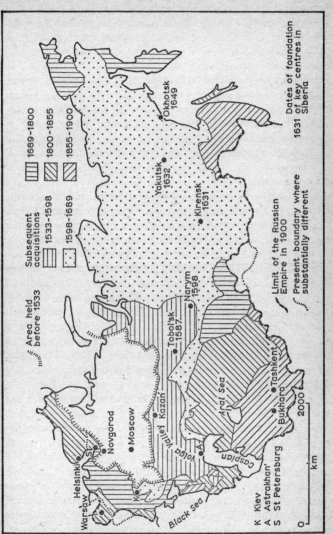

9. Territorial growth of Russia since 1533.

the forest lands of Novgorod and was making incursions into the open steppe land to the south. The territorial explosion of Russia continued in the reign of Ivan IV (the Terrible), who reigned 1533–84. Two lines of expansion were followed. One took the Russians to the shores of the Caspian Sea at Astrakhan'; this drive south-eastwards gave them control of the lower Volga and cut off the steppe lands of southern European Russia from the much more extensive open lands of Asia to the east. The second line of penetration, that along which the greatest expansion took place, was eastwards. The town of Kazan' on the Volga was taken in 1552 and well before 1600 the Russians had reached places beyond the Ural Range (see dates on Figure 9), using relatively low passes in the middle Ural.

Territorial expansion continued eastwards throughout the seventeenth century and the relatively few native inhabitants of Siberia were easily overcome, thanks to the superiority of Russian arms and eventually numbers. The main lines of initial penetration were the east–west stretches of rivers such as the Ob', the Tunguska and the Lena. Yakutsk on the Lena was reached in 1632 and the Pacific Coast by about 1650. Further penetration southwards towards China met resistance from China itself and in 1689 expansion in this direction was checked by the Treaty of Nerchinsk.

In the following century Russian conquest continued in a north-easterly direction, and Kamchatka, and eventually Alaska in North America, were acquired, but impetus in this direction was being lost with increasing distance and possibly loss of interest. Nevertheless, in 1812 the Russians had an outpost in Fort Ross only about 100 km. north of what is now San Francisco in the U.S.A.

It is difficult to appreciate the magnitude of Russian conquests in Siberia without drawing attention to a few distances. In the first fifty years of the seventeenth century the Russians extended their control, if only loosely at first, 4,000 km. eastwards, over some of the most difficult physical conditions in the world. Only a globe shows clearly the staggering distances involved in a journey across the Russian Empire from Moscow to the furthest outposts in North America. The great circle distance[1] from Moscow to

1. A great circle distance is the shortest distance between two points on the Earth's surface actually across the surface as opposed to through the body of the planet itself.

Fort Ross over the North Pole is some 9,000 km., but it was not of course possible to travel to it this way. The great circle distance from Moscow to Lake Baykal is 4,200 km., that from Baykal to southern Kamchatka 3,200 km., and from here to Fort Ross, following islands and the North American coast, the distance is about 7,500 km. Thus the distance from end to end in general terms is 15,000 km., but following recognized river routes, it would be about 18,000 km. It would take someone travelling at 30 km. a day altogether 600 days. The reader will ask why the Russians did not find some shorter or easier way from Moscow to the eastern extremity of their Empire. This would, in fact, have involved even longer sea routes either round Cape Horn to avoid the Spanish Empire or round Africa; the Russians in those days were quite unable to operate reliable services over such distances.

Peter the Great was Tsar of Russia from 1682 to 1725. During this period Russia turned its attention westwards and south-eastwards, and during the eighteenth century acquired new territory in Europe at the expense of a number of neighbouring powers. The extent of these new areas was very small compared with the new possessions in Siberia, but conquest was much more difficult because these were densely peopled lands with inhabitants techno-logically equal to, or superior to, the Russians. An outlet on the Gulf of Finland was established in 1703 and the town of St Petersburg (now Leningrad) built at the head of the Gulf became the capital of the Russian Empire in 1713. Not until late in the eighteenth century, however, did Russia acquire an outlet on the Black Sea, and occupy the Crimea. By this time Russian influence was also growing in the Caucasus area.

After the period of the Napoleonic Wars, Russian empire-building began again, and the Caucasus area was mostly occupied by the middle of the nineteenth century, although there have been fluctuations in the frontier since, and allegiance to Russia has sometimes been in doubt. More impressive and ambitious was the campaign to occupy Central Asia, which took place in the second half of the nineteenth century and caused considerable concern to the British in India. By now far superior technologically, the Russians were able to overcome the old civilizations of Turkestan with the help of modern weapons, and railways were built to consolidate these new possessions, the first line being constructed from the Caspian eastwards; the western side of the Caspian could be reached by the railway from Moscow to Baku. Later, a more direct line was built into Central Asia, passing close to the Aral Sea.

A third area in which Russians showed renewed interest in the nineteenth century was the Far East. Here they pushed east along the Lower Amur valley, established Vladivostok, occupied Sakhalin, and moved south into Manchuria, threatening the northern fringes of the Chinese Empire. During the nineteenth century, therefore, Russia came face to face along its Asian frontier with Turkey, Persia, Afghanistan, China proper and Japan. Eventually expansion in the Far East was checked by the Japanese in the War of 1904–6, and the movement of Chinese settlers into Manchuria with the help of a railway built by the Russians themselves prevented this area from becoming a Russian sphere of influence.

The actual area of the Russian Empire was appreciably reduced in 1867 by the sale of Alaska to the United States for seven million dollars. By the first decade of the present century the Russian Empire was almost exactly as large as the Soviet Union at present, but included Finland and Poland, now separate, and lacked some areas in both Europe and Asia, acquired since.

In the inter-war period territories were lost, but most of these were regained as a result of readjustments immediately before the Second World War or in 1945. The Baltic Republics, and parts of what are now Belorussia and the Ukraine, remained outside in the inter-war years. In the 1930s the Soviet Union claimed as its territorial waters the whole of the Arctic Ocean lying to the north of it. Most fundamental, however, has been the establishment of Communist or pro-Communist régimes in East Europe. Soviet relations with these new Communist countries will be discussed in Chapter 11. It must be made clear, however, that these states are sovereign by their own definition and indeed have grown in independence very considerably since 1956, even though they are still popularly referred to in the West as satellites.

11. SOME FEATURES OF GROWTH

A review of Russian Empire building since 1533 shows that the amount of territory (and the number of people) added has varied greatly during different periods. The following figures summarize this territorial growth (see also Figure 9). Alaska is not taken into consideration at all.

	Amount added Millions of sq. km.	New Total
1533 total		3
1533–98	2½	5½
1598–1630	4½	10
1630–98	5½	15½
1698–1800	2	17½
1800–1900	5 almost	22½
1960	almost	22½

The figures below show approximately the area added per decade. They are suggestive rather than precise. Nor do they take into account the usefulness of new areas in terms of their resources, their accessibility, the number of people in them or the degree of consolidation achieved in the greatly varied areas occupied by the Russians during this period.

Average number of sq. km. added per decade	
1530–1600	400,000
1600–30	1,500,000
1630–1700	800,000
1700–1800	100,000
1800–1900	500,000
1900–1960	15,000

During the present century there have been two major periods of change, the first resulting in the loss of roughly 600,000 sq. km. during and after the First World War, and the second, during 1939–45, resulting in new gains. The area of the U.S.S.R. was 21·7 million sq. km. during the inter-war period, rose to 22·1 million by 1940 and was 22·4 million by 1950.

Some outstanding features of the Russian Empire may now be noted. Its continuity in time is striking when compared with the

Spanish Empire, which lasted for three centuries and then collapsed, and also with the French and British Empires, from which from time to time territories were lost, while other areas were added in different parts of the world. Its compactness also distinguishes it from the sea empires established by West European countries. In these, communications between the mother country and the colonies could easily be interrupted, whereas Russia could reach its farthest colonies, apart from Alaska, without crossing any other country or any ocean. Much of the new territory added to the Russian Empire was acquired in the seventeenth century. In the nineteenth century however there was 'rejuvenation', and a repetition of empire-building on a smaller scale.

The establishment of the Russian Empire has left the Soviet Union with by far the largest sovereign state in the world, although for a time both the Spanish and British Empires were comparable in size. The growth of the Empire was accompanied by an explosion of Slav settlers, the ancestors of the present Russians, Belorussians and Ukrainians, who first moved southwards into the blackearth steppe lands of European Russia, practising agriculture in previously pastoral areas, and then eastwards across the Ural Range and into Siberia. Not until the Trans-Siberian Railway was constructed in the 1890s, however, was it possible for very large numbers of Russians to move or be moved into the virtually empty steppes and forests of the East. The Russians are now in the majority virtually all the way from Leningrad to Vladivostok, although pockets of non-Russian peoples remain in this belt.

In the last hundred years or so Russians and Ukrainians have been moving in increasing numbers into Transcaucasia and Central Asia; in the period since the Second World War particularly into the latter area. They settled there first as administrators and in other professional capacities, mainly in towns. More recently they have gone to be farmers and industrial workers. The proportion of Russians in each of the non-Russian Republics in 1959 is shown in Chapter 4, Section I. Life in Central Asia has now been profoundly changed by the presence of the Russians, who have attempted to eliminate nomadic pastoral practices, have established mines and factories and have, of course, established the Communist Party firmly in the region.

It is perhaps surprising that the Russians who moved to remote parts of the Russian Empire and settled there have not apparently shown signs of disloyalty towards the central government; at all events there have never been moves towards independence of the magnitude encountered in the colonies of the sea empires established by West European powers. In the last hundred years the growth of the railway system has helped to consolidate the vast area, but even now there is nothing so complete as is found in North America.

III. OUTLINE OF ECONOMIC HISTORY

Between 1500 and 1900 the economic life of the Russian Empire changed considerably in many areas even though in total it was still predominantly agricultural at the beginning of this century. In European Russia around 1650 iron was being worked around Tula and Moscow and near Lake Ladoga, the metal being smelted with charcoal from the forest. Hemp and flax were being manufactured to the north and west of Moscow, and furs and clothing processed and made in many centres. Archangel on the White Sea was the principal outlet of the country, but there was relatively little trade with other countries. Nor at this time did Siberia make more than a slight contribution to the economic growth of the country.

During the eighteenth century considerable progress was made, and industrial growth was stimulated by Peter the Great with his policy of looking towards West Europe for new techniques and for technicians. The new outlet on the Baltic, St Petersburg (now Leningrad), had shipbuilding yards and metal-working industries, while the Moscow area had many textile centres including Ivanovo and Kostroma, now important cotton centres. Iron was still widely smelted and worked around Moscow, but one of the main economic advances in the eighteenth century was the establishment of an iron industry in the Ural region on a much larger scale. This was about as far east as it was feasible to put factories at this stage. The products were sent westwards by the tributaries of the Volga, particularly the Kama and Belaya. Towards the end of the century Russia had become the leading producer of iron in the world and was even exporting some to England. Improvements were made to communications by joining the head-waters of some of the European rivers with canals and in particular a link from the Upper Volga to Lake Ladoga and St Petersburg was a great achievement for this period.

In the first half of the nineteenth century modern factories using machinery imported from West Europe were gradually established in certain parts of the Russian Empire, first in St Petersburg, the Moscow area and Poland for the manufacture of cotton textiles, then on the lower Dnepr and on the Donbass coalfield in the Ukraine, to smelt iron ore and make relatively simple iron goods. Towards the end of the century the Donbass, with its more modern and larger metallurgical establishments, eclipsed the Ural region, which however continued to make some contribution, still using charcoal. At first cotton was imported for the textile industry of the country but later it was brought in from the new colonies in Central Asia. By about 1900, six main industrial and mining areas could be distinguished in Russia, the two most important being that around Moscow with its light industry, and that in the Ukraine with its heavy industry (see Figure 10a). The other four areas were the declining Ural region, Poland, the St Petersburg port area, and Baku on the Caspian, which by this time was producing something like half the oil in the world. By 1900, too, there was a reasonably complete railway system in Russia west of the Volga, but little beyond the Ural Range; the Trans-Siberian Railway reached Omsk in 1896 and Krasnoyarsk in 1898 (see Figure 10b).

A study of Russian history is certainly essential for the fuller appreciation of many present features. In understanding present spatial patterns, how far back into the past do we have to go? Metal-working presumably lingers in the area around Tula, where raw materials for the industry are now lacking, because it has been traditional there for so long. Similarly oil reserves are limited around Baku, and exploration costly, yet the industry continues to expand here partly on the past reputation of the Caucasus as an abundant source of oil. Turning to a comparison of the Russian Empire with the sea empires created (and lost) by West European powers, surely we could usefully study the differences between large political units that are continuous and compact and those that are greatly fragmented and discontinuous. Another question that is often asked about the Russians is whether or not they are European. While this question revolves largely round a definition,

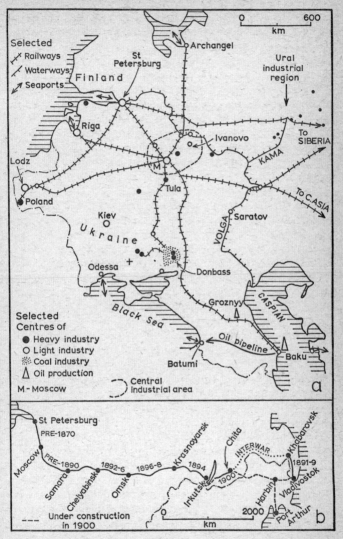

10. a. European Russia around 1900. b. The Trans - Siberian Railway.

it is thought-provoking and leads one to appreciate that while the Russians originated well within Europe, their empire-building put them in close contact with many different peoples and cultures in central and southern Asia. In forgetting the past, the Communists also forgot to give independence back to non-Russian areas such as Transcaucasia and Central Asia; in fact they have even managed to bring in a few more non-Russian areas since 1917.

Chapter 4

POPULATION

THIS chapter gives a general picture of the distribution of population in the U.S.S.R. In the view of the author the distribution of population gives the best introduction to the human geography of the country, since activities such as agriculture, mining and manufacturing, and services such as railways, exist to serve population, are run by people, and therefore reflect the distribution of people. The general distribution of people in the U.S.S.R. reflects the greatly differing usefulness of and use made of different parts of the national area. Clearly, for example, highly urbanized areas tend to be associated with mining and manufacturing. The varying cultural and social backgrounds of the population over the national area is also important in an appreciation of the human geography, even in a Communist framework where these features are not stressed and are theoretically of little importance. In the study of population, it is essential to appreciate too the drastic losses that were suffered during the First and Second World Wars and during the collectivization of agriculture in the early 1930s. In particular the age and sex balance of the country was upset in a spectacular way by the Second World War, with repercussions on man-power ever since.

I. INTRODUCTION

At the beginning of 1965 the population of the U.S.S.R. was about 229 million, some 7 per cent of the world total. The following table summarizes trends this century.

| | 1913 | 1940 | 1950 | 1960 | 1965 | Expected | | |
						1970	1975	1980
Total population	159	194	178½	212	229	250	263	280
Urban	28½	63	69½	104	121½	145	160	190
Rural	130½	131	109	108	107½	105	103	90
Percentage urban	18	33	39	49	53	58	61	68
Percentage rural	82	67	61	51	47	42	39	32

SOURCE: *Nkh S S S R, 1963*, p. 8, and *SSSR v tsifrakh v 1964 godu*, p. 7.

There has been an increase of roughly $3\frac{1}{2}$ million per year during the early 1960s. At the same time the proportion of urban dwellers has increased by about one per cent per year, a trend expected to continue at least to 1980.

In 1963 the birthrate in the U.S.S.R. as a whole was 21·2 per thousand inhabitants, the deathrate 7·2 per thousand and the natural increase therefore 14 per thousand. Infant mortality was 31 per thousand. A characteristic feature of Soviet population for at least half a century has been the higher birthrate in rural settlements than in urban ones. The steady increase in the proportion of urban dwellers has continued in spite of this, and is caused both by the migration of people from rural settlements into urban ones and by the promotion to urban status (by definition) of rural centres, as for various reasons they grow or change function. A further rise in the proportion of urban dwellers will however be one potential cause of a further lowering of the national birthrate, given the generally low birthrate in towns. On the other hand, it must be remembered that as a population increases, the same percentage natural increase means a slightly greater absolute number of people added to the population each year.

As a consequence not only of the Second World War, but apparently also of collectivization in the early 1930s, there has for some time been an imbalance in the ratio of males to females in the U.S.S.R., as the following figures clearly show:

	Population in millions			
	Total	Male	Female	Percentage male
1959	209	94	115	45
1964	226	103	123	45·6

During the Second World War far more adult males were killed or died than females. This has left the Soviet Union in the postwar period with a preponderance of females, especially in employable age-groups (say 15 to 65), one explanation of the common practice of employing women in heavy manual work. By 1964, however, there was a balance between male and female in age-groups below about 35, groups of which the members were either below 16 during the war or not yet born. In some of these age-groups, males actually exceed females.

The population of the U.S.S.R. consists of a very large number of national groups. According to the 1959 census, almost fifty of these had at least 100,000 members, while there are many others as well, some with only a few thousand people. Basically, the U.S.S.R. is divided into fifteen Soviet Socialist Republics, S.S.R.s (see Figure 11), which vary greatly both in total area and in number

11. The fifteen Soviet Socialist Republics and their capitals.

of inhabitants. Each of these S.S.R.s has a core population made up of one particular national group (e.g. the Russians, Estonians, Uzbeks). Each S.S.R., by the way, either has a coast or a common boundary with a country outside the U.S.S.R.

In addition to the fifteen S.S.R.s, there were, in 1962, twenty Autonomous Soviet Socialist Republics (A.S.S.R.s), all but four of which were in the largest S.S.R., the Russian one. These are

T–C

formed round other national groups that are either in the interior
of the country and do not therefore qualify for S.S.R. status
because they have no boundary coterminous with a foreign
country, or are too small to merit the status of S.S.R.s. There are
also some twenty other national areas of one sort or another lower
in administrative status than the A.S.S.R.s. Many nationalities
such as Jews, Germans, Poles, Gipsies and Greeks are too dispersed territorially to form nuclei for national areas. The distribution of nationalities is now mapped in considerable detail in
Atlas narodov mira (Moscow, 1964, pp. 10–30). The following
table shows the number of members of the main national groups
in 1959. Liberty has been taken in deciding a reasonably wieldy
English equivalent for some of these names. Those forming the
titular group of S.S.R.s are listed in column I, those with more
than 300,000 members and forming the titular group of A.S.S.R.s
in column II, and other important groups in column III.

I	Number of members in millions	Percentage of total U.S.S.R. population	II		
Russians	114·1	54·7	Tatars	5·0	2·4
Ukrainians	37·3	17·8	Chuvash	1·5	0·7
Belorussians	7·9	3·8	Mordovs	1·3	0·6
Uzbeks	6·0	2·9	Bashkirs	1·0	0·5
Kazakhs	3·6	1·7	Udmurts	0·6	0·3
Azerbaijanians	2·9	1·4	Mariyts	0·5	0·2
Armenians	2·8	1·3	Komi	0·4	0·2
Georgians	2·7	1·3	Chechentsy	0·4	0·2
Lithuanians	2·3	1·1	Osetinians	0·4	0·2
Moldavians	2·2	1·0			
Latvians	1·4	0·7	III		
Tadjiks	1·4	0·7			
Turkmens	1·0	0·5	Jews	2·3	1·1
Estonians	1·0	0·5	Germans	1·6	0·8
Kirgiz	1·0	0·5	Poles	1·4	0·7
			Bulgarians	0·3	0·15
			Koreans	0·3	0·15
			Greeks	0·3	0·15

SOURCE: P. G. Pod'yachikh, *Naseleniye S S S R*, Moscow, 1961.

The set of members belonging to a particular national group is
almost in a one to one correspondence with the set of people

speaking the language of the group, but there are a few people who in the census were recorded as belonging to one nationality but who put another language, often Russian, as their mother tongue.

Within its territorial limits, each S.S.R. and A.S.S.R. has members of many other groups. Thus the R.S.F.S.R.[1] had in 1959 over 117½ million inhabitants, but only about 98 million, or some 83 per cent, were Russians. This left some 16 million Russians living in other Republics, 7 million of them, for example, in the Ukraine. A comparable situation exists with each national area, and in some cases (e.g. Kazakhstan, Kirgizia), the titular group forms less than half of the total population. The proportion in each area of Russians, and to a lesser extent of their fellow Slavs, the Ukrainians and Belorussians, is of interest and importance. The constant trend to disperse these among the other nationalities is part of a gradual process of Russification, strengthened by the growing relative importance of Russian as the language of technology and presumably even of organization and administration. The percentage of Russians in each of the non-Russian S.S.R.s is given in the table below.

Although the population of the R.S.F.S.R. is greater than that of all the other fourteen Republics combined and should be split up for more detailed consideration, the table is a useful introduction to many basic features of the U.S.S.R. and should be studied carefully. Most of the time in this book, however, data will be given for nineteen economic regions (see Figure 19), a system in which the R.S.F.S.R. is divided into ten parts, the Ukraine into three, and most of the other Republics are grouped. This gives a better overall picture than the S.S.R.s since the units are more comparable in size. In the table the following features should be noted: the great area of the R.S.F.S.R. compared with the other Republics, the great difference in recent population growth rate between the 'European' and 'non-European' Republics, the considerable percentage of Russians in the other Republics, and the great difference in proportion of urban dwellers among the Republics.

1. The Russian Soviet Federal Socialist Republic. This, rather than the U.S.S.R. as a whole, may be referred to as Russia.

	Area[1]	Population in millions		Density of population[2] 1964	Population growth[3] 1959–64 (1959 = 100)	Percentage Russians 1959	Percentage urban 1964
		1959	1964				
R.S.F.S.R.	17,075	117·5	124·7	7·3	105	83·3	58
Ukraine	601	41·9	44·6	74·3	106	16·9	50
Belorussia	208	8·1	8·5	40·7	105	8·2	37
Uzbekistan	450	8·3	9·8	21·8	119	13·5	35
Kazakhstan	2,715	9·2	11·5	4·2	126	42·7	46
Georgia	70	4·0	4·4	63·3	109	10·1	46
Azerbaijan	87	3·7	4·4	50·6	118	13·6	50
Lithuania	65	2·7	2·9	44·6	107	8·5	43
Moldavia	34	2·9	3·2	96·2	113	10·2	25
Latvia	64	2·1	2·2	34·8	106	26·6	60
Kirgizia	199	2·1	2·5	12·6	121	30·2	38
Tadjikistan	143	2·0	2·3	16·4	118	13·3	35
Armenia	30	1·8	2·1	69·4	118	3·2	54
Turkmenistan	488	1·5	1·8	3·7	119	17·3	48
Estonia	45	1·2	1·3	27·9	109	20·1	61
U.S.S.R.	22,402	208·8	226·3	10·2	105	not relevant	52

SOURCE: *Nkh SSSR, 1963*, except for nationalities.
1. Area in thousands of sq. km.
2. Density of population, persons per sq. km.
3. Calculated from complete, not rounded, figures.

II. DISTRIBUTION OF POPULATION

In Figures 12 and 13 the distribution of population over the national area of the U.S.S.R. is shown in two ways. In Figure 12 each of the cells contains approximately one per cent of the total population of the U.S.S.R. or about 2,300,000 people. The cells were worked out on the basis of data for major civil divisions (oblasts, and so on), and the dots, representing the mean centre ('centre of gravity') of the population in each cell, give a reasonable general picture of distribution.[1] From the map the reader can

1. Though many slightly different versions would be arrived at depending on the starting point for the procedure.

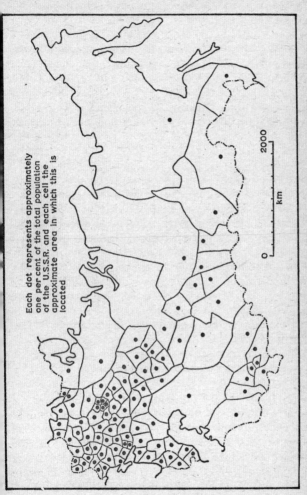

Each dot represents approximately one per cent of the total population of the U.S.S.R. and each cell the approximate area in which this is located

0   2000

km

12. Distribution of population in the U.S.S.R. 1962 figures for major civil divisions have been used as the basis for this map.

quickly work out roughly what percentage of the total population is to be found in any particular part of the U.S.S.R. For example the great concentration in the western part and the emptiness of the east can easily be seen.

In Figure 13 population is represented in a different way. Each major administrative division of the U.S.S.R. (about 150 were used) is shaded according to the density of population in it (1962 data). Thus for example Tula oblast south of Moscow had 76 people per sq. km., Irkutsk oblast in Siberia only 3; these were not the extremes. The mean density of population in the U.S.S.R. as a whole is about 10 persons per sq. km. and shading has been arranged on this basis so that it is easy to distinguish areas with a density above the mean from those with a density below it. Further shading has been applied to distinguish much more densely peopled areas and very sparsely settled ones. The density of population should be thought of against a background of other features. The densely populated areas are not necessarily over-populated, and many of the empty areas could not be expected to attract more than a very small population in the foreseeable future. In other words, notwithstanding the gradual shift of population eastwards there is no reason to expect the basic features of this map to change for a long time; if anything, population is tending to accumulate more and more in a few limited areas, and not to disperse itself over empty spaces. It may be noted here that even the highest densities of population achieved in the Ukraine, in Central Asia and in some industrial areas are a long way below those found in other comparable parts of Europe, in India or in the most densely settled parts of China.

One way of assessing the degree of concentration of population in a given area, with a view to comparing it ultimately with some other area or areas in the world, is to find out what proportion of the total population is found on, say, the most thinly peopled half of the country, what proportion on, say, the most densely peopled 10 per cent of the area, and so on. If population were evenly spread over an area, then any part of it would have the same proportion of the total population on it as it occupied of the total area. This of course rarely occurs in reality. The procedure for summarizing the dispersal of population is to list the major civil

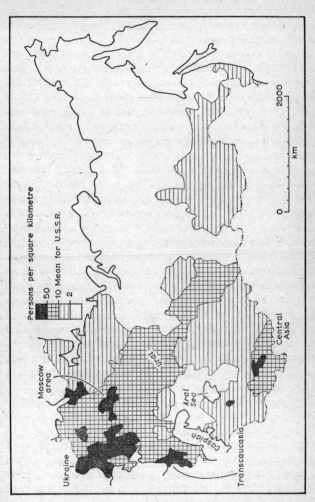

13. Density of population in the U.S.S.R. by major civil divisions, 1962.

divisions in order of density, first from low to high, then from high to low, far enough to work out some meaningful index on the lines described. In the U.S.S.R., the least densely peopled 50 per cent of the national area has only 4·5 per cent of the total population while the most densely populated 7·5 per cent of the area has about half of the total population. It is worthwhile noting that a similar calculation for Latin America as a whole – which has roughly the same area and the same number of people as the U.S.S.R. – gave strikingly similar results, meaning that the degree of concentration and dispersal is similar, even though the pattern of distribution is very different. A Soviet publication[1] points out that only 16 per cent of the total population is to be found on about two thirds of the surface of the U.S.S.R. (West and East Siberia, the Far East and Kazakhstan) and suggests that this area could in fact hold 100–120 million people, instead of less than 40 million at present.

Reconsidering Figure 12, it is not difficult to visualize how, if each of the dots were a weight, and all the weights were equal, then this distribution of weights, resting on a weightless surface, would balance at a point, which would be the mean centre of population.[2] Such a centre can in fact be worked out mathematically, and is near Kuybyshev on the middle Volga. Likewise, the mean centre of area can be calculated; it lies much further east, near the middle Ob'. The movement over time of the mean centre of population of both the U.S.A.[3] and the U.S.S.R. has been studied; that in the U.S.A. has moved steadily westwards from near Washington in the 1780s to near St Louis in 1960. There has been a much less marked eastward shift over the same period in Russia.

III. URBAN POPULATION

Between 1926 and 1961 the urban population of the U.S.S.R. grew more than four times, or by 85½ million people. The growth has been absorbed mostly by existing towns, but also to some extent

1. Vedishchev, p. 22.
2. The centre can also be worked out by drawing median lines but the median centre varies somewhat according to orientation of line.
3. See *Statistical Abstract of the United States 1963*, p. 8.

by the creation of many new ones. Such an increase must have put a far greater strain on urban amenities than contemporaneous urban growth in West Europe, particularly in view of the great destruction in the war. The proportion of urban to total population rose rapidly in the 1930s (18 per cent in 1926, 33 per cent in 1939) and again in the postwar period, passing 50 per cent in 1961. Something like two thirds of the increase in urban population during the period 1939–59 was contributed by the inflow of rural population from the countryside, and many more people are expected from here in the next fifteen years as labour productivity in agriculture rises sharply.

On the whole the R.S.F.S.R. is more highly urbanized than the rest of the country, while Central Asia, the last large area to be added to the Russian Empire, is much less urbanized. The extremes among the fifteen S.S.R.s are Estonia 61 per cent urban and Moldavia 25 per cent, but on the next level of administrative divisions the range of the proportion of urban dwellers is even greater, with very high percentages not only in industrial areas with large towns (e.g. Sverdlovsk oblast 80 per cent) but also in thinly peopled timber and mining areas (e.g. Murmansk oblast 95 per cent). The most deeply rural areas are those with a high density of rural population away from districts of industrial growth. Several oblasts in the western Ukraine are only about 30 per cent urban, while some areas in Central Asia are even less urbanized than this. The proportion of urban to total population is shown for the nineteen economic regions in Figure 14.

Many individual towns of the U.S.S.R. will be referred to at some stage in this book, but the number of towns is too large for a complete study of their growth and functions to be made, even if adequate data were available. It is useful, however, to know where the largest towns are, since the location of other features can be described and remembered in terms of proximity to these. The forty towns that in 1962 had more than 350,000 are therefore shown in Figure 15a. In the table they are ranked according to their growth-rate between 1939 and 1962; this gives the reader a useful introduction to broad differences in regional population growth, which will be discussed in the next section. The names of towns with over 750,000 inhabitants in 1965 are shown in bold print.

Apart from Moscow and Leningrad, the U.S.S.R. lacks 'multi-million' cities, but in 1965 had no fewer than fourteen with between 750,000 and 1,332,000 (Kiev). There is less of a concentration of population in very large cities than is found in North

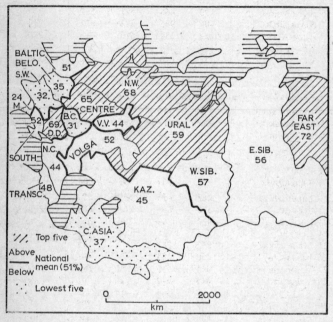

14. Urban population as a percentage of total population. This map shows post-1962 economic region boundaries. Source: *Nkh SSSR, 1963*, p. 13.

America and some parts of West Europe, or even in Japan. Apart from Moscow and Leningrad, which are special cases, many of the larger Soviet cities are either heavy industrial centres (e.g. older ones like Donetsk, Khar'kov, new ones like Novokuznetsk, Ufa) or capitals of S.S.R.s (e.g. Minsk, Tashkent). The eastern Ukraine, Moscow industrial area and Ural region each contain several of the largest. Others are strung out along the Trans-Siberian Railway (e.g. Omsk, Krasnoyarsk). A map showing centres down to

	Population (*in thousands*)				Growth 1939–62 (*1939 = 100*)
	1939	*1962*	*1964*[1]	*1965*	
1 Karaganda	156	459	477	482	294
2 Yerevan	204	583	611	623	286
3 **Chelyabinsk**	273	751	790	803	276
4 Minsk	237	599	688	707	252
5 Novokuznetsk	166	410		475	247
6 Krasnoyarsk	190	465	521	542	245
7 **Novosibirsk**	404	985	1,013	1,027	244
8 Alma-Ata	222	534	610	617	240
9 Krivoy Rog	189	448		488	237
10 Ufa	258	610	651	666	236
11 Perm'	306	701	745	763	230
12 Kuybyshev	390	881	928	950	226
13 Omsk	289	650	702	722	225
14 Nizhniy Tagil	160	359		370	224
15 Sverdlovsk	423	853	897	917	202
16 Krasnodar	193	354	377	385	185
17 **Tashkent**	550	1,002	1,073	1,090	182
18 **Kazan'**	398	711	743	763	179
19 Riga	348	620	649	657	178
20 Khabarovsk	207	363	393	408	175
21 Zaporozh'ye	282	490	529	550	174
22 Saratov	372	631	665	684	170
23 **Donetsk**	466	760	794	809	163
24 **Gor'kiy**	644	1,025	1,066	1,084	159
25 Makeyevka	242	381		399	158
26 Irkutsk	250	385	397	401	154
27 Voronezh	344	516	558	577	150
28 Volgograd	445	649	684	701	146
29 Yaroslavl'	309	443	467	478	143
30 Tbilisi	519	743	794	805	143
31 Kiev	847	1,208	1,308	1,332	143
32 **Moscow**	4,536	6,262	6,353	6,427	138
33 Baku	775	1,067	1,128	1,137	138
34 **Dnepropetrovsk**	527	722	755	774	137
35 Lvov	340	447	487	496	131
36 Rostov	510	661	706	721	130
37 Ivanovo	285	360	380	389	126
38 **Khar'kov**	833	990	1,048	1,070	119
39 Odessa	602	704	721	735	117
40 **Leningrad**[2]	3,015	3,036	3,218	3,636	101

SOURCE: *Nkh SSSR, 1961,* pp. 20–1, and *1963,* pp. 22–3.
1. Where available.
2. The sudden change from 1964 to 1965 is due to boundary changes.

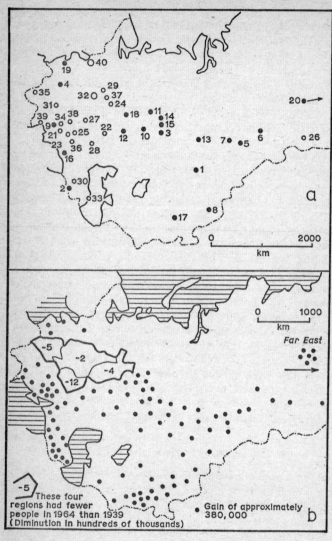

15. a. The forty largest towns of the U.S.S.R. in 1962 (see table p. 73).
b. Where population grew in the period 1939–64 (see text). Source:
Nkh SSSR, 1963.

100,000 or 50,000 inhabitants would bring out these concentrations more clearly. Only in a few instances (e.g. the western part of the Donbass coalfield) do nearby urban centres coalesce to form clusters of towns linked by continuous built-up areas.

In recent years there has been talk of seriously attempting to curtail the growth of the largest towns and trying to divert growth to smaller and medium centres.[1] A population of 250,000–300,000 is referred to as the optimum size for a town, a size large enough for services to be provided economically but small enough to avoid congestion. Very small towns, on the other hand, are as undesirable as very large ones. It may be noted that over fifty towns already exceed 300,000 and many more are approaching that figure. Nevertheless, it is hoped to spread employment among the 'medium' centres, for here labour tends to be more abundant than in large centres. It is considered undesirable, too, that, as in many oblasts, the oblast capital has accumulated much of the industry (e.g. about 75 per cent in Voronezh, Omsk). The encouragement of industrial growth in many medium towns is also considered to be a possible way of reducing the difference in the standard of living between town and country. There does not appear to be any strategic motive in this new appraisal of urban trends. What should also be taken into account is the possibility that if, in the interests of decongesting urban concentrations, industry is spread even more widely over the national area than it is now, then industrial establishments supplying one another will more easily become out of touch, and the average haul of goods between sources of raw materials and factories, and between factories and consumers, may increase substantially.

IV. POPULATION CHANGES

While the population of the U.S.S.R. has increased by almost 80 per cent in the present century there have also been very great changes in the distribution over the national area. Asiatic U.S.S.R. has gained relatively at the expense of European U.S.S.R. although the lack of balance is still enormous. At the same time, some parts of European U.S.S.R. have fewer people than they did a few decades ago, while others have grown very fast. Similarly, much

1. See, e.g. Vedishchev, pp. 33–7.

of Asiatic U.S.S.R. has hardly been affected, and in reality most of the increase there has occurred along the general course of the Trans-Siberian Railway or in Central Asia.

The total population of the U.S.S.R. has grown as follows:

	Number of inhabitants	Percentage urban
1897[1]	124,600,000	15
1926[2]	147,000,000	18
1939[2]	167,000,000	28
1940[3]	194,000,000	33
1950[1]	178,500,000	35
1965[1] (Jan.)	229,100,000	53

1. Within the present area of the U.S.S.R. (22,400,000 sq.km.).
2. In the inter-war area (21,700,000 sq.km.).
3. After the acquisition of areas in Central Europe (to 22,100,000sq. km.).

Some idea of the great loss of population caused by the Second World War will be appreciated from the table. At the end (1945) there were about thirty million fewer than at the beginning. This does not of course mean that all these people lost their lives, though many did; the birthrate fell, too, while many people left the country or were removed and never returned.

Figure 15b gives a general idea of regional population changes in the U.S.S.R. since the late 1930s. Map 15a shows the location of the forty Soviet towns that had the largest number of inhabitants in 1962. These towns have been listed and are divided into two halves, the fastest-growing half and the slowest-growing half. All but one (Irkutsk) of the towns of Asiatic U.S.S.R. are in the half that grew fastest. Most of them more than doubled in population in the period 1939–62, a performance matched and often exceeded by smaller towns in this part of the country. Most of the towns in the European part of the U.S.S.R. grew less rapidly, but a few, including particularly Yerevan and Minsk, S.S.R. capitals, grew very fast. Boundary changes and the great size of Moscow already in 1939 obscure a very large absolute increase especially in the outer suburbs of the national capital, at least two million altogether.

During the period 1939–64 the total population of the U.S.S.R. increased by about thirty-five and a half million people. During this period, however, there was an absolute loss of two million people in the general area formed by four economic regions, Belorussia, the Industrial and Blackearth central regions and the Volga-Vyatka. The other fifteen regions therefore gained by almost thirty-eight million. Figure 15b shows how this gain was spread over the national area, each dot representing approximately 380,000 people or one per cent of the total increase. Almost one quarter occurred in the North-west, Baltic Republics, Ukraine and North Caucasus, almost another quarter in Transcaucasia and Central Asia. Approximately half, however, occurred within a belt of country stretching from the Middle Volga across the Ural, through West Siberia and Kazakhstan to Lake Baykal and the Far East. The gain in the great empty lands lying north of this belt has been only a few hundred thousand.

The first interpretation of these changes, then, is of a great move in the direction of Asiatic U.S.S.R. At least two reservations should be made here, however. Firstly, the picture would be different if the Second World War had not eliminated a considerable proportion of the population in parts of European U.S.S.R. Secondly, precisely because of the war, equipment and people were deliberately moved eastwards, and during the war industrial expansion obviously had to take place east of the Volga for security reasons. In other words, the period 1939–62 is one in which a special event occurred, and may not express the normal trend. Similarly, movement of population eastwards earlier in the century may have been due to the construction of the Trans-Siberian Railway and other railways and the attraction for a time of new opportunities in the east.

A study of population trends since the late 1950s shows that most of the absolute increase is now occurring once again in the European part, although the relative increase tends to be higher in Central Asia, with its particularly high birthrate, and in parts of Kazakhstan and Siberia, with many new developments. In conclusion, it seems that in the mid-1960s there is no particular part of the U.S.S.R. in which urban growth is most rapid, for many towns in the European part are making a striking recovery, while many farther east are stagnating. On the other hand, the rural population in European U.S.S.R. is tending to dwindle still, while that in many parts of Asiatic U.S.S.R. is increasing.

The general features of the present distribution of population in the U.S.S.R. are related first to the availability of resources, secondly to the fact that there has for many centuries now been a large cluster of population in the central part of European Russia. We should be very surprised to find a cluster of population of comparable size in say north-east Siberia, but there is no reason why, in terms of physical conditions and resources, there should not have been one in the belt of country between the Ural Range and Lake Baykal. It will be shown in the next chapter that here, in fact, is much good farmland as well as many other resources. It would be convenient if several tens of millions of people could be shifted from European U.S.S.R. and spread in this general area, left empty for so long. But even with a Communist régime this is not possible to achieve over a short period. Compulsion is used much less now than previously to move people and for some years indeed the eastward movement of population seems almost to have ceased. Neither in the Russian Empire nor since 1917 was there such a massive and spontaneous flow of people into pioneer areas as in North America in the last century. Almost always people would be expected to move voluntarily to new areas only if there was an assurance or at least prospects of better employment opportunities. Siberia offers these, but in theory anyway the Soviet system is against regional differences in wages for the same kind of work. Furthermore, the environment is that much more harsh and unpleasant than in European U.S.S.R.

Chapter 5

NATURAL RESOURCES

GEOGRAPHY not only contains an inventory of resources and of places where these are found. It must also consider how these are related to the distribution of population and to one another. One can safely say that no country in the world has its resources exactly where it would like to have them. In the U.S.S.R. most of the agricultural land (which may be considered as a resource) is to be found in the general area in which most of the population is concentrated. In contrast, most of the best mineral, hydro-electric, forest and fishery resources are separated from the large concentrations of population by great distances. In very broad terms, the U.S.S.R. can tap its more remote resources either by sending a limited number of people to them to extract them and send them elsewhere, or by settling a much larger number of people on them both to extract and to consume them on the spot.

I. INTRODUCTION

Interest in the resources of Russia originated long before the Communist régime and the vast potential natural wealth of the country has often attracted attention from outside. For example in the 1830s the French writer A. de Tocqueville asserted that the United States and Russia had the ingredients for greatness in the future. During the Communist period, however, the work of assessing the inventory of resources has been intensified, with particular attention being given to minerals. The purpose of this chapter is to note the resources of the U.S.S.R., giving an idea of their quantity where data allow, and showing their location in the national area. First, however, a few words are necessary on what is understood in this chapter by natural resources.

Population is often counted as a particular resource when the total resources of a country are being considered, but it is clearly different from natural resources. Population will not therefore be considered here with the natural resources of the U.S.S.R. but rather as something against which these must be balanced. The concept of a population/resource balance in any given area of reasonable size is to be found widely, and is useful as a measure for assessing the favourability of the natural resources of a country. Three main types of natural resource can conveniently be distinguished, although there is some overlap: plant and animal resources (crops, trees, livestock and so on), mineral resources (metals, sources of energy and so on) and finally water. The first are organic, the second and third inorganic, but it is convenient to separate water from other minerals on account of its widespread occurrence and numerous uses. Previously considered to be lacking only in arid areas, water supply has recently become a preoccupation in many industrial countries in which there appears to be no immediate lack.

Most natural resources are not renewable. For example, once coal has been mined and burned it is lost. Similarly, if soil is cultivated excessively its fertility can gradually disappear. On the other hand, falling water used to generate electricity is renewable, assuming that a constant flow of water is maintained, for the water is not destroyed. In assessing the potential resources of any region this distinction must be remembered.

In considering the resources of the U.S.S.R. the following features must be known: the ability to use any particular resource (related to the level of technology achieved in the country), the size of the resources and finally their location within the national territory. Their location often decides whether or not they are worth utilizing at any given time, since some may be placed near the areas where they would be used, while others may be completely inaccessible.

Resources themselves change slowly with time. For example, in certain areas peat is slowly accumulating, while in other areas salts are gradually being deposited. New soil can form quickly under certain conditions, as on lava from volcanoes, while climate, which affects possibilities for cultivation, can change profoundly in quite a short time. That is to say, developments of the kind indicated occur over a matter of several thousand years. But such changes are slow compared with such a short period in history as, say, post-1917 U.S.S.R., and can be ignored; resources can therefore be considered as fixed. At the same time, the usefulness of resources changes with time, provided that technological improvements are being introduced. For example, aluminium was hardly used until the present century, but is now an indispensable ingredient of an advanced industrial economy. In contrast, animal fat for making, say, candles, was in great demand until the present century, but is now hardly needed for this purpose.

If man's ability to use various natural resources has improved gradually over the last few thousand years, irregularly and in different ways in different parts of the world, in the last two centuries or so it has been improving rapidly. More and more resources, particularly minerals, are being used for the first time, while new uses are being found for resources already exploited. Furthermore the attitude and policy towards raw materials may change as a result of progress in technology. For example, peat, hitherto extensively fed as fuel into thermal electric power stations in the U.S.S.R., is now regarded rather as an organic fertilizer for agriculture. Similarly, it is hoped to eliminate the use of grain, potatoes and sunflower-seed oil as raw materials in the chemicals industry.

To use resources at any level of technology other than the most simple, some kind of organization is needed and some equipment. Even in simple agricultural economies, ploughing, irrigation, the storage of products and so on require both organization and the accumulation of capital. In a country as large and complex as the U.S.S.R. most known resources are used and virtually anything can be manufactured. In these conditions a knowledge of resources is essential, and since the establishment of national planning a particular effort has been made in the U.S.S.R. to assess its resources and to plan their exploitation in the most advantageous way. In the Soviet system of course the resources are entirely the concern of the state, and the capital allocated for their utilization comes from the state.

Considering the great size of the U.S.S.R. it would be expected to have a large share of the world's resources. All other things being equal, the larger the area of a country the greater would be its total resources. In practice this is not necessarily true; contrast, for example, France with Greenland, or the Ukraine with Kamchatka. If the U.S.S.R. has some seven per cent of the world's population, it has about fourteen per cent of the world's land area, and might therefore be expected to have more than its share of the world's resources if these were distributed according to population; that is, it would have a favourable population/ resource balance. In reality, it only has an excessive share of certain resources: land suitable for cultivation, forests, coal and probably several other minerals. These are important enough to place it favourably compared with several other large regions of the world, notably West Europe, India and China. But many underdeveloped countries of the world appear to have good natural resources. Unless they have or acquire the ability to organize the exploitation of the resources, the resources are of little use.

The U.S.S.R. appears to be broadly comparable with North America, but if it is expected to supply the rest of COMECON with raw materials, then the situation is not so good. Nor, even though its position appears to be good with regard to total resources, does this mean that all the resources are readily accessible at the moment. In fact, many are at great distances from the areas in which they could be most usefully used, a feature easily overlooked by economists and planners.

Turning to the spatial location of resources, it should be noted that plant and animal resources are closely associated with present-day or relatively recent conditions of climate, vegetation, soil and slope, whereas, with minor exceptions, such as some salts, mineral resources are not. For this reason, about ninety-five per cent of the land at present used for cultivation is in the western half of the U.S.S.R. where physical conditions are most favourable. The fact that most of the population is still here as well is, of course, closely related, since until the 1930s Russia was basically an agricultural country. In contrast, there is no reason to suppose that any particular half of the U.S.S.R. should have such an excessive share of the minerals, for these are related to underlying rocks, the distribution of which may have been determined hundreds of millions of years ago. In reality, minerals are unevenly scattered over the surface of the country. The third main resource, water, is of course closely related to present-day climate, but its particular distribution must be accounted for in terms different from those accounting for the distribution of agricultural land or minerals. Water is a resource of rapidly growing interest in the U.S.S.R. and obviously has a large number of uses. As well, naturally, as being essential in agriculture, either as rain or supplied by an irrigation system, it supplements energy minerals in the generation of electricity, is used in considerable quantities for domestic purposes, and in very large quantities for certain mining and manufacturing processes. Finally, it can be used for transportation. Many water-supply projects satisfy the needs of two or more branches of the economy.

II. PLANT AND ANIMAL RESOURCES

Those features of the physical environment that set the limits to agriculture can broadly be considered under four headings: temperature and precipitation, both of which are climatic, slope (or lack of it) and soils. The physical environment of the U.S.S.R. has already been briefly considered in Chapter 3. In this section, therefore, it will be considered only in so far as it affects agriculture.

Owing to the high latitude of the U.S.S.R. (almost all lies closer to the Pole than to the Equator) cold conditions are the most widely found obstacle to cultivation. Plant growth takes place above a certain temperature (the threshold temperature), which differs greatly from plant to plant. For example, many grasses and some green vegetables can begin to grow only a few degrees Centigrade above freezing, while others, such as cotton and sugar cane, require much greater heat. Of course, the higher above the threshold the temperature rises, the more rapidly plant growth takes place.

The influence of temperature on agriculture can be assessed in various ways. Figure 16, for example, shows the mean July temperature, which only gives a rough picture of conditions. But a more precise assessment of temperature can be obtained by finding how many days in the year, in any given place, plant growth could be expected to occur (see Figure 16a). Better still is an assessment of what are called degree days; this takes into account how high above a given threshold temperature the temperature actually rises each day during the growing season. Other features of temperature that have to be considered in relation to agriculture are the duration of snow cover (see Figure 7a) and the occurrence of permafrost, while local conditions such as exposure to the sun resulting from aspect also have an influence. It may be noted here that in the northern part of the U.S.S.R. summer months are characterized by very long days and higher temperatures tend to occur for longer each day than they do farther south. Not all plants can benefit from this.

Figure 16a shows the areas of the U.S.S.R. in which there are fewer than 120 days above a temperature of 5°C, a temperature below which even the least exacting commercial plants cannot grow. In these areas cultivation is virtually impossible except locally where there are specially favourable conditions or in artificial conditions such as hothouses. Part of the area is forested, but the quality of the timber is not usually high. Figure 16a also shows the area in which between 120 and 150 days with a temperature of over 5°C occur each year. Here, given that other natural conditions are suitable, cultivation of a limited range of crops should be possible. To the south of this area more and more crops can be grown. Some of the most northerly plants grown are rye, wheat, flax and potatoes (since their introduction from the New World after 1500). Passing south, maize and the sunflower are now cultivated successfully at about 55°N, but cotton and tea only at about 45°N. Tropical plants such as the rubber and oil palm trees cannot of course be grown anywhere.

Some two thirds of the area of the U.S.S.R. is rendered completely or almost completely useless for agriculture by low temperature alone. Almost all of the eastern half of the country can be ruled out. A major feature of the widespread long cold season is the fact that virtually no work can be done on the land for anything up to several months of the year even in the main area of cultivation to the south of the two thirds already excluded. Agricultural activities are therefore carried on with a rhythm quite different from that in the tropics, and it is tempting to think that this has contributed to forming some features of the Russian character and way of life.

In agriculture, lack of water can be as restricting as low temperatures. Rainfall (to be precise, precipitation, which includes snowfall as well) can be assessed in various ways with regard to its usefulness to agriculture. Figure 18a shows the distribution of mean annual precipitation and indicates roughly the availability or lack of water for agriculture. But with greater heat and evaporation the effectiveness of a given amount of precipitation diminishes. In other words, 60 cm. of rain per year goes a long way in the Moscow area but does not amount to much in Central Asia,

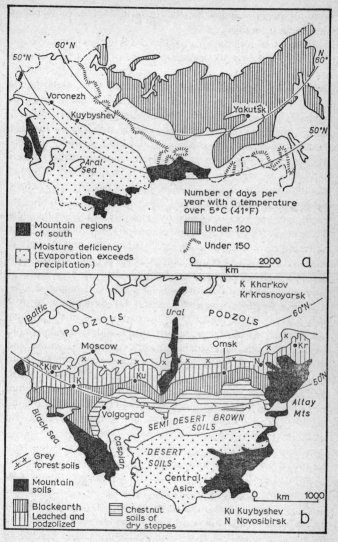

16. Physical conditions affecting agriculture. a. Unfavourable features. b. Soils in the western half of the U.S.S.R.

where temperatures are much higher and evaporation much greater. If the rain or snow comes largely in the season in which temperatures are too low for plant growth then it is not of much use either. In other words, the season in which rain comes must be considered.

Map 16a does not show the actual amount of precipitation but that area (shown by dots) in which water is not considered to be adequate for agriculture. The assessment is made on the basis of the actual amount of precipitation measured against the evaporation that would be expected to take place given the temperature conditions. This does not mean that nothing grows but that with increasing distance south of the line conditions become more and more difficult. Nor does it mean that there is always adequate water in areas north of the line. For some distance to the north of it droughts are not unknown, but other features rather than lack of water also begin to make agriculture difficult. To the south of the line not only does total precipitation diminish and evaporation increase, but reliability of precipitation diminishes, with the result that in some years abundant rain may fall while in other years there may be so little that no harvest can be gathered at all. Dry winds are an added hazard and may ruin crops at an early stage of growth.

The suitability of land for agricultural purposes can also be profoundly influenced by conditions of slope. An area may be either too broken to be convenient for ploughing or, less often, too flat to drain properly, and therefore too damp to be easily cultivated. Broken areas with steep slopes occur in the U.S.S.R. particularly in the mountain regions of the Caucasus and Central Asia where, of course, altitude and consequent reduction of temperatures also make conditions difficult. In these regions steepness of slope is sometimes overcome by terracing, but often soil is too poor anyway. Steep slopes are also found widely in areas of hill country in the southern half of European U.S.S.R. and gullying occurs frequently. Soil erosion is a problem especially in drier areas where slopes are steep. In central parts of European U.S.S.R., particularly in areas where glaciation took place in the Ice Age, considerable areas of badly drained land occur. The best known and most extensive of these is the Poles'ye (Pripet Marshes).

Even if conditions of temperature, precipitation and slope are suitable for cultivation this does not mean that agriculture can necessarily be practised. Soils vary enormously in quality and are not necessarily fertile in areas where climatic and other conditions are satisfactory. For example, a large part of the U.S.S.R. is covered by very poor tundra soils, while large tracts in the driest part of the country consist of bare rocks or useless blown sand. Map 16b shows the distribution of blackearth (*chernozem*) soils. These stretch over a distance of some 3,000 km. from west to east, between the Black Sea and the Altay Mountains, and include the most fertile soils in the U.S.S.R. The quality of soils deteriorates both north and south from this belt, northwards, with increasing cold and humidity into the zone of podzols, southwards into the belt of desert soils. A careful comparison of Figures 16a and 16b would show that the blackearth belt lies on the northern fringe of the area already described as deficient in moisture. In other words, the best soils do not coincide with the best climatic conditions, which are to be found some distance to the north. While fertility is not in doubt, yields are often poor in the blackearth belt because precipitation is inadequate and unreliable. In the area shown as having desert conditions, soils are not everywhere infertile. If water can be brought in for irrigation to appropriate places, very high yields can be obtained here.

A soil map of the U.S.S.R. published in 1960 gives the approximate proportion of cropland to total area in five soil zones. The figures below show the proportion of each zone under crops and the proportion of the total area of the U.S.S.R. occupied by each zone.

Soil type	Percentage under crops	Percentage of total area of U.S.S.R.
Tundra zone	0	8
Forest zone	5	34
Wooded steppe and steppe	50	14
Semi-desert and desert	2	14
Mountain	2	30

Given the poor quality of most natural pastures in the U.S.S.R. a study of the sown area is sufficient to give a broad picture of the distribution of agricultural production. The sown area has increased as follows in the last fifty years:

	Million hectares sown area
1913	118
1940	150
1953	157
1958	195
1960	203
1963	219
1964	213

There was a gradual, though irregular, rise to 1940. This trend was interrupted by the Second World War. After the war there was some recovery but then stagnation until 1953, after which a great increase of the sown area was achieved by ploughing new lands lying mainly east of the Volga. No further comparable large areas remain now to be brought under cultivation, and the total sown areas seem likely to remain at somewhat less than ten per cent of the total national area. In other words, land as a resource is being used as fully as can be expected under technological conditions of the present or foreseeable future, for the difficulties of extending cultivation into new areas are great.

Northward expansion encounters poor soils, stony areas, and permafrost and can only be achieved by reclaiming small patches of land often unsuitable for mechanization. Penetration into drier areas requires irrigation and therefore costly works of construction. Indeed, soil erosion appears gradually to be reducing the cultivable area along the present southern fringe of cultivation. Grandiose plans to change the climatic conditions of large areas by planting tree belts appear to have been abandoned after Stalin's death in 1953 though the idea has not died entirely. The present position then is that greater agricultural production can be achieved only from the more intensive use of the existing areas of cultivation. This requires the wider use of fertilizers, improvement in the quality of seed and livestock, more and better farm machinery, and the cultivation of particular plants in the areas best suited for them. Such improvements depend on better organization, the allocation of more capital to agriculture and to branches of manufacturing producing fertilizers, tractors and so on, higher wages for farm workers and possibly reconsideration of land tenure. These matters will be discussed again in Chapter 8.

One of the major resources of the U.S.S.R. is its forests. About one third of the total national area is forest covered, some 738 million hectares. Figure 8 shows the distribution of forests. They lie mainly between the blackearth lands in the south and the tundra in the north, thinning appreciably towards their northern and southern margins and also in ill-drained areas, and in mountain areas east of the Yenisey. A limited number of species account for a large part of the total area. In the west the forest was originally broadleaf, but much has now been cleared for agriculture. Eastwards broadleaf species, except for the birch, disappear, and most of the forest in Siberia and the northern part of U.S.S.R. consists of the pine, spruce and fir while the larch predominates in much of East Siberia. The quality of timber varies greatly from one region to another but the degree of exploitation so far depends largely on distance from the main concentrations of population rather than on quality. In the west, good stands of timber have mostly been cut, whereas east of the Ural Range many areas have not yet been touched. Forests are found also in the mountain areas of southern U.S.S.R. but are not extensive, and timber is deficient in the steppe and drier areas of the country.

Fishing is becoming a major economic activity in the U.S.S.R. and there are a number of favourable fishing areas along the coasts. In addition to the inland waterways of the country, the Caspian Sea, which is an area of interior drainage, has been one of the most heavily used areas, especially the shallow northern third. In contrast, the Black Sea is disappointing and the Baltic Sea offers only limited scope. Other coastal areas are further from the main markets in European U.S.S.R. but have been developed in recent decades. The Barents Sea and the North Atlantic are not too distant from Murmansk, but fishing grounds in the Far East, including the Okhotsk Sea and the coasts of Kamchatka, while being excellent, are far from areas of consumption in the U.S.S.R. Soviet fishing fleets also use more distant fishing grounds in the Atlantic and Pacific.

III. MINERALS

The distribution of economic minerals in the U.S.S.R. is related
to a different set of conditions from those affecting agricultural
land. In the first place climate has virtually no influence. Secondly,
there is no one main concentration as there is of cultivated land,
but rather a considerable number of major deposits and an
enormous number of minor ones, at first sight scattered haphaz-
ardly over the total area. If, however, three main types of mineral
are distinguished, firstly energy minerals, secondly most metallic
minerals and thirdly other, often widespread, minerals, then the
distribution can be better understood and is clearly related to
geological and structural features. The energy minerals are found
in sedimentary rocks, coal having been deposited in Carboniferous
times and more recently, and oil and natural gas trapped in
sedimentary rocks of various ages and at various depths, where
these have not been excessively disturbed. In contrast, metallic
minerals are most frequently found in areas in which mountain
building has taken place and in which deposits of ores have appeared at some stage. Metallic minerals are largely confined to a
few areas. On the other hand, certain minerals, such as sand, clay,
limestone and iron in various forms occur very widely. In general,
therefore, energy and metallic minerals occur in quite different
parts of the U.S.S.R. The map of tectonic features is perhaps the
best clue to the two different distributions.

The possibilities of finding important new mineral deposits are
of course far from exhausted. For example, in 1964 alone geological exploration revealed more than a hundred new sources of
oil and gas as well as new sources of twenty-seven other minerals.
Even now, however, it is claimed that the U.S.S.R. has larger
reserves of iron, manganese, copper, lead, zinc, nickel and asbestos
than any other country in the world and that it is one of the first
for proved reserves of gas, oil and coal.

Of the metallic minerals, iron is the one used in largest quantities
and it is found in several different ores. Soviet data for iron ore
reserves show that supplies are sufficient for the foreseeable future.
One figure for 1960 is 93,000 m. tons of which 43,000 m. has an
iron content greater than 40 per cent and about 10,000 m. tons

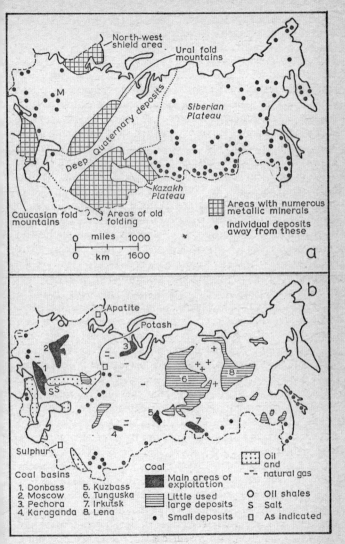

17. Mineral resources. a. Metallic minerals. b. Non-metallic minerals.

is high grade. Some of the best reserves are at Krivoy Rog in the Ukraine and Kursk to the south of Moscow, but some areas in which coking coal, which is used for smelting iron ore, is found, do not have iron ore deposits, and in some cases iron ore is taken up to 1,000 km. by rail. Many new iron ore deposits have been found in the eastern part of the country in recent years but they are too inaccessible to be useful at the moment. Among these are the Kustanay (Kazakhstan) and Angara (East Siberia) areas. More than half of the iron ore extracted in the U.S.S.R. is obtained by opencast methods. The country appears also to have large deposits of the main ferro-alloys, including manganese, chrome, nickel and cobalt.

Little information is available on non-ferrous metals, but Soviet foreign trade in the postwar period suggests that some of these are or have been short. Silver, lead and zinc often occur together; these are mined at the moment mainly in the Ural region, eastern Kazakhstan and the Caucasus. Copper is also mined in these areas, but comes mainly from mid-Kazakhstan. It seems that many of the more accessible deposits of these minerals have already been worked intensively. Bauxite and other minerals in which aluminium occurs are found widely in the U.S.S.R. and appear to be abundant. Gold and tin deposits are found mainly in East Siberia and the Far East. For various reasons, costs of mining gold are very high by world standards.

Other minerals not used as a source of energy include a special set of limited occurrence from which phosphates, potash and sulphur are derived. Large deposits of salt are found in the Donbass area and to the north of the Caspian Sea. Limestone, for cement and for use in the iron and steel industry, sand and clay are widely found in European U.S.S.R. but there is a lack of stones suitable for building and for laying the foundations of roads and railways over much of this part of the country. The discovery of large deposits of industrial diamonds in Siberia in the mid 1950s was of great importance to the Soviet economy since they are of vital importance in the engineering industry and in mining, and the country had hitherto depended somewhat precariously on foreign sources.

Turning to energy minerals, coal in terms of heating value is by far the largest single source. Soviet geologists have calculated that possibly the U.S.S.R. has more than half of the total coal reserves of the world, some 9,000,000 m. tons, but only a small proportion of these, assuming they exist, would be exploitable. Proved reserves some years ago stood at about 200,000 m., which should last several hundred years at present rates of production. These reserves vary greatly in quality, of course, and range from anthracite and coking coal to lignite of limited heating value. The hard coal is almost entirely mined, but much of the lignite (brown coal) is obtained by opencast methods. Of these proved reserves the Donbass has about 26 per cent, the Kuzbass 20 per cent and Kazakhstan 16 per cent. The reserves in the Pechora basin and in the Moscow basin (3–4 per cent each), in the Ural region, the Caucasus and Central Asia (even less), are much more limited. About 25 per cent is in coal-fields east of the Kuzbass. At present, therefore, about one third of the reserves are in European U.S.S.R. and two thirds in Asiatic U.S.S.R. Almost all future discoveries will presumably be in the Asiatic part and will therefore bring down the European share. For example, the reserves of brown coal in the Kansk–Achinsk area of central Siberia have recently been estimated to contain 1,000,000 m. tons. Some of the seams are up to 100 metres thick, many are horizontal and usually they are near the surface. Vast reserves are also thought to occur in two main areas, the Tunguska and Lena basins, but no major developments are expected here this century.

In the last century all the coal mined in the U.S.S.R. came fom the western part, and two thirds is still mined in European U.S.S.R. but in the long run the relative importance of the coal in central and eastern Siberia should increase, even if at the moment it is highly inconvenient, if not impossible, to consider bringing coal westwards to European U.S.S.R. from anywhere east of the Kuzbass. As the better seams of the Donbass and Pechora are worked, however, longer hauls will be necessary to supply not only European U.S.S.R. but presumably East Europe as well. Although coal reserves are so large, one particular type of coal, coking coal, is missing in many coalfields in areas of metal smelting. Since coal is not only a non-renewable source of energy but also a raw material with many uses, Soviet planners will presumably eventually attempt to replace its use as a source of energy by renewable sources, but reserves are so large that there is no likelihood of this happening yet.

Although coal was regarded as the principal source of energy in the Soviet Union until the late 1950s, great progress has recently been made in the oil and gas industry. Many new reserves have been discovered in the last twenty-five years or so and the initial monopoly of the Caucasus–Caspian area no longer exists. Moreover, exploration is continuing, and several new deposits have been discovered in Asiatic U.S.S.R. in the early 1960s. According to one source[1] the proved reserves of oil are five times as great as they were in the early 1950s. There are about a hundred oilfields within the general oil bearing area extending through the middle Volga valley and up to the western flanks of the Ural Range. Once a suitable system of oil and gas pipelines is installed, these minerals emerge as a cheaper source of energy than coal, but the drawback is that no long-term planning can be based on oil and gas since proved reserves are only sufficient for twenty or thirty years at present rates of production. This, at least, is the conclusion of a number of reports on the subject. In 1960 oil reserves were put at 4,700,000,000 tons. In contrast to coal, most of the oil so far discovered appears to be in European U.S.S.R., mainly in the Volga–Ural area, but also in the western Ukraine and in the Ukhta area. But in the last few years there have been many reports of very large deposits in the West Siberian Lowland.

Gas reserves, which in the early 1960s were put at 930,000 m. cu.m., are only partly associated with oil. Gas is found in a broad zone stretching from the western Ukraine to the North Caucasus and middle Volga. Large new reserves are also claimed in Central Asia, including about one third of the national total in the Bukhara–Khivinsk–Gazli area. The eastern half of the U.S.S.R. has been regarded as deficient in both oil and gas but the search continues in Siberia and new deposits of gas have been found in the Lena basin. Like coal, both oil and natural gas are raw materials as well as sources of energy, and since Soviet plans for the next two decades envisage a great expansion of the petrochemicals industry, it would seem unwise to consume greatly increased quantities of these minerals as a fuel in power stations and for other purposes if they could be replaced by coal.

1. Vedishchev, p. 55.

Other sources of energy are of limited importance at the moment. Oil is derived from oil shales in Estonia, while peat is widely available in the central part of European U.S.S.R. and is cut for burning in power stations. As yet nuclear power stations make only a negligible contribution to total electricity production, but the U.S.S.R. appears to have discovered deposits of nuclear fuels and is less dependent on East Germany and Czechoslovakia than in the decade following the Second World War. As well as hydro-electric energy, which will be discussed in the next section, Soviet planners have thought of making use of energy from the tide, sun and wind, while geothermal sources have also been considered.

IV. WATER

The need to assess, and to utilize as economically as possible, water resources, has been a consideration of Soviet planners throughout the Communist period, but awareness of, or at least widespread discussion and concern about, a water shortage in the southern part of European U.S.S.R. is of recent origin. This 'discovery' gives added interest to the study of water supply. The competition between various users of water has already been suggested.

Figure 18a showing the distribution of precipitation in the U.S.S.R. gives an idea of the availability of water in different parts of the country. We have already seen that in the desert and semi-desert area of Kazakhstan and Central Asia and in other areas of unreliable and limited rainfall and great evaporation, agriculture is difficult. In these areas agriculture is clearly one of the greatest potential users of water from rivers for the purposes of irrigation. Most irrigation in the U.S.S.R. takes place in areas with less than about 400 mm. of rain. Here irrigation is essential if any worth-while crops are to be grown. At present the main source of water is the high mountain region of the Caucasus and Central Asia, which receives a considerable rainfall and is drained by rivers flowing to the Caspian, the Aral Sea or into the desert. Water is taken off in irrigation canals to agricultural land in interior valleys, at the foot of the mountains and along the courses of rivers stretching out into the desert. Between Transcaucasia in the west and the Chinese boundary in the east there is a string of oases of varying

T–D

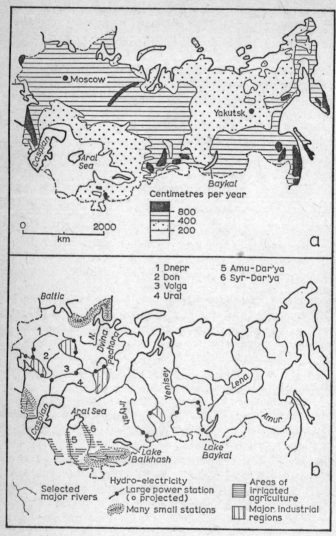

18. a. Mean annual precipitation. b. Water resources.

shape and size containing most of the irrigated land in the U.S.S.R. (see Figures 26 and 51). This only amounts however to a very small proportion of total arable land in the country, but high yields are obtained.

Hydro-electric power stations use falling water to generate power. Electricity has been generated in this way in West Europe since the 1890s but very little was generated in the U.S.S.R. before the mid 1920s. Hydro-electric power stations have received great publicity in the U.S.S.R. but even now they contribute only about a quarter of all electricity produced. They are usually costly to build, but once completed, cheap to run. At least, so it has seemed to Soviet planners up to now. But various disadvantages of building large dams and reservoirs have become evident, especially in lowland areas of western U.S.S.R. In addition to drowning land and submerging farms and settlements, large water surfaces greatly increase evaporation, and it has been noted, for example, that the Volga, among other rivers, has been bringing less water into the Caspian Sea since the creation of reservoirs along its course. In addition water can be lost through the wide bed of a reservoir more easily than through the much narrower bed of a river. Finally, in the long run reservoirs are likely to silt up and their usefulness to be reduced in this way. Up to a point, too, hydro-electric power stations compete with agriculture for water, for once the water has been dropped to the generators it may be at too low a level to be distributed to adjoining land for irrigation without being pumped there, thus using some of the electricity generated by it.

Industrial and domestic consumption of water is also increasing rapidly in European U.S.S.R. and there is concern over the amount of water in the Don and Dnepr rivers. It is therefore proposed to divert water from rivers flowing north into the Arctic Ocean into the headwaters of the Volga and Dnepr (see Figure 21c). This would obviously reduce the water reaching the Arctic along these rivers but would not create a new shortage here since at present needs are small. Some idea of the preoccupation over water in the southern part of U.S.S.R. is summed up in the following quotation from *Izvestiya*, 26 July 1963. 'We know what deposits of coal, iron ore and other economic minerals have been discovered [in the country]. But do we have a lot of water?' Undoubtedly water is abundant in the U.S.S.R. as a whole, but like several important mineral reserves, it is not always present where it is most needed.

Until the construction of railways began in the second half of the past century waterways were the main form of transport in Russia. Their relative importance has declined, but certain rivers still carry heavy goods traffic and navigation has been improved by schemes directed primarily towards obtaining hydro-electric power. Navigation will be considered more fully in Chapter 7.

V. SUMMARY

The actual utilization of the various resources described in this chapter will be considered in later chapters. The table below summarizes the distribution over the national area of the main resources. To achieve a simple but reasonably useful summary, the U.S.S.R. has been divided into five main regions. The location of each of these can be worked out from Figure 19. Resources have also been divided into five groups, some, of course, more important than others. The existing population of each of the five regions has been calculated, figures being available to do this, and the share of each of the five groups of resources has been estimated (this cannot be done with great accuracy). If the region has an appreciably larger share of total population of the country than of a particular resource, its balance is rated as Poor. If the reverse is true, then its balance is rated as Good. For example, Transcaucasia, Central Asia and southern Kazakhstan have about 10 per cent of the total population of the U.S.S.R. but have only about one per cent of the forests, so their balance is Poor. Where the shares of population and of a particular resource do not appear to differ greatly, the rating is given as Moderate. Favourability of location merely indicates the position of each region in relation to the one major concentration of population in European U.S.S.R.

Some of the assessments made and conclusions reached in this chapter have been based on very approximate statistical data. Even so one must conclude that many of the best resources of the country, including the largest forest reserves and fisheries, coal and several metals, water and good sites for hydro-electric power stations, are in the eastern half of the U.S.S.R. This half of the country so far has only a small percentage of the total population.

Potential Resources

Region	Agricultural land	Forest	Metals	Sources of energy	Water	Favourability of location
I	Poor	Moderate	Poor	Poor	Moderate	Good
II	Good	Poor	Moderate	Moderate	Poor	Good
III	Good	Moderate	Good	Good	Good	Moderate
IV	Poor	Poor	Moderate	Moderate	Poor	Moderate
V	Poor	Good	Moderate	Good	Good	Poor

I Northern part of European U.S.S.R.
II Southern part of European U.S.S.R. (excluding Transcaucasia).
III Ural, West Siberia, northern Kazakhstan.
IV Transcaucasia, Central Asia and southern Kazakhstan.
V East Siberia and Far East.

Perhaps the greatest single problem facing economic planners in the U.S.S.R. is to decide whether to move population to the resources or to move the resources extracted and suitably processed to population.

Chapter 6

ADMINISTRATIVE DIVISIONS AND REGIONAL PLANNING

THE national territory of any country is divided into many sets of sub-areas for ecclesiastical, military and other purposes as well as for local government. The U.S.S.R. has a system of political administrative units for regional and local government which has remained fairly stable since the revolution of 1917. Indeed, the European part still reflects the pre-1917 system based on towns and their service areas, a system found in France and some other European countries since the beginning of the nineteenth century. On the other hand, the economic planning regions, which are established to help planners in the development of the country rather than to serve as convenient areas for performing services and organizing the Communist Party, have been changed and regrouped many times since the Revolution.

I. ADMINISTRATIVE DIVISIONS

The U.S.S.R., like virtually every other country in the world, is divided into a number of politico-administrative units for the purposes of government. In the U.S.S.R. these units serve both for local government, organizing services that can be done better regionally or locally than centrally, and also as part of the Communist system of organization, each division having its Party committee. Unlike most other countries, the U.S.S.R. is also divided into a number of economic planning regions. The top level of economic planning regions consists of groups of contiguous administrative units, which is convenient but which may lead to a splitting of areas that are economically integrated and continuous; thus for example the Donbass coalfield lies mostly in the Ukraine but partly in Rostov oblast of the R.S.F.S.R., and is therefore shared by two major economic regions and cannot be planned as a single unit.

Both the administrative units and the economic regions have frequently changed in number and shape. For example, as a town grows in size or influence to a certain level it may form the centre of a new unit carved out of existing adjoining ones. On the whole, however, the Soviet Socialist Republics (S.S.R.s) have not been modified much since the Second World War, although the Karelo-Finnish Republic was abolished in 1956, and some of the Republics of Transcaucasia and Central Asia have recently been trimmed to eliminate unwieldy protuberances.

The highly complicated administrative hierarchy of the U.S.S.R. may be summarized as follows. At the top level the fifteen Soviet Socialist Republics cover the whole of the country. Incidentally, three of these, the R.S.F.S.R., the Ukraine and Belorussia each have a seat in the United Nations. At the next level there are approximately 140 major civil divisions. Twenty of these are Autonomous Soviet Socialist Republics (A.S.S.R.s), mostly in the R.S.F.S.R., eight are autonomous oblasts, and 112 are krays or oblasts. Below this level there were in 1964 almost 2,000 rayons (*rayony*) which may be considered minor civil divisions. At the lowest level of all there are some 40,000 rural Soviets. The oblasts have tended to replace the *guberniya* of pre-Communist and early Communist times, but the Republics are a new idea, designed to give to the main non-Russian peoples a sense of participation in the running of their own affairs.

There are great variations in the size and population of the major civil divisions. They tend to be larger in thinly populated areas than in the main concentration of population in European U.S.S.R. West of the Volga, major civil divisions resemble those in France and some other European countries in having a town of some importance at or near the centre. Their average size is however considerably larger. In Siberia some krays and oblasts are enormous, and extend from the Trans-Siberian Railway as far as the Arctic coast. Statistical data are available both for the Republics and for the next level of political divisions, and for this reason alone it is essential for the geographer to have an idea of the system of units.

II. ECONOMIC REGIONS AND THEIR PROBLEMS

Very broadly there are three kinds of economy in the world today, a traditional economy, not greatly interested in economic growth, a command economy (highly planned, Communist), and a market economy (capitalist). In most countries of the world today at least two kinds and sometimes all three, are found together, but one is usually dominant.[1] At the moment the Soviet economy is of the second kind since it is run almost entirely on centrally planned lines and almost all economic enterprises are owned and operated by the state.

The idea of limited centralized planning is not new, for governments have often intervened to operate or stimulate some economic activity in West Europe in recent centuries. But nowhere has there been for so long in such a large country a planned economy as thorough as that in the Soviet Union. Central planning in the U.S.S.R. determines the division of national income between investment and consumption, decides to which branches investment should be allocated, and finally which parts of the country should receive the investment. The tasks to be accomplished during particular periods are stated formally in national plans such as the First Five Year Plan, 1928–32. It is assumed in the Soviet Union that such a system ensures the most rational use of resources and the fastest possible increase in material production. If possible the consumer is not excessively sacrificed to achieve rapid growth of the economy.

Of great geographical interest is the way in which new investment is distributed over the national area. Decisions made here obviously result from an assessment of the relative favourability of different parts of the country for economic development. In order to facilitate decisions about the allocation of investment over the national area it is useful, if not essential, to divide the country into an appropriate number of compartments, the resources of which can be explored and their possibilities assessed. Understandably, therefore, the U.S.S.R. has been divided into economic planning regions of one sort or another virtually throughout the Communist period, and an appreciation of their nature is important for the geographer since the distribution of many economic activities at the present day is at least partly explained by the regions.

1. These three 'systematic types' are proposed and discussed by R. L. Heilbroner in *The Making of Economic Society*, Prentice Hall Inc., Englewood Cliffs, N.J., pp. 9–17 in the 1964 paperback edition.

The kind of decision to be made by Soviet planners with regard to the allocation of investment in areas may be illustrated by the following example. The cost of extracting a given amount of coal varies greatly from one coalfield to another in the U.S.S.R. In the 1930s most of the production had to come from the Donbass because this was nearest to most of the industrial centres, rather than from the Kuzbass or certain other fields, where production costs are much lower. In the Second World War the high cost Pechora coalfield in European U.S.S.R. was exploited through necessity, and production has also continued here ever since. Now fields in West and East Siberia offer the lowest production costs of all, but the cost of transporting coal from here to European U.S.S.R. is so great that it is still worthwhile to continue producing in the older European coalfields. Once it has been decided by how much coal output should be raised over a given period, it must be decided what proportion of the total shall come from each producing area and therefore how much investment each area is to be allocated. Soviet planners are constantly facing problems of this nature and an understanding of differences in production costs in different places is essential. The presence of a system of economic regions at least facilitates comparisons between different parts of the national territory.

Long before 1917 the need for economic planning regions was being discussed in Russia, but not until after the Revolution were economic planning regions formally adopted as an essential part of national life. In the early 1920s some twenty regions were tentatively sketched out, and as time went on these took more precise shape and have been used in planning almost throughout the last forty years. These regions tended to focus on some major industrial centre or on a physical feature, or were designed to contain certain more remote and fairly distinct parts of the country. The whole system has been somewhat distorted however by the need to avoid splitting Union Republics (S.S.R.s), and by the reluctance to amalgamate parts of the R.S.F.S.R. with any of the other Republics.

In 1957, regional planning was taken to a lower level, when over a hundred *sovnarkhoz* regions were established, each with its own planning body. For a time much publicity was given to these new planning regions and they were still in existence in the early 1960s, but they did not achieve the success initially hoped. In average size they were about as large as the United Kingdom and had about two million people. Their purpose was to give to local people with on-the-spot knowledge of conditions in their areas the opportunity to plan the development of their resources, while still maintaining central planning to coordinate the activities of all the sovnarkhozes. For various reasons, including possibly the excessively small size and large number of the sovnarkhozes, and the over-enthusiasm of local planners to develop all their resources indiscriminately and

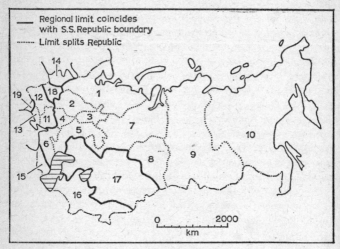

19. The economic regions of the U.S.S.R. The regions shown on this map were established in 1963. 1. North-west. 2. Centre. 3. Volga–Vyatka. 4. C. Blackearth. 5. Volga. 6. N. Caucasus. 7. Ural. 8. W. Siberia. 9. E. Siberia. 10. Far East. 11. Donets–Dnepr. 12. South-west. 13. South. 14. Baltic. 15. Transcaucasia. 16. C. Asia. 17. Kazakhstan. 18. Belorussia. 19. Moldavia.

to try to obtain some degree of self-sufficiency, attention has returned in the early 1960s to the more limited number of nineteen major regions, with fifty subdivisions. The present main regions are shown in Figure 19. Examples are the central industrial region (now the Centre) focusing on Moscow, the Volga and Ural regions, arranged about distinct physical features, a mountain range and a major river respectively, and Transcaucasia, a distinct, fairly self-contained peripheral area. The latest version of the nineteen major economic regions dates from 1963.[1] Some of the nineteen are further divided, giving altogether fifty regions on the next level.

The area of and number of people in each economic planning region depends of course on the total number of regions in the system, but population and resources tend to be so unevenly spread over a national area that it is impossible to devise compartments that are equal in area, in population and in resources. Usually a network is designed with reasonably compact rather than fragmented units, and with smaller units in the more densely peopled parts. Since population is constantly shifting and new resources are discovered or become exploitable with advances in technology, it is useful, in practice, to be able to change the number and shape of the economic regions from time to time, although if overdone this is inconvenient when continuity of planning is desired and comparison of past with present data is needed.

The frequent territorial changes affecting the number, location and resource composition of the economic planning regions reflect the uncertainty in the Soviet system of the relative advantages of territorial against production branches of planning. Either system requires some kind of regional breakdown, but a sensible choice of regions is more vital for the first type of planning than for the second. Moreover, a given network of regions, suitable as a basis for territorial planning, might not be so satisfactory for production planning.

At best, the economic region in the U.S.S.R. is a group of major civil divisions with certain mutual interests. Theoretically such a region consists of a characteristic part of the country in which suitable natural resources and an adequate labour force are combined to ensure low production costs and the production of something useful to the national economy as a whole. In practice, with certain exceptions such as Transcaucasia, which is very obviously distinct and physically separate from any other part of the U.S.S.R.,

1. See A. N. Lavrishchev, *Ekonomicheskaya geografiya SSSR*, Moscow, 1965, pp. 28–33. Boundary changes introduced in 1963 in some of the regions and consequent difficulties in comparing post-1963 data with pre-1963 data will be noted in Chapter 12.

or the Far East which is so remote from the rest of the country that it must be considered individually, any network of economic regions, whatever its number and form, is an arbitrarily devised system superimposed on many different sets of objects distributed in different ways over the surface of the country.

Vedishchev (p. 158) lists the following features as the essentials of an ideal economic region: (i) the best combination possible of economic activities, with cooperation among different branches within the region and specialization in appropriate branches, (ii) universal availability of electricity, (iii) engineering and chemicals highly developed, (iv) regional production forces adequate to take care of construction and light manufacturing needs, (v) self-sufficiency if possible in food requirements. At present, many of the economic regions of the U.S.S.R. fall short of these requirements.

In any assessment of the usefulness of economic regions, there are two main considerations. Firstly, how strong the planning powers of individual regions should be, or in other words, how independent they can be of central planners. Secondly, how they can possibly be largely self-sufficient and at the same time make some important contribution in the form of specialized products to the national economy as a whole.

The first consideration raises the question as to whether economic regions are useful at all. At present there seems no doubt that in a country the size of the U.S.S.R. compartments of some kind are necessary at least for the planning of certain economic activities. Thus it would seem better to plan locally rather than nationally the production of such items as bricks, vegetables or firewood. On the other hand certain activities, particularly those with a homogeneous product such as electricity, are becoming more and more amenable to central planning, and if and when an all-Union electricity grid is established, then obviously any additional generating capacity contemplated will potentially affect the whole country and not only the region in which it is established. Ideally, there would be a set of regions of appropriate number, size and shape for each economic activity, some, as for example for steel, having only a few units, but others, organizing say the marketing of vegetables, with a very large number of compartments. But if all these networks were combined the resulting picture would be so complicated that while reflecting the true complexity of spatial aspects of economic activity, it would be useless for any planning purposes.

Having devised a suitable system of regions, it is possible to use these first to assess the regional distribution of resources and to decide which to develop, and secondly to ensure that roughly an equal amount of development takes place in each region and therefore throughout the country. This second recognized function of regions in the U.S.S.R. originates from the view that in capitalist economies with empires, colonial areas have been neglected and the metropolitan countries have become over-developed, with resulting high standards of living in the latter and a potential for industrialization wasted in the former. Ultimately in the Soviet Union it is hoped to achieve uniform living standards all over the country by raising the level of industrialization in former colonial areas, such as Central Asia. There is considerable evidence to suggest that in any kind of economy, state run or otherwise, highly industrialized areas tend to be the ones with the highest income per inhabitant.[1] At present, Soviet data suggest that there are still very great disparities in income per inhabitant among the economic regions of the U.S.S.R.

In the inter-war period, balance and a large degree of self-sufficiency in the various regions of the country were considered desirable both for the economic reasons already noted, and for security reasons. It was assumed (rightly in retrospect) that in a future war, some parts of the country might be occupied and other parts would therefore have to carry on completely independently. Thus the presence of the regions has been used to discourage the inter-regional movement of goods and to encourage the establishment of basic industries such as steel production in regional centres. To achieve this, freight charges have been artificially stepped up at regional boundaries, making it considerably more costly to transport something to a place just across a boundary than to one just inside. Another reason for discouraging inter-regional hauls at least of bulky goods has been to keep the railways free for the movement of more specialized items produced only in certain parts of the country. Thus the economic regions of the

1. See for example N. Ginsburg, *Atlas of Economic Development*, University of Chicago Press, 1961, especially Part VIII by B. J. L. Berry.

U.S.S.R. have definite functions and are therefore quite different from those used for descriptive purposes by geographers in certain other parts of the world, regions such as the cotton belt in the U.S.A., in which one particular item of production is or has at some stage been dominant or at least characteristic.

Assuming that some clear-cut if arbitrary system of economic planning regions is desirable, then the principal question to be solved about them is how far they should be balanced and self-sufficient, and how far specialized. It seems safe to say that no planning region yet devised in the U.S.S.R. has been either completely self-sufficient or completely specialized; rather it is a question of moving in one direction or the other. A completely self-contained region would be against the division of labour over the country as a whole and in fact no single region can be expected to contain all the ingredients it would need to build up a self-contained economy anyway. On the other hand the U.S.S.R. is so large that it seems absurd to have the total national production of many items in a single economic region. An example will illustrate the nature of the problem. In the United States virtually all the motor vehicles (several million each year) are produced in the vicinity of Detroit. Similarly, in the interests of economies of scale, until recently most of the motor vehicles produced in the U.S.S.R. came from Gorky. In the case of the U.S.S.R. however it appears to have been found desirable to open motor vehicles factories in certain other regions of the country, thus decentralizing the industry, though still having a situation far from regional self-sufficiency in motor vehicles.

In studying the economic regions of the U.S.S.R. one expects, on the whole, to find some degree of regional self-sufficiency in the production of items that are bulky, perishable or in some other way inconvenient and costly to move over considerable distances. Regional specialization on the other hand may be expected in the production of certain agricultural, mineral or manufacturing products which for climatic, geological or other reasons only certain regions can produce cheaply. On the whole, building materials such as cement, glass and bricks are produced locally, and also where possible, fuel and food supplies. In contrast, extreme specialization has occurred in the case of certain agricultural products, such as tea and cotton, which can be grown only in the extreme south, in certain minerals, such as diamonds, most of which come from the Yakut A.S.S.R. since the only large deposits in the country are found here, and in some manufactured goods including cotton textiles, most of which still come from the Moscow area.

A rough idea of the degree of self-sufficiency or specialization in different items of production in each region of the country can be achieved by comparing the share of the total population of the country to be found in a region with its share of the national production of any particular item (see Chapter 12, Section II). Thus, for example, some years ago the so-called central region of European U.S.S.R. contained about 20 per cent of the total population of the country but only accounted for about 13 per cent of agricultural production and about 7 per cent of pig iron production. While it cannot be said that because it has 20 per cent of the population it must consume 20 per cent of the agricultural production and of the pig iron of the country, thus having to make up its balance by 'importing' precise amounts of these from other regions, it is obvious that some agricultural products and some pig iron must have been brought in. Similarly, it produced about 80 per cent of the cotton textiles, and therefore must have had a very large surplus of these for distribution among other regions.

The last word has not been said on the economic regions of the U.S.S.R. and undoubtedly experimentation will continue. It is certain however that economic regions are a drawback rather than an asset unless they ensure that each part of the country is specializing in what it is best endowed to do. There is one major snag here, however, for quite obviously some regions of the country have very little or nothing that they can produce cheaply and excel in. Thus, for example, Belorussia, which is badly endowed in resources and also suffered badly in the Second World War, does not seem to have found anything that it can produce more cheaply than some other part of the country. Even the Moscow and Leningrad areas, the Baltic Republics, the western part of the Ukraine and Transcaucasia are in almost as serious a position. Quite clearly the less favoured regions have to continue producing some items that can be produced more cheaply elsewhere in the country. Coal production costs will again serve as an example. The cost of producing a given quantity of coal is ten times less in

parts of West Siberia and East Siberia than in the Pechora coalfield
or parts of the Donbass coalfield in European U.S.S.R., yet no one
would contemplate stopping production overnight in the less
favourable coalfields. Similarly, production costs of oil vary
twenty-three times, those of iron ore seventeen times and those
of pig iron several times between different regions. These drastic
regional differences in production costs are, of course, to some
extent, though certainly not entirely, offset by the additional cost
that would be necessary to distribute the products of the lowest
cost areas over the rest of the country, if these came to produce for
the whole national market.

In reality, then, it is not possible to say that any given region
should produce only those items for which it has the lowest
production costs in the country. Rather an attempt should be
made to ensure that high-cost production is discontinued when
items can be brought in easily from not too far away, and the
closing of mines or factories would not disrupt the life of the region
too drastically. An example of this situation is the continuing but
gradually diminishing production of peat and lignite for fuel in the
Moscow area in the face of the increasing availability of low-cost
oil and gas supplies within distances of a few hundred kilometres.

III. BACKGROUND TO PLANNING

In Chapter 3 it was shown that by the beginning of this century
considerable progress had been made in industrializing parts of the
Russian Empire, although the level reached was far behind that in
West Europe or North America at the time, and large parts of the
country were predominantly agricultural. In spite of the chaos and
conflict following the Revolution in 1917, one of the first tasks
undertaken by the Communist Party when it achieved power after
the Revolution was to attempt to industrialize the country. There
had in fact been a fairly steady build-up of industrial capacity in
Russia for several decades. This was followed by a period of
decline, which started during the First World War and continued
during the Civil War, bringing industrial production around 1920
to a standstill in many branches. Pre-First World War peaks were
not achieved again generally until the late 1920s.

One of the first steps was to take over most industrial activities, transport and internal trade. Agriculture however was left almost entirely in private hands and under the New Economic Policy (NEP) farmers were left to produce what they chose and to dispose of it freely, a situation that prevented complete national planning for a whole decade. The first branch of the economy to be considered by planning bodies was electrification. In 1919 GOELRO[1] was founded, and in 1920 state planning (GOSPLAN) began to take an interest in other branches of industry, but planning was difficult at first for various reasons. One was lack of data on which estimates could be made of possibilities for development. A more serious drawback was the fact that the peasants could not easily be taxed to obtain capital for investment in new industries. With what at this stage would have been the chief source of capital for economic growth restricted, planning was extremely difficult. Even by 1928, the year in which the first Five Year Plan was started, only 44 per cent of the national income was contributed by the state-owned sector of the economy. Over 80 per cent of industry and over 75 per cent of wholesale trade were by then nationalized, but in spite of the establishment of some collective and state farms, nearly 97 per cent of agricultural production came from privately run farms. In other words very little was done beyond rehabilitating the economy during the first decade of Communist power.

The first Five Year Plan (1928–32) was one of drastic change, with two main aims, first to socialize agriculture and second to build up a heavy industrial base away from those parts of the country most vulnerable to invasion from Western (or Central) Europe. During this Plan period agriculture was almost entirely socialized (either collectivized or nationalized), while many new coal mines and metallurgical plants were built both in the Donbass area and in the Ural–Kuzbass *kombinat*. There was however a lag of several years between the beginning of new heavy industrial construction and the period, roughly 1932–8, during which the production of steel (see Figure 36), one of the leading links in the planning system, and of other heavy industrial items, achieved substantial year-to-year increases.

The second Five Year Plan in 1933–7 continued the work started in the first but tended to put somewhat less emphasis on heavy

1. The initials of the title of the body established to electrify the country.

industry. The third Five Year Plan, which started in 1938, was interrupted by the German invasion of 1941, and during 1938–41, possibly owing to uncertainty in the years immediately before the war, not much progress was made, and the rate of expansion of heavy industry achieved in the mid-1930s tailed off.

As a result of the Second World War very serious damage was done to factories, mines and housing in much of European U.S.S.R., while the sex ratio of the population was upset, as explained in Chapter 4, with repercussions on the nature of the labour force lasting even to the present day. For anything from a few months to almost four years the Germans held an area lying roughly south-west of a line through Leningrad, Moscow, Volgograd (then Stalingrad) and Groznyy. Here rehabilitation was necessary, whereas in regions east of this, particularly the Volga and Ural regions, growth had continued during the war, and these emerged, therefore, relatively much more important than they had been in the 1930s.

It took the first postwar Five Year Plan (1946–50) to restore the economy to immediate pre-Second World War levels. The next Five Year Plan (1951–5) continued the expansion of the economy more or less on the rapid lines that the pre-war Plans had been doing, but in 1953 Stalin died and perhaps because of the new personalities who emerged in the country, or simply because of the inadequacy and inflexibility of the rigid planning used up to then, changes of one sort and another were made which began to introduce an element of uncertainty in Soviet economic life. During the mid-1950s certain apparently disconnected events took place, all of which in some way affected the economy. From 1953 a deliberate attack was made on the backwardness of agriculture, which included the ploughing of many large areas of new land east of the Volga. In 1956 there was opposition to the U.S.S.R. in Poland and Hungary. One result of restlessness in East Europe at this time was the establishment of financially more favourable terms of trade with the U.S.S.R., which among other things agreed to pay realistic prices for such items as Polish coal. Moreover Soviet leaders realized that the allegiance of these countries could more satisfactorily be held by the Soviet Union if they were integrated economically with it rather than organized as more or less self-sufficient communities.

Around 1957 there was a review of the relative merits of coal on the one hand and oil and natural gas on the other as to which was the cheaper source of energy. At all events the next Five Year Plan (1956–60) was abandoned not long after it was started, one of the pretexts being that new resources (presumably oil and gas) had been discovered in certain parts of the country and that the new discoveries made the directives of the Plan useless. After a short period with no plan at all, a Seven Year Plan (1959–65) was introduced and in 1965 this was still being referred to, though since 1959 it had clearly been modified in several ways. In spite of uncertainty over the organization of planning, Soviet leaders were more optimistic than ever around 1960, and were talking of overtaking the United States and of building Communism during the course of their new perspective plan 1960–80. Since 1960 some of the enthusiasm has evaporated, as it has become evident both in the U.S.S.R. and in some East European countries, especially Czechoslovakia, that industrial production is not showing such a high rate of increase as expected or as achieved previously. At the same time bad harvests, culminating in 1963 in one of the worst since the Second World War, brought home the fact that after ten years of attempts to improve agriculture this branch of the economy could still let the country down quite unpredictably.

In December 1963 (*Pravda*, 17 December 1963) the latest aims of the economy were outlined. Firstly, progressive branches of manufacturing should be developed. These included the chemicals industry, from which fertilizers, pesticides, plastics, synthetic fibres and rubber could be expected to help agriculture and consumer industries, the manufacture of equipment for the chemicals industry, an increase in the extraction of oil and gas, and the development of petro-chemicals as a basic source of raw materials for the chemicals industry, and the expansion of cellulose and paper production. Secondly, agricultural production should both be increased and made more reliable by the raising of productivity in crop and livestock farming through the greatly increased use of fertilizers, and by extending the scope of irrigation works. Thirdly, science and technology should lead the way towards greater specialization and productivity of workers, should take up the slack by using existing productive capacity more efficiently, and should help to improve the quality and increase the variety of products, particularly consumer goods. All these would lead to the fourth requirement, the raising of living standards.

For the provisional plan 1964–5 it was expected that industrial production would increase in two years by 17·5 per cent, with an increase of 18·6 per cent in heavy industry (group A) but only 14·5 per cent in light industry (group B). During this period the increase in chemicals, refined petroleum products, cellulose and paper, gas and electricity, should in all cases be considerably above the average for all industry, while the output of fertilizers should go up by 75 per cent in the two years and that of equipment for the chemicals and oil industry even more rapidly. Less precise and longer-term aims were set out for agricultural production, including roughly a doubling of grain, meat and milk production by 1970.

Planning at the moment has come to revolve very much round the needs of the chemicals industry and this has tended to move into the prominent place held by coal and steel in the inter-war period, by electricity and engineering throughout, and by oil and gas in the late 1950s. In the end, however, every branch is connected with every other one, though often indirectly, and any scheme of priorities differs in emphasis rather than fundamentally from others that could be drawn to summarize the links in the economy at previous periods. Even by 1965, however, there was some doubt about the prominent place of the chemicals industry and there were hints that all was not well. For example, the lack of skilled management and suitable labour in some areas has been mentioned, as well as the failure to complete the construction of, or equip properly, some of the new chemicals factories. When the 1964 production figures were published in *Pravda*, 30 January 1965, the chemicals industry no longer headed the list as it had done a year previously.

IV. PROBLEMS OF CENTRAL PLANNING

During much of the Soviet period, state planning has encountered difficulties. These appear to have grown in the last few years and various reasons for the present crisis in planning have been suggested. Reasons suggested include a new interest in production costs, the fact that the economy is now much more complex than previously, difficulty in predicting farm production and lack of appropriate data about production.

In the inter-war period there was a tendency to develop any resources indiscriminately, regardless of production costs. Behind this seems to have been the idea that under Communism everything was feasible. Decisions were made intuitively and arbitrarily by Stalin or under Stalin. Now there is a much more discriminating approach and greater interest in the relative merits and production costs of different sites producing the same thing. On account of the arbitrary prices fixed for the sale of various goods it has however been difficult to detect which factories and farms are efficient, with low production costs, and which are not.

Quickly, too, the economy has become much more complex than it was up to the end of postwar reconstruction around 1950, and central planning has become much less straightforward.[1] Now it is often a question of determining the best location for a whole complex of interrelated factories rather than one individual factory. There is an interest in the idea of industrial 'knots', one set of which is illustrated in Figure 20.[2] The unwieldiness and inefficiency of the existing system of organization is often implied in cartoons and even openly debated. Lack of contact between units of production supplying one another is a built-in defect of central planning and has been overcome only thanks to local initiative and to the use of specially employed people, *tolkachi*, who have smoothed out bottlenecks in the flow of commodities. At the same time both failure to fulfil planned targets and over-fulfilment (although the latter is naturally praised[3]) make the task of the planners and the continuity of plans difficult. Obtaining items not produced in

1. L. Smolinski and P. Wiles, 'The Soviet Planning Pendulum', *Problems of Communism*, Vol. XII, No.6 November–December 1963. The authors suggest that the volume of planning tasks tends to increase at least as the square of the output. By the early 1960s the Soviet economy was something like 1600 times more complex than in 1928, while planning methods were virtually unchanged.

2. See Vedishchev, p.11. Vedishchev recommends the use of mathematical models for ensuring the optimum combinations of resources and productive forces in each region.

3. e.g. during the Seven Year Plan period (1959–65) it was expected that the Donetsk and Dnepropetrovsk oblasts would each produce almost ten million tons *more* steel than had originally been planned (*Pravda*, 5 February 1964).

sufficient quantity from abroad at short notice is not necessarily easy, while suddenly disposing of items that have been over-produced and cannot be absorbed at home can cause consternation in world markets.

Other difficulties confronting the Soviet planner have been concerned with labour regulations and with the unpredictability of weather conditions and the consequent difficulty of predicting farm yields. Since the relaxation of the drastic labour regulations

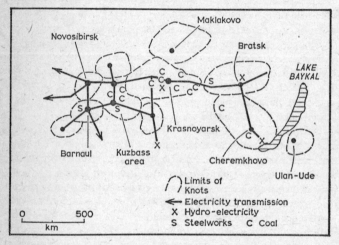

20. Industrial 'knots' in Central Siberia. Based on map in Vedishchev, p. 139.

of the Stalinist period workers have tended to change jobs very frequently and it was estimated that in the early 1960s something like a hundred million working days were lost each year and productivity suffered. Worse now for the planners is the difficulty of persuading people to settle in unattractive areas where in the past they would have been compelled to go.

So far no solution has been found to the unpredictability of weather conditions, but planners seem to be optimistic in this respect, for no more than a few months after the bad harvests of

1963, yields expected in 1965 were being discussed (*Pravda*, 17 December 1963). It is hoped that within the not too distant future the much wider application of fertilizers and the extension of irrigation facilities will both raise yields in agriculture and lessen the adverse effects of dry seasons. But the only answer to a bad harvest is to have large reserves of farm products stored in readiness.

One of the biggest complaints against central planning is that under such a system large amounts of capital become tied up in unfinished works of construction. For example, even a hydroelectric dam that is nine tenths of the way towards completion and gets held up at that stage is still producing absolutely nothing. It is noteworthy that the construction of new power stations in East Siberia is now being carried out much more quickly than that of the Volga power stations. In short, capital is not always being used as efficiently as it should be. An article in *Pravda*, 11 August 1963, criticized this and called capital construction the question of questions.

Another feature of central planning that has achieved only mixed success has been the propensity to embark on large-scale campaigns to transform over a short period some particular aspect of the economy or the environment, or to construct some new project, the advantages and disadvantages of which have not been thoroughly worked out beforehand. This tendency has been called 'campaignology' by Professor A. Nove.[1] One of the most devastating campaigns in Soviet history was collectivization in the years around 1930. This reorganization of land tenure led to a great diminution in the livestock population and to diminished enthusiasm among farmers in general. Almost as massive was the grandiose plan to plant tree belts throughout the drier agricultural lands of the country and even in semi-desert areas, in order to reduce soil erosion and to improve moisture conditions in the soil (see Figure 21). Indeed it was hoped eventually to transform the climate. Few of the tree belts planted seem to have materialized and this project has not been mentioned for some time now. Other ambitious projects since 1950, some of them successfully carried out, include the ploughing of new lands in central U.S.S.R.

1. *The Soviet Economy*, Allen and Unwin, 1961, p. 289.

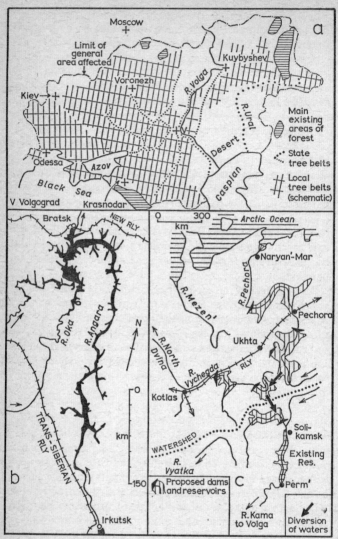

21. Examples of large-scale projects undertaken or projected in the U.S.S.R.
a. Afforestation scheme to change the climate of the steppe. b. The Bratsk
reservoir, completed by 1965. c. Proposed diversion of Arctic rivers to the
Volga.

(particularly Kazakhstan), the construction of very large power stations on the Volga at Kuybyshev and Volgograd, and on the Angara at Bratsk (see Figure 21b), the extension of irrigation in Central Asia and the southern part of Kazakhstan, plans to divert rivers at present flowing into the Arctic Ocean to the Volga system (see Figure 21c) and into the arid parts of Kazakhstan. The plan for a dam across the northern part of the Caspian Sea, and the scheme to build, in collaboration with the United States, a dam across the Bering Strait between the U.S.S.R. and Alaska, are too ambitious to consider seriously at present.

Building big reservoirs and diverting rivers, opening large hydro-electric power stations, and similar achievements catch the imagination, and receive frequent references in the Soviet press. Central planners seem less able to cope with such small-scale tasks as supplying collective farms with electricity and making local roads usable throughout the year. Moreover, even the grandiose projects have not escaped criticism. For example, there was a discussion (*Pravda*, 23 June 1964) as to whether it would be better to drown a considerable part of the Ob' valley in the West Siberian Lowland for a reservoir to supply a large hydro-electric power station, or to use it for extracting timber, possibly growing crops in the future, and exploring for oil and gas, recently found widely in this part of the U.S.S.R. In some cases large-scale projects may even lead to disaster, as in the new lands, for example, where excessive ploughing appears to be causing widespread soil erosion.

V. CRISIS IN PLANNING

In 1957, the Sixth Five Year Plan was abandoned. It was replaced in due course by the 1959–65 Seven Year Plan. This was the first time since large-scale national planning had been started in 1928 that any plan had been dropped, apart from the abandonment of the Third Five Year Plan in 1941 when the war started. In the early 1960s there was talk of a 'rolling' plan that would carry on indefinitely, giving greater flexibility and allowing adjustments to be made more frequently than in the fixed framework of regular five year plans. Clearly either central planning had suddenly become more difficult or it never was satisfactory in the first place. The frequent use of such vague terms as rational, sensible, effective and efficient does not solve the problem. Indeed, planning on a national scale seems threatened in its entirety, and the whole economic system of the U.S.S.R. is in doubt.

The basic reason for the crisis in planning seems to be the sheer difficulty of collecting and processing adequate and suitable data on which decisions about the economy can be based. These are looked after in a private enterprise economy by innumerable individuals. Nor is it possible in a centrally planned economy to take into account the wishes of every individual consumer. Disregard for consumer sovereignty was possible when goods were scarce, as indeed they have been during most of the Communist period. People could then be counted on to buy more or less anything. As standards of living have risen, thus beginning to fulfil one of the aims of Communism, consumers have become more particular about the type and quality of the goods they buy. The certainty that the consumer would buy virtually everything offered has been replaced by a more probabilistic situation.

Another drawback of the planned economy is the use of unsuitable incentives. In general, the idea that people should have financial rewards for high quality work, rather than just praise, has only recently been accepted, though, of course, large differentials exist between wages paid to people in different types of employment. Things have been changing, however, and there is growing criticism of incentives of the kind that encourage producers to go in for quantity rather than quality or that make road hauliers carry goods as far as they possibly can to accumulate as many ton-kilometres as possible. The idea of private shareholders is of course out of the question and the concept of profit is frowned upon, but the idea of rewarding efficiency on the part of managers and of workers is being taken seriously. For example, it was stated in *Pravda*, 6 August 1964: 'We consider that the wages of the managers and specialists in state farms ought to grow as productivity is raised by them.'

More revolutionary have been the ideas of Professor Y. Liberman, openly expressed as early as 1962, that a market economy rather than central planning would be better at least for some industries. In May 1964 the readers of *Pravda* were introduced in an unobtrusive article (*Pravda*, 17 May 1964) to the idea of direct contact between factories and the people consuming their products.

Mention was made of two factories, Bolshevik and Mayak, that were working on this basis. It was hoped that a better idea could thus be obtained of the kind of goods wanted by consumers, and that these goods would be manufactured, rather than items made to fulfil production targets as easily as possible. In January 1965 (*The Times*, 14 January 1965), it was announced that almost four hundred consumer goods factories would be converted to such a supply and demand system. Ironically, then, just as state participation is becoming respectable in some capitalist economies, the U.S.S.R. seems to be moving towards the dreaded profit motive and market economy capitalism.

It is hoped, however, that central planning may be saved by cybernetics, or in more concrete terms, by electronic computers. For some years now there have been references to the usefulness of these. For example, in *Pravda*, 31 May 1963, V. Nemchinov pointed out the possibility of coordinating different branches of the economy and linking different regions with the help of a system of computers. It was argued that plans could then be worked out better, and also that the theoretical question of a transformation from socialism to communism could be studied more satisfactorily. In January 1965 (*Pravda*, 17 January 1965) Nemchinov wrote a long article on computers. The gist of it was that by 1980 the economy of the U.S.S.R. would be so complex that the whole employed population of the U.S.S.R., about a hundred million people by that time, would be needed to collect and process manually enough data to work out the next plan. The situation could only be saved by a network of electronic computers linked to one central organization and by insuring that proper statistical data were made available by all units of production. Such a system has grave implications for party decision makers at all levels, for it means in fact that the best course in any particular circumstances could satisfactorily be found through the massive calculations that only computers could make quickly enough.[1]

The idea of computerized planning may seem novel and even impracticable, but already many large industrial establishments in Western countries keep a check on, and work out daily, the items they are producing and should produce. It is ironical that only in

1. See also an interesting article by A. Zauberman in *The Times*, 2 February 1965, entitled 'A new phase opens in Soviet planning'.

November 1964 (see *Pravda*, 25 November 1964) the shortage of computer programmers in the U.S.S.R. was being lamented.[1]

1. One consequence of the development of such a system of computers would inevitably be a strengthening of centralized planning, the position of which was for a time threatened by the creation of 104 *sovnarkhoz* regions in 1957. For example, *The Times*, 4 March 1965, reported a move towards the recentralization of the Soviet economy and the creation of six new ministries to coordinate the activities of certain branches of manufacturing, mainly in engineering. Also *The Times*, 20 October 1965, reports the creation of twenty-eight new Ministries to replace the fifty economic planning councils.

Chapter 7

TRANSPORTATION

I. INTRODUCTION

IT goes without saying that a transportation network is a pre-requisite of any but the simplest kind of economy and that the greater the degree of specialization in different parts of a country the more complicated and complete the system must be. Although Soviet planners have tried to keep to a minimum the inter-regional movement of goods, the integration of the economy of the U.S.S.R. involves many long hauls even of bulky items. In the U.S.S.R. different forms of transportation tend to be complementary, for competition between different means of transport for goods or passengers has not usually been encouraged or allowed. New routes are provided rather to relieve congested existing ones than to put them out of business.

At least the following five aspects of a system of transportation may be considered: the actual direction of the road, rail and other services, the kinds of distance covered, the things carried, the means used and their advantages and disadvantages, and the adequacy of the system as a whole. It should be appreciated that the existence of a means of transport can be both a cause and a result of a particular distribution of population and economic activities. For example, in the last century a railway was built from Moscow north to Archangel, since a good rail link was needed between the Moscow area and its outlet on the White Sea. The decision to put the railway where it is depended therefore on the location of the two major centres. But since the railway has been in use it has attracted at places along its course numerous saw mills, paper mills and small towns, and has been the cause of an accumulation of population here giving a belt of country with a much higher density of population than is found in adjoining areas away from the railway.

Turning to the first aspect of a transportation system, the actual location of the various routes, it is possible and even useful to obtain a preliminary idea of the kind of system necessary in a given context by studying the distribution of the main concentrations of population, mapping them, and joining them by lines, the technical term for which is 'desire lines'.[1] This has been done in Figure 22. Obviously, given the weight of population and economic activity in and near Moscow and the Donbass, it might be expected that much traffic would be generated between these two places and, similarly, between Moscow and Leningrad, and even Moscow and Central Asia, or to take a regional example, between Baku and Tbilisi. It is unlikely that a major route will be provided into an area where there is little or no population unless there are plans to develop this area.

With regard to the second aspect of the transportation system, distance, it hardly need be stressed that in many cases great distances are involved in the movement of goods in the U.S.S.R. The average length of rail haul of goods is known, and is many times greater than that in the United Kingdom. But it would be more realistic to compare the U.S.S.R. with, say, the British Commonwealth for a comparison of distances, while an interesting comparison could be made between the U.S.S.R. and North America by taking say the largest ten or twenty urban centres and comparing the sum of distances of all journeys between all those in the one area with the sum of distances of all journeys between the corresponding towns in the other. In the U.S.S.R. in fact, most road journeys are less than 100 km. in length, whereas rail journeys average about 800 km., the kind of distance involved in journeys between major regional centres, for example, Moscow–Kiev, Moscow–Riga, Moscow–Kuybyshev. On the other hand journeys of several thousands of kilometres occur between more distant regions: for example, Moscow and Central Asia, the Volga region and East Siberia. It has been noted already, however, that although the U.S.S.R. is a hundred times as large as the United Kingdom, the difference in distance across is only roughly equal to the square root of the difference in area, or about ten times as great.

With regard to what is carried on the Soviet transportation system, it is necessary to consider the value, weight, bulkiness and

1. Desire lines have been mapped in a few Soviet papers already, in one case to make it clearer where new routes would be useful. See e.g. 'Ekonomicheskiye svyazi i transport', *Voprosy Geografii*, No. 61, Geografgiz, Moscow, 1963. The use of desire lines may be seen in an English publication, *Traffic in Towns* (H.M.S.O., 1963, p. 92).

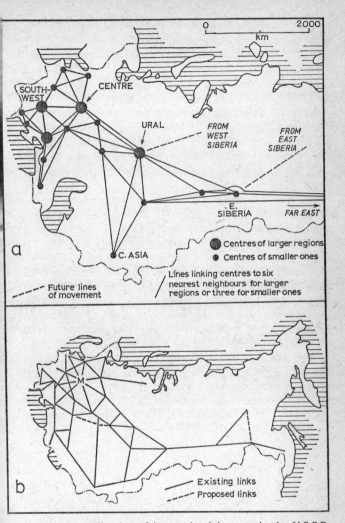

22 a. The general direction of inter-regional journeys in the U.S.S.R.
b. Generalized scheme of inter-regional transportation and econmic links.
Based on a map in 'Ekonomicheskiye svyazi i transport', p. 15, in *Voprosy Geografii*, No. 61, Moscow 1963.

perishability of the items to be moved. Obviously the difference in value between gold or diamonds on the one hand, timber or iron ore on the other, in relation to their weight, is so great that in the first case the only problem in transportation involves security, while in the second case every effort has to be made to move such items about as little as possible, or at least to process them and reduce their weight and bulk. Some goods like cement, petroleum products and sulphuric acid require special forms of transport.

It is not necessary to distinguish which goods are carried most on the Soviet transportation system, for almost everything is carried some distance from the place where it is produced to the place where it is consumed, sometimes in several stages. The amount of different goods carried on the railways, which still handle about 75 per cent of the ton-kilometres, is little more than a reflection of the amount (in weight) of goods produced. Obviously, therefore, coal, oil, iron ore and other minerals, timber and grain, occupy a very large proportion of the total.[1]

Turning to the means of transport used, Soviet figures make it possible to assess the relative importance of different means of transport in terms of ton-kilometres of goods carried and passenger-kilometres of people carried. Assessment by ton- or passenger-kilometres seems to be the fairest way of determining the relative importance of different means of transport. In the case of goods, the number of ton-kilometres carried in thousands of millions has risen as follows since the beginning of the First Five Year Plan:

1929	120
1950	713
1960	1,886
1963	2,302
1964	2,516

The railways have accounted for between 75 per cent and 85 per cent of the total in almost every year since 1928. Their contribution in 1963 was 76 per cent, that of sea transport 10 per cent, inland waterways 5 per cent, road 5 per cent and pipelines 4 per cent. The

1. Figures for 1963 in millions of tons were: coal 380 m., oil and oil products 270 m., timber 220 m., building materials 187 m., iron and steel 140 m., ore 97 m. and grain 77 m.

assessment in terms of ton-kilometres hides of course the great difference in average length of journey between the various means of transport. The railways accounted for 60 per cent of the passenger-kilometres travelled in 1963, road transport for 30 per cent and air transport for less than 10 per cent, but the use of road and air transport has increased relatively, particularly in the last decade, for short and for very long journeys respectively.

The advantages and disadvantages of the different forms of transport depend on the particular kinds of goods being carried, on environmental circumstances and on other influences, but the comparative cost of transporting a given amount of goods a given distance is at least a rough measure of efficiency. Expressed in kopeks per 10 ton-km., the striking contrast between rail (2·6), inland waterway (2·6) and sea (1·7) on the one hand, and road (61·6) on the other can easily be appreciated. The efficiency of the Soviet railway system and/or the inefficiency of water transport compared with that in most Western countries is also evident, for here water transport is in general many times cheaper than rail transport. In spite of the apparently high cost of road transport, it is still best for goods to be carried over very short distances by road, while sea and waterway journeys are only advantageous when goods are carried over considerable distances. Moreover, a good road system, which is still lacking in most of the U.S.S.R., is more flexible than a rail system, and far more flexible than waterways. Since pipelines and electricity transmission lines carry highly specialized products they can only be considered in relation to other means of transport when these are carrying the products they carry.

Perhaps the most difficult question of all is to determine how satisfactory the present transportation system of the U.S.S.R. is, considering the needs of the economy as a whole. Certainly it would seem to be inadequate if one considers the aims of the 1959–65 Seven Year Plan. According to this, 13,000 km. of new railway were to be built during the period, and 20,000 km. of new route electrified, while the length of motor roads with a tarred surface was to be increased by 120,000 km. The most spectacular increase of all was planned in the length of oil and gas pipelines, to be extended from 24,000 to 80,000 km. In spite of these improvements however, the distance of road, rail and pipeline systems measured against population or area is still greatly inferior to that of North America.

Sheer distance is not the only measure of completeness of a transport system. Whether it is satisfactory or not depends on whether or not goods may be taken by cheap means between all important places without making an excessively large detour. Of course, a direct journey between two places is unlikely except by air, for land routes are forced to make detours to avoid natural obstacles. Thus, for example, only two railways enter Trans-caucasia from the north, picking their way round the eastern and western extremities of the Greater Caucasus Range (see Figure 50), and a rail journey between pairs of towns on either side of the range (e.g. Groznyy–Tbilisi) is many times greater than the straight line (or air) distance between the two towns. Sometimes, however, a reasonably direct journey by a given means of transport is im-possible, not on account of the presence of a physical obstacle such as a mountain area or inlet of the sea, but because no line has been provided. For example, between the northern part of the Ural region and the Vorkuta coalfield a great detour has to be made on any rail journey, since no attempt has been made to link the places directly. On the whole, Moscow is particularly well placed to reach most other major centres of the country by a direct route.

Some geographers have started to study transportation networks in terms of their layout and connectivity.[1] Basically a transporta-tion network increases in efficiency the fewer the dead-end lines it has. A comparison of the railways of say the Baltic Republics on the one hand and Central Asia on the other (see Figure 23) shows that in the first area there are few projections to individual centres, and rail journeys between most towns in the area are fairly direct, whereas in Central Asia the system consists basically of one major rail axis picking its way through the various oases of the area and providing the framework from which individual lines project into the adjoining desert and mountain areas. Journeys between places on these projecting lines often involve very great detours. A study of this aspect of the Soviet transportation system could be rewarding.

1. e.g. K. J. Kansky, *Structure of Transportation Networks*, Chicago, University of Chicago Press, 1963, and R. E. Taaffe, *Rail Transportation and the Economic Development of Soviet Central Asia*, Chicago, University of Chicago Press, 1960.

II. RAIL TRANSPORT

The rail system of the U.S.S.R. has a slightly broader gauge (apart from some local lines) than those of central and western European countries, the gauge being 5 ft instead of 4 ft $8\frac{1}{2}$ ins. This makes the construction of somewhat larger rolling stock possible, but it makes little difference otherwise except that on rail journeys between the U.S.S.R. and most of its neighbours goods, containers or trucks themselves have to be trans-shipped or transferred to new flat trucks. Over most of that part of the U.S.S.R. in which there are any railways at all, relief is easy and curves, tunnels and steep gradients few. On the other hand the presence of many wide rivers has required the construction of large bridges.

The U.S.S.R. is one of the few countries in the world in which many new railways have been built in recent years. Even now the length of route is only one third of that in the U.S.A., where, however, the total route distance is actually declining. It is hoped to construct some 60,000 km. of new route in the Soviet Union between 1960 and 1980, in contrast to the increase from 70,000 km. to 128,000 km. between 1917 and 1962. Even then nothing like the present U.S. distance will be reached. Most of the new lines will be east of the Ural Range, in that part of the country where existing lines are among the most heavily used in the country.

There is no doubt that Soviet planners regard their railway system as the leading link in the total transportation system, and some idea of its usefulness may be obtained from the fact that, while the U.S.S.R. has only 10 per cent of the railway route distance in the world, its railways handle 45 per cent of all the goods traffic. It must be admitted, however, that on the Soviet railways, as on other forms of transport, plan incentives and targets are such that they give credit to an increase in the amount of goods carried from place to place, and many instances have been cited in the Soviet press of goods being moved about simply to boost the amount of ton-kilometres achieved. Given the amount of goods and passengers carried, however, they seem reasonably efficient in terms of manpower, employing only some 2·3 m. persons.

Great improvements are envisaged in the railway system of the U.S.S.R. and these will increase the speed of movement and the

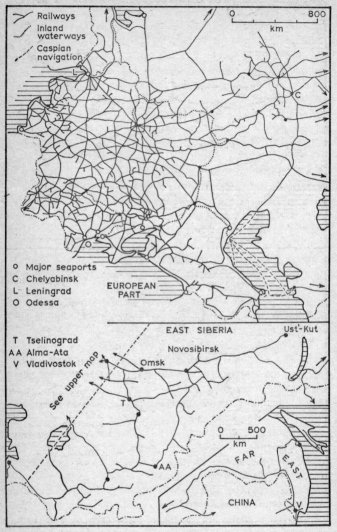

Railways
Inland
waterways
Caspian
navigation

0   800
km

EUROPEAN PART

O Major seaports
C Chelyabinsk
L Leningrad
O Odessa

T Tselinograd
AA Alma-Ata
V Vladivostok

EAST SIBERIA

Ust'-Kut

Novosibirsk

See upper map

Omsk

T

0   500
km

FAR

EAST

AA

CHINA

V

23. The Soviet rail system. All railways are shown. Note the difference in scale between the upper map and the lower ones.

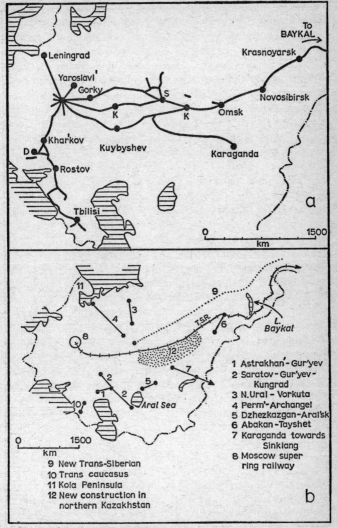

24 a. Main stretches of electrified railway completed or under construction in 1963. b. Selected proposed railways (see text). The existing Trans-Siberian Railway (T.S.R.) is also shown.

volume of traffic that can be handled on many lines. The track itself is being improved by the introduction of heavy rails, reinforced concrete sleepers and automated points and signals. Electric or diesel traction is to replace steam traction almost entirely in the next few years. These forms of traction handled less than 10 per cent of the traffic in 1953 but over 70 per cent in 1963. New diesel and electric locomotives are far more powerful than their steam predecessors (up to 6–7,000 h.p.), can travel at 2–2½ times their speed and haul trains of 5–7,000 tons. Recently it was stated that the average speed at which goods were moved was 9·5 kilometres per hour, this presumably including the time when trains were stationary. This contrasts with a proposed average speed for goods trains of 60 k.p.h. For passenger trains on main routes, 100 k.p.h. is thought to be possible and on some major routes (e.g. the Moscow–Leningrad express) 160 k.p.h. The electrified Trans-Siberian Railway has now reduced the time from Moscow to Irkutsk to eighty-five hours.

In the early 1950s it was found that 12 per cent of the rail network was carrying one third of all the traffic, and 35 per cent of it, over two thirds. A rough idea of the relative importance of different lines may be obtained by finding whether they are single or double track, while a further indication is whether or not they are electrified or are to be electrified. For technical reasons it is worthwhile only to electrify routes with a reasonably heavy traffic (a minimum yearly capacity of 25,000 ton-km. per km. is quoted in one source). During 1956–70 it is proposed to electrify some 40,000 km. of route, almost all of it double track, and this route will take about two-thirds of all goods carried. For routes with a capacity of up to about 20,000 ton-km. per km. each year it is better to introduce diesel trains. In 1963 there were about 20,000 km. of electrified route, while diesel traction is used on 43,000 km. In that year electric traction handled 34 per cent of all the traffic and diesel traction 37 per cent. The electrified lines are shown in Figure 24. The stretch Moscow–Irkutsk is the longest electric line in the world. The most recent addition has been the line Moscow–Gorky –Kirov–Perm'–Sverdlovsk.

The layout of the Soviet rail network can be seen in Figure 23, and it is hardly necessary to draw attention to the different densities in different parts of the country. The closest network is in the area west of the Volga and south of Leningrad. Hardly any new lines are to be built here. There is a less dense network in the area between the Volga and the Kuzbass. Elsewhere (Transcaucasia, the northern part of European U.S.S.R., Central Asia and the Trans-Siberian Railway) there is little that can be called a network at all, but rather individual lines branching off, while in almost half of the U.S.S.R. north of the Trans-Siberian Railway and east of the Ural Range there are no railways at all, apart from one or two short special lines. From Figure 23 it is less easy to see the main gaps in the system and to detect where new lines might be built in the future. The rest of this section is devoted to notes on the gaps and on new lines proposed, and is not an attempt to describe the whole rail system in detail.

Three gaps in the rail system, the filling of which would involve the construction of relatively short stretches of railway, and would bring considerable benefits to large areas by facilitating inter-regional movement, may be noted. Firstly, there is a gap between Astrakhan' and Gur'yev, a direct distance of some 300 km. A rail link here would give direct rail access between the Ural region and Transcaucasia. Secondly, the gap between Kungrad, Gur'yev and Saratov, if filled, would give much more direct access than at present between the western part of Central Asia on the one hand and the Volga region and Moscow on the other. This line would not be expected to attract much local traffic, however, since it passes mainly through a desert area. The third possible link is between the Vorkuta coalfield and the northern part of the Ural region. This could take coking coal to the iron and steel industry of the Ural region, which at present derives its coke and coal from the Kuzbass, much further away.

The general direction of new railway lines of penetration into the empty part of the U.S.S.R. would presumably be towards the north-east from appropriate points on the Trans-Siberian Railway. Eventually, for example, a useful line could run north-east from Sverdlovsk towards the mouths of the Ob' and Yenisey. Another proposed line would run north-east from the Baykal area to Yakutsk.

Other lines that have tentatively been suggested for the next decade or two are worth noting since they throw light on the way Soviet planners regard their country and the relative importance of resources in different parts of it. The following lines may be noted: Archangel–Perm' (this would give more direct access to the coast from the Ural region than exists at present), Kungrad–Makat, Dzhezkazgan–Aral'sk, Abakan–Tayshet (1,100 km.) continuing the South Siberian Railway (already complete from Magnitogorsk to Abakan) as far as Lake Baykal, a direct line from Karaganda into Sinkiang (China), and a super ring railway round Moscow, 500 km. in length. More ambitious than any of these individual projects is the concept of a railway from the Ural region to the Pacific, well to the north of the present Trans-Siberian Railway. Such a line would duplicate the Trans-Siberian Railway all the way from the Ural region to the Okhotsk Sea, covering a distance of some 6,000 km. and running at a distance of 500–700 km. north of the Trans-Siberian Railway. This line would help to push the frontier of development several hundred kilometres further north into Siberia, bringing within reach enormous forest and mineral resources, but it would encounter many physical difficulties in areas that are easily flooded, have steep slopes or permafrost. This line could usefully be supplemented by a line from the Lena basin to the southern part of the Soviet Far East region.

Other areas in which new lines are proposed include one across the central part of the Greater Caucasus Range, several new lines in the Kola Peninsula, and some 12,000 km. of new line in Kazakhstan, completing the mid-Siberian railway, planned to run for 2,500 km. between the existing Trans-Siberian and South Siberian lines.

III. ROAD TRANSPORT

The average length of haul of goods by road in the U.S.S.R. in 1963 was a mere 12 km. compared with over 800 km. on the railways. In fact, more individual road journeys are made than rail journeys, but given the great disparity in their average length, the railways handle more than fifteen times as many ton-kilometres. This situation is strikingly different from that in the U.S.A., where road traffic now exceeds rail traffic in ton-kilometres. The unsatisfactory nature of road transport in the U.S.S.R. is appreciated and often referred to. Both the roads themselves and the variety and quality of motor vehicles are too restricted. In fact, bad road surfaces can put up road transport costs several times by slowing down movement, wearing out vehicles, and so on. It has been pointed out that 35 per cent of the goods are carried on the railways over distances of less than 200 km. and that many of these could better be handled by road. For example (*Pravda*, 28 September 1962), virtually all journeys of less than 100 km. have been calculated to be cheaper by road, and some food products can be carried more cheaply by road than by rail up to 200 km., parts for the engineering industry 300 km. and cloth 500 km. Further, where only small quantities of goods are involved, rail transport is unsatisfactory.

The road transportation system, measured in terms of length of good road or of number of vehicles, against area or population, is greatly inferior even to that in West Europe. Although the total length of roads is very large, those with a hard surface was only 177,000 km. in 1950 and 330,000 km. in 1963, while the 19,000 km. with a proper asphalt or concrete surface in 1950 might have been looked down on even by a much smaller under-developed country, and the 108,000 km. in 1963 is still far from satisfactory. Quality of roads and their availability differs from region to region, but without data for different regions of the R.S.F.S.R., it is possible only to indicate that certain Republics in the western part of the country, particularly the Baltic Republics and Belorussia, are much better provided than the Central Asian Republics.

The number of vehicles produced each year in the U.S.S.R. over the last ten years has been about 500,000. Even if all these are still in circulation, which seems unlikely, given the bad condition of many roads, this would still only give the country appreciably less than 10 per cent of the number in circulation in the U.S.A. The disparity is not so great perhaps as these figures suggest, because about 75 per cent of the motor vehicles produced in the U.S.S.R. are lorries or buses, and some of the residue, the light vehicles, are used as taxis, whereas private cars account for most of the U.S. total.

The principal road systems and individual roads of the U.S.S.R. are of several different kinds. Not counting the network of roads and tracks used for carrying farm produce throughout the farming areas of the country, the best road networks appear to be in and around certain large towns, including of course Moscow and

Leningrad, while there are also a number of good inter-city roads, including the highway from Moscow through Minsk to Warsaw, and one south from Moscow to the Crimea. Road transport is also used in areas in which rail construction is difficult or impossible owing to the presence of mountain areas, permafrost and so on, or in which a road may be preferred in circumstances where a railway would not be expected to carry much traffic. Examples of these roads occur in Central Asia, where one serves the Pamir area, and in the Far East, where roads cross the coniferous forest to serve gold-mining centres and other settlements (e.g. Never to Yakutsk, Magadan to the Upper Kolyma and Indigirka valleys).

The importance of local roads is often overlooked and their existence taken for granted. However, articles required on farms, such as seeds, fertilizers, cement for construction, and so on, obviously have to be moved into and out of farms by road, as well as farm products themselves, which have to be taken either to near-by towns for consumption or to railway yards to be sent further afield. It is most disturbing for Soviet agriculture therefore that, except in limited areas such as the Baltic Republics and around big towns, properly surfaced secondary and minor roads are still lacking or non-existent. The tracks that often serve as roads may be adversely affected by the severe winter conditions in many parts of the U.S.S.R. Lack of good building materials locally in many of the farming areas has also hindered road construction. Altogether, therefore, rural life is much more sluggish, and the movement of farm products, and especially perishable ones, tends to be much slower than in North America where there is both a much closer rail network in the farming areas and a far superior road system. Local mobility is far superior in Western Europe also, where not only are the rail systems denser and the roads better, but settlements tend to be closer and average hauls shorter than in the U.S.S.R.

In under-developed countries, subsistence agriculture is common and roads therefore less important, since each community tends to be reasonably self-sufficient. In the advanced industrial countries, as already shown, rural roads are adequate. The U.S.S.R. at the moment has the worst of both worlds, for basically it aims at specialization rather than subsistence on farms, yet it tries to achieve this with a road system worthy of some decades ago rather than now. The cost of improving rural roads and maintaining them at North American standards would be very great indeed.

IV. OTHER FORMS OF TRANSPORT

While the actual volume of traffic carried on the inland waterways of the U.S.S.R. has increased several times since 1913 the share of the national total handled by the waterways has dropped from 25 to 5 per cent. Before the railway era an even bigger proportion was carried on them. It is claimed that 140,000 km. of waterways are used for some kind of movement of goods, if only for floating logs. In fact, about two thirds of all traffic is on the Volga system. Thanks to canals, through navigation is possible between the Black Sea, Caspian, Baltic and White Sea but until the very recent improvement of the canal (Volgobalt) between the Upper Volga and the Baltic, the size of vessels able to pass the whole length was very limited. A considerable part of the remaining traffic is carried on the Dnepr and on rivers flowing to the Baltic and Arctic in European U.S.S.R. Many of the rivers of Siberia are navigable over great distances, but their usefulness is limited because they do not usually link places between which many goods need to be moved. The rivers on the Mid-Siberian Plateau are difficult to navigate on account of rapids.

The construction of reservoirs for hydro-electric stations has to some extent improved navigation, particularly on the Volga itself. In general, however, waterways make detours and, unlike manmade routes, do not necessarily form direct links between regions or towns of importance. The construction of navigation canals is a very costly and lengthy matter and with the exception of the Volga–Don Canal, the only area where this has been done thoroughly is in the north-central part of European U.S.S.R.

As early as 1799–1810, a major piece of canal construction was carried out between the Upper Volga (where the Rybinsk reservoir is now) and Lake Onega, the Mariinsk Canal, about 360 km. in length. This has been inadequate for some time and goods from the Volga system have usually been transferred by rail at Yaroslavl' or Cherepovets for shipment further north. The old canal only took 700-ton vessels, whereas the new Volgobalt can take 2,700-ton

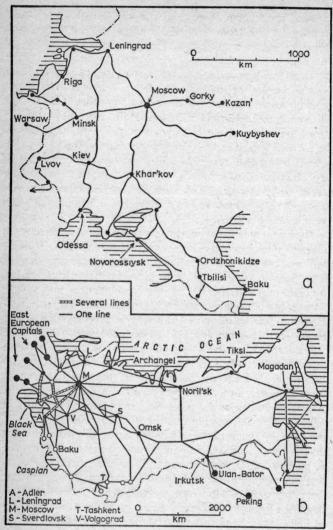

Map a labels:
Leningrad
Riga
Moscow · Gorky · Kazan'
Warsaw
Minsk
Kuybyshev
Kiev
Lvov
Khar'kov
Odessa
Novorossiysk
Ordzhonikidze
Tbilisi
Baku

a

0 km 1000

Map b labels:
≋ Several lines
— One line

East European Capitals

ARCTIC OCEAN

Archangel
Tiksi
Magadan
L
M
Noril'sk
A
S
V
Omsk
Black Sea
Baku
Caspian
T
Irkutsk
Ulan-Bator
Peking

A – Adler
L – Leningrad
M – Moscow
S – Sverdlovsk
T – Tashkent
V – Volgograd

0 km 2000

b

25. Selected roads and air routes. Only the principal inter-regional links are shown.

vessels. The amount of cargo that can be carried has increased from 600 to 5,000 tons, the cost of transporting it is five to seven times lower than previously, and the time between Rybinsk and Leningrad three or four days, not eighteen. This new link has some strategic significance, for it allows the passage of smaller military vessels between the Black Sea and Baltic without their having to pass through embarrassingly conspicuous stretches of sea such as the Bosphorus and Strait of Gibraltar. It also offers the prospect of inter-COMECON movement of goods in small sea-going vessels, as between Poland and the Volga or between the Danube and the northern part of European U.S.S.R. There is talk of speeding up river transport further by using containers easily transferred from rail to river vessels and back at convenient transhipment points, and the need to mass produce large river and small sea-going vessels has been stressed.

The role of the inland waterways is nevertheless restricted, since in terms of the cost of moving goods they are not cheaper than the railways, and their slow speed and many detours are a great drawback. In practice, virtually all the goods carried by inland waterway are bulky materials. Of the total of some 240 m. tons moved, 74 m. tons were floating logs, 88 m. tons mineral building materials and 24 m. tons oil and oil products. Surprisingly, the average length of haul by waterway, 478 km., is much less than that by rail.

Sea transport in the Soviet Union may be divided into two parts, internal traffic between Soviet seaports, and foreign trade between the U.S.S.R. and other countries. Internal traffic may be further divided into that between ports on the same sea (e.g. Batumi to Odessa on the Black Sea) and that between different seas. Journeys between ports on the same sea are mostly no more than several hundred kilometres, whereas distances between different sea areas are enormous. The journey from Odessa to Riga, for example, passes through the Atlantic, that from Odessa to Vladivostok uses the Suez Canal and Indian Ocean, and that from Archangel or Murmansk to the Far East follows the Northern Sea Route close to the floating ice of the Arctic. It is not surprising that the average distance over which goods are carried by coastal shipping in the U.S.S.R. is 1,305 miles (2,100 km.). Altogether about 94 m. tons of goods were carried in 1963, including coal, oil and oil products, timber, ores and mineral

building materials in particular. Sea transport is vital for inte-
grating the Arctic and Pacific coastlands of the country into the
economy of the country as a whole, since these areas are not served
by rail.

Russia has long been interested in movement by sea along the
Arctic coast and into the Pacific, and the route was used a little in
the nineteenth century to move manufactured goods into Siberia.
Around 1930 there was an increase in its use. Penetration from the
coast into Siberia is largely confined to the Ob', Yenisey and Lena,
however. More important, the period during which the route is
open is normally only a few weeks, with prolongation up to ten to
twelve weeks with the help of ice-breakers. The route has however
been attractive both strategically and economically, and in the last
few years it appears to have been exploited more than ever before,
thanks to the availability of the atom powered ice-breaker *Lenin*.
Fuel, salt, metals and timber are moved along the route.

There is some uncertainty about the exact size and composition
of the Soviet merchant fleet, but the U.S.S.R. was estimated to
have some 3,500,000 gross tons of shipping by 1960, including
fishing and whaling vessels. Moreover it was hoped roughly to
double the size of the fleet during the Seven Year Plan 1959–65,
concentrating especially on dry cargo vessels (rather than tankers).
Even now however the fleet is not sufficient to carry all Soviet
foreign trade. Another drawback is the lack of facilities for
handling large vessels in most Soviet ports. By 1970 it is hoped to
bring the tonnage of shipping to 10–11 m. tons and by 1980 to
18–22 m. tons. By then the country should be able to carry all its
own trade and even serve some other countries.

Air transport has been used in the U.S.S.R. for many purposes
in addition to its main function of carrying passengers and mail.
Remote areas of the country, far from a road or railway, particularly in Siberia, have been developed thanks to the availability of
air transport, and equipment and construction materials flown in
(at enormous cost) to allow gold and other particularly valuable
minerals to be extracted. More exotic uses have been to hunt
wolves and to land explorers on floating ice in the Arctic. Now
there is even talk of reintroducing airships to transport heavy,
particularly cumbersome pieces of equipment (for example, for
hydro-electric stations) that cannot easily be moved by rail. It has

been estimated that the cost of airship transport is only about one fifteenth that of helicopter transport.

At the moment the amount of goods traffic handled by air is negligible in terms of weight – in 1963, 910 m. ton-kilometres or 1/2500 of the national total – and the principal function is the movement of passengers (about 8 per cent of all passenger-kilometres in 1963). A study of air routes on a Soviet atlas map (see also Figure 25) suggests that Moscow is the outstanding centre for both international and internal air routes. There are at least sixty scheduled routes to first stop places, and most of the routes lead on to a series of other places. Sverdlovsk appears to have the second largest number of services. Among the top ten are also Leningrad, Kiev, Kuybyshev and Tashkent, great regional centres, as well as Simferopol' (Crimea), Mineralnyye Vody (North Caucasus) and Adler (Black Sea resort coast), in holiday areas.

Oil and gas pipelines and electricity transmission lines will be discussed more fully in Chapter 9 but their growing importance in the general transportation system must be noted here. The length of oil and gas pipelines has increased greatly since the Second World War, and more particularly, the actual capacity and volume of goods carried:

	Length in kilometres	Ton-kilometres carried (thousands of millions of tons)
1953	5,400	5
1960	17,300	51
1963	23,900	91

SOURCE: *Nkh SSSR*, 1963, p. 420.

Some idea of the cheapness of pipeline transport and the quantity of goods that can be carried may be gathered from the fact that the pipeline from the Bashkir A.S.S.R. to Omsk carried oil at about one quarter the cost of the rail haul. A 72-cm. diameter pipeline can carry up to 16 m. tons of oil per year, one and a half times as much as a single-track railway. Long-distance electricity transmission can also relieve the railway system by moving energy in the form of electricity generated close to a source of coal or oil rather than distributing the actual fuel itself by rail to power stations near markets. In the case of gas, it is in fact considered cheaper to pipe it from gasfields to power stations near markets, at least when the distance exceeds 1,500–2,000 km., rather than to generate the electricity on the gasfields, since power is lost in transmission, whereas the amount of energy needed to move gas along a pipeline is very small. It goes without saying, of course, that hydro-electric energy has by its nature to be moved by transmission lines.

Chapter 8

AGRICULTURE, FORESTRY AND FISHING

WHILE there have been great advances in many branches of mining, manufacturing and transportation in the U.S.S.R., few people either inside or outside the country would claim more than partial success for agriculture during the Communist period. Indeed, a crisis in agriculture has been proclaimed from time to time since 1953. There seem to be three principal reasons why agriculture is in such a poor state in the U.S.S.R. at the moment. Firstly, the devastation and neglect of the Second World War was entirely negative as far as agriculture was concerned, whereas while industry suffered in some parts of the country, it was expanded in others, and research and the introduction of new technology were even stimulated by the war. The second reason seems to be the Soviet attitude to rural life in general and to the peasant in particular. This, broadly, is a matter of organization, and the policy has been to keep to a minimum the allocation of capital to agriculture. There is something about plants and animals, however, which makes them less easy to plan in economic terms than mines, factories, railways and so on. Economists and politicians tend to hold the view that if only enough money is put into Soviet agriculture then all will be well.

The third reason is that the environment in physical terms may not be all that favourable anyway. This is a view that the geographer should investigate, though without preconceived ideas. It was suggested somewhat inconclusively in Chapter 5 that the environment plays an important role and should not be overlooked.

I. INTRODUCTION

This chapter deals with the geography of production of plant and animal commodities. It includes forestry and fishing, which depend on the gathering of products largely without growing or raising them first. These topics are dealt with in separate sections at the end, leaving the rest of the chapter to deal with agriculture, which for organizational reasons is at present distinct. Reafforestation is taking place, however, and fish are being 'farmed' on a limited scale;[1] indeed it may only be a matter of decades before these two 'extractive' activities become organized on farming lines.

For over a decade now there has been a drive in the U.S.S.R. to achieve greatly increased farm production. This drive has arisen from dissatisfaction with agriculture in the early 1950s. As a result, the geography of farming has recently been profoundly modified in the U.S.S.R., and further spatial changes in the distribution of different crops, livestock, the consumption of fertilizers, and yields, may also be expected to occur. Increased farm production can be achieved broadly in two main ways: by extending the area of land under cultivation, or by improving techniques, land tenure and incentives to obtain higher yields in existing areas of cultivation.

Land as a resource was discussed in Chapter 5, and it was made clear that with the technology of the present day and even of the next few decades it seems unlikely that the cultivated area of the U.S.S.R., now about 10 per cent of the total area, could usefully be increased beyond at the most 12 per cent. On the other hand, by increasing the application of fertilizers, improving the quality of livestock, seeds and so on, and by improving incentives to farm workers, much more could be grown within the existing farm belt, a conclusion reached simply by comparing Soviet standards with those in certain other countries with comparable physical conditions. As it is, agriculture has been deprived of capital and has not been allocated the equipment and experts needed to improve yields. Workers have left the land in large numbers. This is a desirable trend, since labour thus becomes available for industry and service activities, but only if the productivity of those remaining on the farms goes up sharply. The productivity of farm workers has risen much more in similar circumstances in recent decades in North America and West Europe than in the U.S.S.R.

In the U.S.S.R. agriculture has either held an anomalous position, as in the 1920s, or has been devastated or seriously neglected, as during and after the Second World War. Under the circum-

1. Great progress in fish farming appears in fact to have been made in the U.S.S.R. in recent years (see *The Times*, 23 September 1965). About one million tons of fish, or one fifth of the entire Soviet fish consumption, comes now from internal waterways and farms.

stances, recovery from climatic setbacks, particularly the several serious droughts of the last three decades, has been slower than it might have been had there been greater sympathy towards farming. For example, during 1958–9 140,000 people left the new lands area on account of bad living conditions. It has been precisely these bad living conditions, coupled with widespread mechanization, that have helped to keep grain production costs low compared with those in other parts of the country. The basic problem in Soviet agriculture therefore has been that this sector of the economy has been squeezed in different ways and has been sacrificed to allow the accumulation of capital for industry. Unless agriculture gets more investment, little improvement can be expected.

II. ORGANIZATION AND MEANS OF IMPROVEMENT

Although there has been talk of reorganizing land tenure and of finding new ways of paying for farm products, the farmland of the country remains basically either in state farms (*sovkhozes*) or in collective farms (*kolkhozes*). Until 1958 the collective farm system included machine tractor stations (M.T.S.) as well as the kolkhozes themselves, the M.T.S. hiring out equipment to the farms. This system was convenient when equipment was scarce but the M.T.S. were abolished during and after 1958 and their machinery was sold to individual collective farms. In addition to the collectively owned land, collective farms usually have small private plots for each farm family, a concession widely criticized as being anti-socialist in concept, but extremely useful in practice since large amounts of vegetables, meat and milk have been produced from these. In 1963, private plots covered about 44,000 sq. km. or some 4 per cent of all the arable land of the collective farms. From this 'private' land, however, comes about half of the vegetables produced in the U.S.S.R., while 40 per cent of the cows and 30 per cent of the pigs in the country are on them.

In contrast to kolkhozes, the members of which, in theory at least, jointly own the land, the sovkhozes are owned and run directly by the state. Workers on them are paid regular wages and do not therefore depend on sharing the profits, often small, from the sale of products, as happens on the collective farms. On the whole, state farms are much larger, more highly mechanized, more specialized and generally more efficient than collective farms. Most of the new land brought under cultivation since the early 1950s appears to have been allocated to state farms, while recently some collective farms have been transformed into state farms.

The relative importance of state and collective farms in agriculture may be judged roughly by the following figures for 1963:

	Total area in thousands of sq. km.	Arable area
In collective farms	5,095	1,213
In state farms	5,470	1,010

Almost half of the arable land was accounted for by state farms by 1963, a great increase since the period around 1950. The proportion of state purchases of many key crops derived from state farms has risen during the decade between 1949/53 and 1959/63. The following are examples: grain from 10 to 40 per cent, potatoes from very little to 25 per cent and vegetables from 15 to 50 per cent. Livestock state farms have also gained in importance. A comparison of the total number of state and collective farms in the last decade also shows great contrasts:

	1950	1963	1964
State farms	5,000	over 9,000	10,075
Collective farms	124,000	under 40,000	38,300

As the number of collective farms has shrunk, partly by transformation to state farm status, but mainly by amalgamation in the supposed interest of efficiency, their average size and number of inhabitants has increased. Thus the average number of families per collective farm rose from 165 in 1950 to 411 in 1963 and 416 in 1964, constituting a sizable community with around 1,500 inhabitants. In 1964 the average number of workers on a state farm was 717. With families and supporting services this means about 4,000 inhabitants per state farm. It appears to be taken for granted by Soviet economists and planners that farms benefit from economies of large scale just as many industries do. *Pravda* (24 April 1964) quoted one example of a specialized farm employing only

126 people to raise a quarter of a million pigs, to criticize the many collective farmers who each raise a pig or two on their private plots.

In practice, both state and collective farms deviate appreciably from the average size. The layout of farms and settlements inherited from the past varies greatly, while different kinds of crops and livestock need different sizes of farm. Thus for example farms tend to be small in the farmlands, originally forested, of European U.S.S.R., but very large in the more open steppelands further south, particularly in the southern Ukraine and North Caucasus, where large nucleated villages are common. One reason for trying to group settlements and make collective farms larger has been the greater ease and lower cost of providing amenities for larger villages rather than for many small hamlets and scattered dwellings.

On the basis of data for the nineteen economic planning regions a fairly strong positive correlation can be seen between the proportion of sovkhozes to all types of farm, and the proportion of land brought under cultivation in the last decade or so. Thus sovkhozes are weakly developed in most of European U.S.S.R., especially the Ukraine (under 20 per cent of the area farmed) where little new land has been brought under cultivation recently, but strong in Siberia, and dominant in Kazakhstan, where they make up 87 per cent of the total farm area. Of the 10,075 state farms in the U.S.S.R. in 1963, 1,423 were in Kazakhstan.

One theme has been stressed frequently in the Soviet Union in recent years, the desirability of bringing all farms, state or collective, up to the level of the foremost (e.g. *Pravda*, 14 January 1964). This is rather like saying that there is room at the top for everyone, or that everything should be raised well above the average. When, however, a comparison of two collective farms in similar physical conditions (e.g. *Pravda*, 14 July 1964) shows that one is achieving yields two to three times as high as the other, then obviously there is some slack to be taken up in the more backward one. The idea that it may not really be fair to pay the same pensions to members of both farms is an interesting indication of current thought on incentives. Unfortunately physical conditions vary so considerably from place to place that often great differences in yield between two farms that have been compared may be the result of differences in the quality of soil, in slope, aspect or some other environmental influences. An assessment of the value of land seems essential before allowance can be made for differing physical conditions in comparing yields. It would be more illuminating perhaps to compare the generally poor state of farms in, say, Belorussia, not with farms growing the same things under *different* physical conditions elsewhere in the U.S.S.R., but with farms in southern Sweden or in Denmark, where physical conditions are fairly similar.

Great advances in agricultural productivity are expected in the Soviet Union in the next few years from the much wider application of fertilizers. Although the raw materials for these are available in the form of numerous suitable mineral deposits, the expansion of fertilizer production has tended to be half-hearted. Possibly not enough was known about the techniques of the industry, possibly the complex nature of the products and their bulkiness and perishability discouraged planners from giving them high priority. At all events, the 5 m. tons delivered to farms in 1950 and even the 10 m. tons in 1958 seem inadequate in retrospect, given the great size of the U.S.S.R. and the generally somewhat low fertility of soils in the forest zone of the country. In 1963 the volume delivered had reached 16 m. tons and in 1964 about 20 m., and it is hoped to provide over 30 m. tons by 1966. In view of the apparent lack of experience in many farms in using fertilizers it does not seem likely that suitable types will necessarily be delivered to the areas needing them, at least for some years to come. This may be why it was announced (*Pravda*, 11 February 1964) that the application of fertilizers in Western countries would be studied and that a national 'agro-chemical' advisory service would be established with some two hundred local laboratories by 1966.

Another problem facing the fertilizer campaign is that rural roads are in many places inadequate to ensure the smooth delivery of such a bulky and often perishable item. At present the application of fertilizers per unit of area appears to vary enormously between different regions. In 1963 an average of 16·2 kg. was applied per hectare in the U.S.S.R. as a whole but the amount was much higher in parts of Central Asia (125 kg. per hectare in Uzbekistan), Transcaucasia (63 in Georgia), the Baltic Republics (about 80) and Belorussia, and extremely low in Kazakhstan (only 3 kg. per hectare).

The improvement and extension of irrigation systems has for some time been given prominence as a valuable way of increasing farm production. For example *Krasnaya Zvezda* in 1961 (11 February) had an article about irrigation entitled 'Here they are, our second virgin lands (*tselina*)'. Irrigated land must have become attractive to planners particularly since the poor harvest of 1963, for yields are generally both high and reliable. The article in *Krasnaya Zvezda* suggested that eventually the 9 m. hectares of irrigated land in the U.S.S.R. might be extended to 50 m. Certainly, if cotton is to occupy 12 m., as planned, then some extension will be needed.

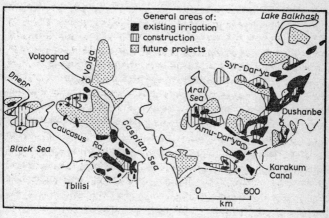

26. Irrigation in the U.S.S.R.

In 1963 the U.S.S.R. had nearly 9 m. hectares of irrigated land. Almost 50 per cent was in Central Asia alone, with over 10 per cent in adjacent areas of Kazakhstan, while Transcaucasia accounted for almost another 20 per cent. The hottest and driest parts of the U.S.S.R. therefore have altogether about 80 per cent of the total. Most of the remainder was in the drier southern parts of European U.S.S.R. The irrigation systems of Central Asia and Transcaucasia are fed by rivers from nearby high mountain regions (see Figure 26) and serve lowland areas with such a low rainfall that crop farming would be virtually impossible without them. Those in European

U.S.S.R. outside Transcaucasia receive water mainly from the Volga, Don and Dnepr in areas in which irrigation water tends to supplement rainfall rather than replace it.

Several irrigation works have been completed or started in the Soviet Union in recent years including the Karakum Canal, which strikes west from the Amu-Dar'ya as it leaves the mountains of Tadjikistan, to bring water to a number of areas with suitable soil in the desert of Central Asia, and a canal from the lower Dnepr conveying water to the dry steppes of the Crimea. About 35 per cent of all the irrigated land is under cotton, 25 per cent under cereals and 15 per cent under vegetables, but a wide range of other crops occupy the remaining area.

In contrast to the dry condition of the steppe and desert areas requiring irrigation, considerable areas in the forest zone both of European U.S.S.R. and east of the Ural Range are too badly drained to be suitable for cultivation. Such areas, once drained, often provide more fertile soils than those generally associated with the higher, better drained areas already cleared for cultivation. Altogether some 6,600,000 hectares have been improved in some way by draining, almost exclusively so far in European U.S.S.R., with 2,600,000 hectares in the Baltic Republics alone, and about 2 m. in the Ukraine and Belorussia, much of it in the Poles'ye. Large tracts still remain to be improved however, both in Belorussia and in the central regions around Moscow.

Yet another way in which the backwardness of Soviet agriculture is being attacked is by improving electricity supplies and the availability of equipment, especially in collective farms. Even by 1950, thirty years after the establishment of GOELRO, only 15 per cent of the collective farms used electricity for agricultural purposes. By 1963 it was claimed that 88 per cent of the collective farms were using electricity and that between 1950 and 1963 the consumption of electricity on them had increased tenfold. Even the state farms, although generally better equipped, were not all using electricity in 1950 (only 76 per cent). Obviously the introduction of many useful labour-saving devices on farms has to await a supply of electricity.

The tractor position has not altogether been satisfactory on many Soviet farms even in spite of the great efforts and publicity given to mechanization in the 1930s. In 1963 there were 2,661,600 units of 15 h.p., but this figure stood in reality for only 1,442,000 actual tractors. The resulting average of one tractor per 130 hectares of crop land is low by North American and West European standards. In practice some farm areas are considerably more mechanized than others, at least in terms of tractors per unit of cropland. These include the Baltic Republics and the North-west, Transcaucasia and Central Asia, and the Far East. Kazakhstan is less well provided but its large fields and generally flat or gently sloping surface presumably enable greater use to be made of each tractor unit and other equipment. Moreover Kazakhstan, and the Volga, Ural and West Siberian regions, together have over half of all the combine grain harvesters (270,000 out of 517,000 in 1963) compared with little more than 10 per cent in the Ukraine, the former granary of Russia.

III. AGRICULTURAL PRODUCTION

It is claimed in Soviet statistical sources[1] that total agricultural production was somewhat more than twice as great in 1963 as in 1913 (1913 = 100, 1963 = 216). Whatever the true increase in the last fifty years, it has been achieved primarily by bringing new areas into cultivation, including over 40 m. hectares of new land in Kazakhstan and West Siberia alone since 1953. The increase in basic livestock products (meat, milk, eggs, wool) has been roughly twofold during the last fifty years, but a comparison of the average yearly volume of production during 1909–13 with that during 1959–63 shows that grain production has increased almost 3 times, and production of industrial crops and vegetables even more in most cases (cotton 7 times, sugar beet $4\frac{1}{2}$ times, sunflower seed about 6 times and vegetables about 8 times). In addition, the cultivation of grasses and other plants specifically for animal fodder has increased enormously, particularly in the last decade.

In the last few years state purchases of grain have fluctuated very considerably, as the following figures suggest (millions of tons purchased by the state or sold off farms): 1958, 62; 1959, 53; 1960, 54; 1961, 58; 1962, 62; 1963, 48; 1964, 68. Sugar-beet has dropped since a peak in the late 1950s and flax and hemp are declining.

1. e.g. *Nkh SSSR 1963*, p. 227.

Òilseeds, cotton, vegetables, including potatoes, tea and fruits on the other hand, are on the increase at present.

One fairly steady trend since the 1930s, when a considerable part of the animal population was slaughtered during collectivization, has been the growing share of value of total agricultural production contributed by livestock. This means in fact that more products of the land are now reaching the factory and the consumer via livestock, thanks to the drive to improve fodder supplies and the quality of stock itself. The respective shares of the two branches have been as follows:[1]

	Crops (*percentage*)	Livestock products (*percentage*)
1940	61	39
1949–53	58	42
1954–58	56	44
1959–63	53·5	46·5
1963	51·5	48·5

IV. CROP FARMING

In the early 1960s about half of the total surface of the U.S.S.R., or 10,600,000 sq. km., belonged to collective or state farms. Of this, about half (5,330,000 sq. km.) was put to some agricultural use, whether to grow field or tree crops, or to serve as natural pasture. Of this used part, in 1963, about 2,250,000 sq. km. were classed as arable (*pashnya*), but about 3 per cent of this or 60,000 sq. km. was fallow. The remaining 2,185,000 sq. km. of the arable land, after excluding fallow, is defined as sown area (*posevnyye ploshchadi*) and is divided into four main categories according to the crops grown on it (1963 figures): cereals, occupying 59·5 per cent; industrial crops 6·8 per cent; potatoes, vegetables and crops such as melons, 4·8 per cent; and fodder crops 28·9 per cent. The main types of cereal and fodder are displayed in Figure 27.

The relative importance of different crops in Soviet agriculture may also be assessed by taking into account value and weight, as well as area occupied. In general the industrial and vegetable crops

1. *Nkh S S S R 1963*, p. 228.

tend to be much more valuable per unit of area than the cereal or fodder crops, and in several cases, notably sugar beet and potatoes, much heavier as well. Unfortunately figures are not readily available to compare the values of the harvests from units of area under, for example, wheat, cotton and potatoes. From experience in other countries however, it may be inferred that some crops are several times more valuable per unit of area than others. Certainly

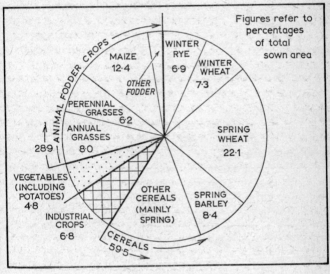

27. Use of the sown area of the U.S.S.R. in 1963.

the sectors occupied by industrial crops and vegetables in Figure 27 would be two or three times larger if they reflected the percentage of value rather than of area.

Before turning to the distribution of cropland and of individual crops over the surface of the U.S.S.R. it is helpful to summarize, if only roughly, the main features of distribution of prominent crops. In the table below, each crop is placed in one of nine possible compartments according to the actual extent of the area on which it is grown (vertically) and according to how widely over the farmlands of the country it is actually found (horizontally).

	All or most regions	*Several regions*	*One or two regions*
Large extent	Wheat Fodder grasses	Maize	(Unlikely)
Medium extent	Barley	Sunflower Rye Oats Sugar-beet	Cotton
Small extent	Vegetables	Flax Potatoes	Rice Tea Citrus fruits

From this table it can be seen, for example, that wheat both occupies an extensive area and is cultivated almost everywhere; at the other extreme, tea is limited in area and confined to a small part of the national territory.

Although one would not expect arable land to be spread evenly over the Soviet Union, it is surprising to find how concentrated it actually is. About 90 per cent is found in a belt of land narrowing eastwards and extending from the extreme south-west of the country as far east as the Yenisey (see Figure 28). This belt lies between the coniferous forest in the north and the deserts and higher ranges of Transcaucasia, Kazakhstan and Central Asia in the south. Within the main belt of arable land there are districts in the North Caucasus and middle Ukraine where over 80 per cent of the land surface is under crops. The proportion falls off northwards to less than 40 per cent around Moscow, only a small percentage around Leningrad, and a mere 1 per cent around Archangel near the Arctic Circle. It tends to diminish even more sharply southwards into the desert region east of the Caspian Sea. The proportion of cropland to total area is lowest in parts of Siberia, being only about one five thousandth in Kamchatka and negligible in the Chukhotka Peninsula in the extreme north-east of the country. In the East Siberia region it was only 2 per cent of the total area in 1963 and in the Far East region as a whole a mere 0·5 per cent. Contrast this with nearly 70 per cent in the Blackearth Centre.

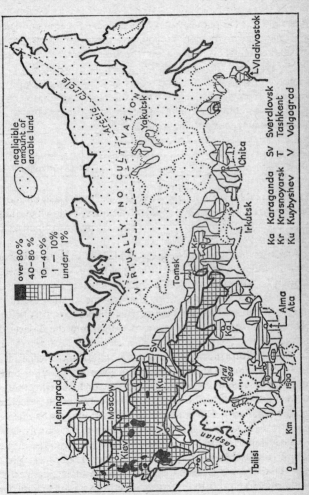

over 80%
40-80%
10-40%
1 - 10%
under 1%

negligible
amount of
arable land

VIRTUALLY NO CULTIVATION

ARCTIC CIRCLE

Vladivostok
Yakutsk
Chita
Irkutsk
Tomsk
Leningrad
Moscow
Kiev
Aral Sea
Caspian
Alma Ata
Tbilisi

0   1500   Km

Ka Karaganda   Sv Sverdlovsk
Kr Krasnoyarsk   T   Tashkent
Ku Kuybyshev   V   Valgograd

28. Distribution of arable land in the U.S.S.R. *Pashnya* includes fallow and is therefore somewhat more extensive than *posevnyye ploshchadi* (sown land). Source: *Atlas sel'skogo khozyaystva SSSR*, Moscow, 1960, p. 62.

Between 1950 and 1963, the total sown area of the U.S.S.R. increased by about 50 per cent, from 1,463,000 sq. km. to 2,185,000 sq. km. This increase of some 700,000 sq. km., an area almost three times the size of the whole of the United Kingdom, took place largely in one main belt of country, the so-called virgin and long-fallow lands extending from the Volga to the Yenisey. Between 1953 and the early 1960s the regional distribution of farmland in the U.S.S.R. was thus greatly modified and the dominance previously held by the southern part of European U.S.S.R. was eliminated. The increase was distributed (using as a basis the nineteen economic regions) as follows:

Kazakhstan	nearly 35 per cent
Volga, Ural, West and East Siberia	41 per cent
The southern half of European U.S.S.R.	about 15 per cent
The northern half of European U.S.S.R.	about 7 per cent
The dry and empty parts	about 2 per cent

SOURCE: *Nkh SSSR 1963*, pp. 254–5.

More precisely, the increase was largely confined to the southern part of the Ural, West and East Siberia regions and the northern third of Kazakhstan.

V. CEREALS

In terms of sown areas occupied, cereals are by far the largest user of farmland in the U.S.S.R. If maize grown for green fodder rather than for grain is excluded, cereals cover about two thirds of the total area under crops. Thus the fortunes of Soviet agriculture are obviously still closely tied to grain harvests, though less so now, probably, than at any time previously in this century. It is therefore important to appreciate that in spite of a large increase in the area sown, the amount harvested varies greatly from year to year. The following official Soviet figures are reproduced for reference, but the absolute amount of grain harvested seems large, and even the year-to-year changes may have been distorted by the inclusion of extra high figures around 1960 to prove the success of Khrushchev's campaigns in farming.

	Tonnage of all grain harvested (millions of tons)	Percentage (1940 = 100)	Yield in tsentners per hectare
1940	95·5	100	8·6
1950	81·2	85	7·9
1958	134·7	141	11·1
1960	125·5	131	10·9
1962	140·2	147	10·9
1963	107·2	113	8·3
Average 1949–53	80·9	85	7·7
Average 1954–58	110·3	116	9·1
Average 1959–63	124·7	131	10·2
1964	151·1	158	11·4

SOURCE: *Nkh SSSR 1963*, p. 225; 1964 figure: *SSSR v tsifrakh v 1964 godu.*

Most of the increase between 1940 and the present has been accounted for by the extension of the area under grain rather than by higher yields per unit of area. Compare in the third column of the table 8·6 tsentners per hectare in 1940 with an average of 10·2 during 1959–63 and only 8·3 in 1963 itself. The population of the U.S.S.R. is larger now than in 1940, and in 1963 the grain produced *per inhabitant* was actually less than in 1940.

Between 1950 and 1963 the area under grain increased roughly from 1,030,000 sq. km. to 1,300,000 sq. km., an increase of 270,000 sq. km., an area somewhat larger than that of the United Kingdom. But the increase was distributed very unevenly over the main farming belt of the U.S.S.R. Grain actually occupied a smaller area in most regions of European U.S.S.R. in 1963 than in 1950. There was a decline of altogether 70,000 sq. km. as both the blackearth lands of the Ukraine and the forest areas to the north switched to other crops, particularly fodder. In contrast, there was a gain of 340,000 sq. km. in a belt stretching north-east, then east, from the North Caucasus, along the Volga, and east to the Yenisey; in Kazakhstan alone there was a gain of 180,000 sq. km.

In retrospect it can be seen that this great shift of grain cultivation eastwards has had its drawbacks. At the same time it is obvious that as things were in the early 1950s, European U.S.S.R., together with those limited areas under grain in Asiatic U.S.S.R., could not have coped with the growing needs of the country. On the other hand, even after the enormous increase in the area under grain, grain production is clearly inadequate. What is more disturbing is that grain yields in the newest areas appear to be diminishing. This is so particularly in Kazakhstan, as a result of the virtual monoculture of wheat. A comparison of recent yields in the Ukraine and Kazakhstan shows convincingly that yields tend to be about twice as high in the Ukraine, in which the area under cereals is diminishing, whereas in Kazakhstan the area under cereals is greatly expanding.

Grain yields in tsentners per hectare

	Ukraine	Kazakhstan
1958	16·8	9·5
1960	15·8	8·5
1962	17·9	6·5
1963	12·9	4·4

SOURCE: *Nkh SSSR 1963*, pp. 274–5.

In practice the two areas are so far apart that in any one year there is not necessarily a connexion between their yields. Indeed, on occasions, high yields in one area have helped to compensate low yields in the other. But when low yields occur in both areas, as in 1963, the result is most serious.

Much of the grain grown on Soviet farms is actually consumed on the spot either by the farmers themselves, or by livestock. State grain purchases are generally somewhat less than half of the total volume produced. Thus in 1963, for example, total grain production was 107 m. tons, while state purchases were 45 m. The contribution made by the different regions to the latter total is of interest since it concerns grain available for consumption in non-agricultural communities and also represents the grain moved about the country over distances of varying length, as opposed to that used on the farms themselves. The following figures show the state grain purchases in selected economic regions (in millions of tons):

	1950	1958	1960	1962	1963
Ukraine (whole)	8·7	9·1	5·9	10·6	9·7
N. Caucasus	3·2	7·0	5·4	8·2	8·8
Volga	3·8	8·7	7·3	11·4	8·0
W. Siberia	3·1	7·7	6·5	2·9	0·6
Kazakhstan	2·1	14·8	10·5	8·2	4·8
U.S.S.R.	32·3	56·6	46·7	56·6	44·8

SOURCE: *Nkh SSSR 1963*, p. 289.

The glamour of West Siberia and Kazakhstan has certainly been wearing off since 1958, and it is remarkable that in 1963 the North Caucasus and Volga together provided about 40 per cent of all state purchases of grain, compared with less than 30 per cent from the new granary of the Ural, West Siberia and Kazakhstan regions. As a result of the bad harvest in 1963 the U.S.S.R. has purchased some 12 m. tons of grain from North America. According to the Soviet press, however, it was clear that the 1964 grain harvest was much better than the 1963 harvest, even in Kazakhstan. A figure of 151 m. tons is claimed for 1964, compared with only 107 m. tons for 1963.[1] But the 1965 harvest was again inferior.

Figure 27 shows the main types of cereal grown in the Soviet Union. These vary greatly in their properties and application, differ in their regional distribution, and have changed appreciably in relative importance over time. Wheat is now the cereal most widely used for direct human consumption, having replaced rye except in a few regions. Barley, oats, and more recently grain maize are largely grown for animal fodder or industrial uses. Certain cereals, such as rice, are limited in importance. Chickpeas and other bean crops are generally classified with cereals.

Rye, barley and oats are all relatively less important now than before the Revolution, for in 1913 they together occupied over half of the sown area of Russia, but in 1959 only a third. Rye is still widely grown in European U.S.S.R. north of about 50°N, particularly in Belorussia and in the Volga basin east of Moscow. Barley, in contrast, is grown virtually everywhere in the U.S.S.R., including very cold areas well north of 60°N, and very dry areas in the extreme south, though the quantity is usually limited. The

1. See *Pravda*, 25 October 1964, and *SSSR v tsifrakh v 1964 godu*.

T – F

cultivation of oats, on the other hand, is largely confined to farmlands between about 50° and 60°N. All three cereals may be sown either in the winter, where conditions are not too severe, or in the spring.

By far the most important single cereal in the U.S.S.R. is now wheat, which occupies over half of all land under cereals. About one quarter of the wheat is winter sown, including that grown in the Ukraine, the North Caucasus and the Blackearth Centre. The area under both winter and spring wheat has risen between 1950 and 1963, winter wheat from about 125,000 to 165,000 sq. km., spring wheat from 260,000 to 480,000, with a gain of 280,000 sq. km. of spring wheat in the belt between the Volga and Yenisey, and a diminution in some other areas.

It is difficult to represent satisfactorily on a map the regional distribution of such a widespread cereal as wheat, but the relative importance of this crop to all crop farming may be seen approximately in Figure 29a. It is evident that in the new lands, where wheat usually occupies over 60 per cent of the total sown area, it is the dominant crop, whereas in the central and western part of European U.S.S.R., where it is usually under 20 per cent of the total sown area, it is of secondary importance. If the distribution of total wheat production and total urban population are compared, an idea of regional deficits and surpluses in wheat can be estimated. Currently there is probably roughly a balance in the Ukraine and the North Caucasus, an area once with a large wheat surplus. The rest of European U.S.S.R. has a large deficit, while there is a large surplus in the new lands, and the main interregional flow of wheat is therefore now in a westward direction. Other smaller deficiencies occur in Central Asia, and in Siberia away from the main wheat belt.

The position of maize in Soviet agriculture is less straightforward than that of other crops since it is now widely grown for ripe grain, when it is classed as a cereal, or for silage or green fodder when it is classed as a fodder crop. Since the grain cannot be relied on to ripen every year even when the crop is sown for this product, unripe grain maize may be used as green fodder instead. The area under maize of all kinds has grown in a most striking way, rising from under 50,000 sq. km. in 1950 to nearly 200,000 in 1958 and over 340,000 in 1963. The comparable

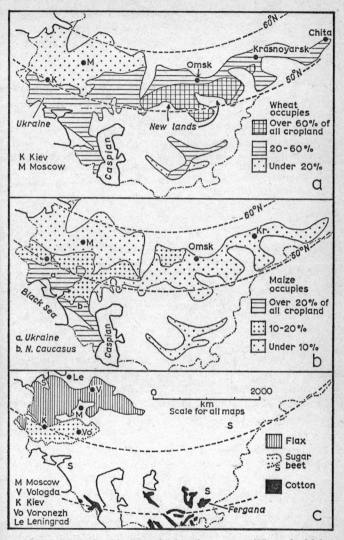

29. Distribution of cultivation of selected crops. a. Wheat. b. Maize.
c. Industrial crops.

figure for 1964 was however only 270,000 sq. km. Of the 1964 area under maize, only 50,000 sq. km., or less than a fifth, provided ripe grain, while 220,000 sq. km. was used for silage and green fodder.

Undoubtedly the introduction of maize to Soviet agriculture on a large scale and over much of the country has been one of the reasons for the general improvement in livestock farming. Clearly, however, the initial optimism about the crop in the mid 1950s, which led to its being grown in areas as far north as Archangel, has diminished somewhat, and the small proportion that actually provides ripe grain is disappointing. It is a result of the high latitude and insufficiently high temperature over most of the farmland of the U.S.S.R. No less critical for maize is the low rainfall in many areas in which it is widely grown, including, for example, the south-east Ukraine (see Figure 29b) where it occupies well over twenty per cent of the sown area in places, but receives only about half as much rain as maize grown in the Middle West of the U.S.A. By the early 1960s, maize was being widely grown in the U.S.S.R. south of about 55°N, but most of the ripe grain comes from areas south of about 50°N, particularly the Ukraine, Moldavia and the North Caucasus, for although physical conditions are ideal for it in the irrigated lands of Transcaucasia and Central Asia, other crops can more profitably be grown there.

Other plants classed as cereals are grown less extensively than the five so far mentioned. Millet is grown mainly in the drier southern part of European U.S.S.R., while rice is confined largely to the oases of Central Asia and Transcaucasia, and to the Kuban valley in the North Caucasus. Beans and peas of various kinds are of considerable importance locally, but the area of cultivation of some has actually declined recently. Chickpeas are fairly widely grown in central European U.S.S.R., beans mainly in a belt between the forest and steppe of this part of the country.

VI. INDUSTRIAL CROPS AND VEGETABLES

Industrial crops and vegetables together occupy little more than ten per cent of the total sown area of the U.S.S.R. but several make a major contribution to the national economy as foodstuffs or as raw materials for industry. In the last decade, the area under each has tended to increase at about the same rate as the total sown area of the country.

The category of industrial crops is somewhat arbitrary since it contains some food plants, some fibre plants, and some crops, such as the sunflower, that yield products both for human consumption and for industry. On the whole the industrial crops of the U.S.S.R. are characterized by the large amount of processing needed in their preparation after harvesting, and their presence is usually associated with a system of processing plant, such as sugar beet factories or cotton gins. The principal industrial crops are cotton, hemp and flax, grown mainly for fibres; the sunflower and linseed (flax grown for its oil) for oils; sugar-beet, the residue of which can be fed to livestock once the sugar is extracted; and tobacco and tea.

The percentage of total sown area under industrial crops is far from even in the nineteen economic regions. Compared with 7 per cent in the U.S.S.R. as a whole, both the Far East (the soybean) and Central Asia (particularly cotton) have about 40 per cent of their sown area under industrial crops, while the Ukraine, Moldavia and Transcaucasia also have an above average proportion. Industrial crops are relatively least important in the cereal belt stretching east from the Volga through northern Kazakhstan.

In spite of recent interest in artificial and synthetic fibres, cotton remains the outstanding textile fibre in Soviet industry. The demand for cotton, which has risen steadily throughout this century with decreasing dependence on imported cotton, is expected to rise still further. Whether East Europe will in the future receive the bulk of its supplies of raw cotton from the U.S.S.R. or from elsewhere must influence this to some extent. Russian interest in the Republics of Central Asia has been closely connected with cotton cultivation, and the desire to extend irrigation here is a result of the need to have a larger sown area for cotton.

In 1963 the U.S.S.R. produced 5,210,000 tons of raw cotton. Over 90 per cent of this came from Central Asia and southern Kazakhstan, 71 per cent from Uzbekistan alone, whereas Transcaucasia, mainly Azerbaijan, contributed little over 5 per cent. In the U.S.S.R. yields of cotton are closely related to temperature conditions. The cultivation of cotton in the Ukraine and North

Caucasus, tried earlier in the Communist period, has been abandoned, and there is also some doubt about Transcaucasia, where a yield of 11·3 tsentners per hectare of raw cotton in 1963 was only half the national average (21 tsentners), and even about southern Kazakhstan (14·3 tsentners). Not surprisingly, Tadjikistan, with the hottest conditions of all, managed 25 tsentners per hectare.

Throughout the U.S.S.R. cotton is grown with the help of irrigation. This is an advantage as far as the quality of the lint is concerned, since the dry atmosphere of the arid climate makes diseases less likely than in more humid areas and allows the formation of superior fibre. It may be noted in passing that in the U.S.A. cotton cultivation is declining in the traditional areas of heavy rainfall in the south-east and is increasing in the drier irrigated lands of the south-west, including California. The total area under cotton in the U.S.S.R. has only risen from 23,000 sq. km. in 1950 to about 25,000 in 1963 and 1964, but yields have gone up appreciably and much effort is put into providing fertilizers for the crop. In 1963 the area under cotton was distributed among the republics as follows:

	per cent
Azerbaijan and Armenia	10
Uzbekistan	66
Turkmenistan	10
Tadjikistan	9
Kirgizia and Kazakhstan	5

SOURCE: *Nkh SSSR 1963*, p. 263.

The main areas of cotton cultivation are indicated in Figure 29c.

Sugar-beet is another major crop of the U.S.S.R., although it occupies less than 2 per cent of the total sown area. The area under sugar beet has risen greatly since 1950 (1950: 13,000 sq. km.; 1963: 37,500 sq. km.; 1964: 41,000 sq. km.). Since the establishment of a socialist government in Cuba and the signing of an agreement to import large quantities of cane sugar from there, however, the continuing expansion of sugar beet in the U.S.S.R has seemed less sound economically. Beet sugar cannot compete with cane sugar unless protected, and at the same time, it takes up good quality land and quickly exhausts the soil unless grown in rotation and given fertilizers.

In 1950 about 65 per cent of the sugar-beet area was in the Ukraine, but this Republic accounted for only 50 per cent in 1963. As the area has increased, so cultivation has tended to become decentralized, with the crop spreading both into neighbouring economic regions, notably into Moldavia, the Blackearth Centre (21 per cent in 1963) and North Caucasus, and into more distant areas such as West Siberia. It seems reasonable to decentralize the industry, since the consumption of sugar is presumably spread according to population and it must have been inconvenient to transport the commodity to distant regions from one main producing area, the Ukraine. On the other hand, a study of regional sugar yields in the period 1959–63 (*Nkh SSSR 1963*, p. 279) shows that, compared to a national average yield of 157 tsentners of beet (before processing) per hectare, the Ukraine had a yield of 185 and the oases of Transcaucasia and Central Asia 250 and 340 respectively, whereas areas into which cultivation was being extended further north in European U.S.S.R. were giving yields only around half the national average. Figure 29c shows the main areas of sugar beet cultivation in the U.S.S.R.

Flax has long been grown for its fibre for the linen industry in the forest zone of European U.S.S.R., and here is still found about 80 per cent of the cultivation, most of it in the North-west, Central and Belorussia regions. The actual area under flax has recently been declining. The sunflower, a key source of vegetable oil, surprisingly perhaps to the West European reader, is widely grown in the steppe zone of European U.S.S.R., about 75 per cent coming from here, especially from the Ukraine (about 35 per cent) and North Caucasus (about 20 per cent), the Blackearth Centre and Volga. Between 1950 and 1963 the area under the sunflower rose from about 36,000 sq. km. to 44,000. Hemp is grown mainly in the central part of European U.S.S.R. and tobacco widely in the warmer parts of the country, but tea is almost entirely confined to the warm, humid hillsides of parts of Transcaucasia.

Vegetables, including potatoes, which are considered separately in the Soviet statistical sources, together with fruits, occupy an even smaller part of the total crop area than industrial crops, but in general they are of very high value per unit of area. The area under vegetables of all kinds has remained fairly consistently around 10–11,000 sq. km. for many years now, and it is revealing to find (*Nkh SSSR 1963*, p. 249) that about half of this area is accounted for by private plots on kolkhozes, allotments and other comparable kinds of holding, less than one fifth by state farms, and the remainder by collective land on kolkhozes. Presumably, therefore, the cultivation of vegetables of one sort or another is as widespread as collective farms themselves. Potatoes do however seem to make a larger contribution to farm production in certain areas than in others, and the Baltic Republics and Belorussia, which have about 20 per cent of the area under potatoes, have appreciably higher yields than most other regions. In 1963 for example they had 110 and 105 tsentners per hectare respectively, compared with 84 in the country as a whole. In 1963 the total area under potatoes was 8,500 sq. km., that under other vegetables 1,400 sq. km.

The cultivation of fruit in the U.S.S.R. is characteristic particularly of the southern part of European U.S.S.R., where deciduous fruit orchards are widespread. Vineyards are largely confined to warm hilly localities in the extreme south, including Moldavia, the Crimea and Transcaucasia, while citrus fruit cultivation, like tea cultivation, is a speciality of Georgia.

VII. FODDER CROPS AND LIVESTOCK

One of the most striking developments in Soviet agriculture in the last decade has been the great increase in the area of farmland devoted specifically to the growth of fodder crops for livestock. In the past, the raising of animals, including the large number of horses kept for work of various kinds on the farms, has tended to depend either on natural pastures or on the residue from crops grown for human consumption. The area under fodder crops, including grasses of various kinds, cereals fed green, including maize, and plants such as lucerne, rose sharply from 207,000 sq. km. in 1950 to 502,000 in 1958 and 632,000 in 1963, reaching 29 per cent of the total sown area of the U.S.S.R. in 1963. The 1964 figure, however, was only 534,000 sq. km.

The proportion of sown area devoted to fodder crops varies greatly from region to region. The cultivation of fodder crops in relation to all arable farming is most strongly developed in the northern and central parts of European U.S.S.R., particularly the

North-west, Baltic and Central regions. In the North-west and Baltic the area under fodder crops actually exceeds that under cereals. Fodder crops are most weakly developed in Transcaucasia, Central Asia and the Far East, but Central Asia in particular has very large, if poor, natural pastures. In the new lands of Siberia and Kazakhstan the area under fodder crops appears to be growing at the expense of cereals, as the initial virtual monoculture of wheat is abandoned, but in 1963 the area under cereals in Kazakhstan was still four times that under fodder crops.

In addition to the fodder available for livestock from arable farmland, some contribution is made by the natural pastures of the Soviet Union. Excluding the vast but very poor pastures on which reindeer are grazed in the north, natural pastures (*pastbishche*) cover about 10 per cent of the total area of the country. They are mainly concentrated in the driest areas, however, precisely where precipitation and soil conditions are unsuitable for arable farming, at least without irrigation. The amount of fodder to be expected per unit of area in such conditions is many times less than that obtained in the areas of arable farming. The great sand deserts of Central Asia and Kazakhstan, for example, are classed as pasture, but these produce nothing but occasional crops of ephemeral plants in periods following the rare and unpredictable downpours in the desert. The high mountain pastures such as those in the Caucasus and Central Asia are likewise restricted in scope, providing fodder only in the summer. Figure 31a shows that whereas a high proportion of the driest part of the U.S.S.R. east of the Caspian contains natural pastures, these are clearly limited in extent elsewhere.

The following figures (in millions) give an idea of the relative importance of different types of livestock in Soviet agriculture at six selected dates:

	1916	1938	1951	1959	1964	1965
Cattle	58·4	50·9	57·1	70·8	85·4	87·1
of which cows	28·8	22·7	24·3	33·3	38·3	38·7
Pigs	23·0	25·7	24·2	48·7	40·9	52·8
Sheep and goats	96·3	66·6	97·0	139·2	139·5	130·6
Horses	38·2	16·2	13·8	11·5	8·5	—[1]

SOURCES: *Nkh SSSR 1963*, p. 311; *SSSR v tsifrakh v 1964 godu*, pp. 78–9.

1. not available.

There seems to be no reason to suspect the general picture given by these figures. For one reason they are far from flattering to Soviet agriculture. In using them however certain considerations must be borne in mind. Firstly, the population of the U.S.S.R. has increased substantially during the five decades covered. Secondly, no indication is given of possible changes in the quality of livestock. Thirdly, since cattle and horses are much larger than the other animals, and are therefore greater both as consumers of fodder and in value, livestock figures must be weighted to allow for this. The precise weighting depends on detailed information about the various types in the U.S.S.R., but a rough idea can be obtained by dividing the number of pigs, sheep and goats by six. This calculation gives some 70 per cent of the weight to cattle, a few per cent to the horses and under 25 per cent to pigs, sheep and goats combined. A comparison of the total number of livestock units in 1916 and 1964 on this basis shows that while the number of cattle, pigs and sheep has increased, the number of horses has declined by 30 m. Moreover the increased number of cattle (some 27 m.) and smaller livestock (60 m.) would be expected to consume roughly as much fodder as the 30 m. horses replaced by mechanization. In other words, Soviet agriculture is producing little if any more fodder now than fifty years ago, unless of course the average size of animal is now greater.

Another surprising feature of Soviet livestock farming is the shareout of animals among the different kinds of land tenure. A large though diminishing share of the livestock is still kept on private plots in collective farms. The 1964 figures are as follows:

	Total (millions)	On private plots (millions)	Percentage on private plots
Cattle	85	24	28
of which cows	38	16	42
Pigs	41	13	32
Sheep	134	27	20

SOURCE: *Nkh SSSR 1963*, pp. 312–13.

Given the very small extent of the private plots and the fact that a large part of their area is devoted to the cultivation of vegetables, one cannot help concluding that much of the private plot livestock is either grazed on or fed from the collective land. It is interesting to note from Soviet figures that the reduction in livestock numbers, especially pigs, following the bad 1963 harvest, hit the state and collective animals much more than those on the private plots. Thus total pig numbers diminished by thirty million between January 1963 and January 1964, but the decline on private plots was only three million.

The reverses in 1963 are only the last part of a long story of set-backs. Following a gradual build-up of livestock to the First World War, there was a period of several years of decline. During the N.E.P. period, from about 1922 to 1930, there was an impressive increase. This was followed by a sharp drop in the early 1930s during collectivization, a further rise to the Second World War, a decline followed by only slow recovery to the early 1950s, then fairly steady progress until the 1963 setback. The effect of this extraordinary series of fluctuations on the other branches of the economy cannot be assessed here, but it must have been detrimental in many ways.

In Figure 30 the distribution of production of two of the principal livestock products, meat and milk, is mapped, rather than that of individual types of animal. While there are regional variations in the density of cattle and of pigs per unit of arable land, their distribution over the national area is so similar to the distribution of arable land itself (see Figure 28) that only detailed and reasonably large-scale maps can bring out subtle differences. In general, however, it may be noted that the density per unit of arable area of cattle (more particularly of dairy cows) and of pigs, tends to decline eastwards across the main farm belt of the country, and is also low in the extreme south of the country. The distribution of sheep and goats, on the other hand, shows a different pattern. Although these are not entirely absent from the main farm belt, they occupy a much more prominent place in and around the high mountain areas of Transcaucasia and Central Asia, using high pastures in the summer and lowland areas in the winter. They, rather than cattle or pigs, use the natural pastures of the drier part of the U.S.S.R. (see Figure 31a). In contrast, the reindeer herds of the country are largely confined to the tundra and northern part of the coniferous forest belt.

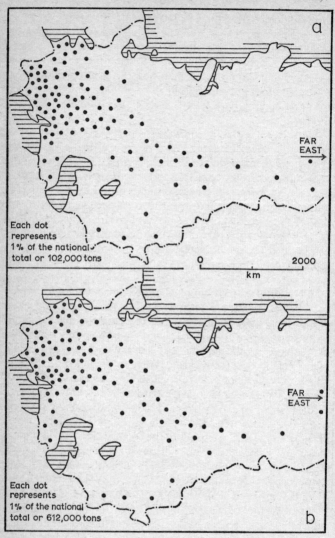

Each dot
represents
1% of the national
total or 102,000 tons

FAR
EAST →

0   2000
              km

Each dot
represents
1% of the national
total or 612,000 tons

FAR
EAST →

a

b

30. Distribution of production of livestock product in 1963 a. Meat. b. Milk.

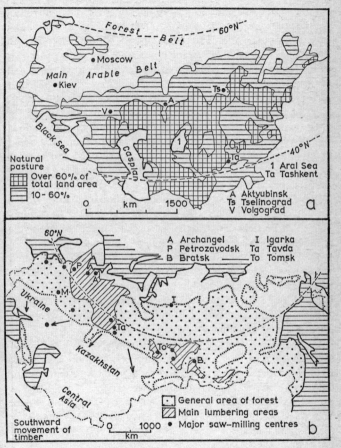

31. a. Natural pasture. (*pastbishche*) b. Forestry.

The distribution of production of meat and of milk (see Figure 30) shows that livestock products are closely related to the main arable belt. Areas of surplus and deficit may be tentatively located by comparing meat and milk production with the number of people in each region, and assuming a fairly uniform consumption of these products related to the number of people. On this basis, meat must be deficient in the North-west and the Centre on account of the large industrial populations here, while Transcaucasia and Central Asia, lacking particularly cattle, and the Far East, short of fodder, probably also receive meat from other regions. The Ukraine would appear now to have roughly a balance.

Owing to the greater proportion of dairy cows to total cattle in some regions than in others, the distribution of dairying is not exactly the same as that of beef production. The extreme western part of the U.S.S.R., including the Baltic Republics and Belorussia, appears to have a surplus, while a new surplus area is emerging in West Siberia and Northern Kazakhstan. In addition to the main urban areas, Central Asia and Siberia east of the Yenisey appear to be deficient in dairy products. The efficiency of the dairying industry, or at least the quality of cows and suitability of fodder, vary regionally to such an extent that (in 1963) compared with an average yield of 1,584 kilograms per cow in the U.S.S.R. as a whole, the Baltic Republics, North-west and Central regions had yields of 1,800–2,000 (still low by West European standards) whereas in Transcaucasia and Central Asia the yields were only about half this amount.

In 1963, 373,000 tons of wool were produced in the U.S.S.R. Of this about 35 per cent came from the Volga region and North Caucasus, from flocks of sheep kept largely on the drier fringes of the steppe belt and adjoining semi-desert areas. Over 40 per cent came from Transcaucasia, Central Asia and Kazakhstan, where even drier pastures are used and a characteristic product is the fur of karakul lambs.

VIII. FISHING AND FORESTRY

The rise of the Soviet fishing industry since the Second World War has been impressive, since the U.S.S.R. was not previously considered to be a major fishing power at all. The industry is characterized by the inevitable division of forces among several distinct sea areas and also by the great distances over which some of the fleets now travel to fishing grounds. An interest in other matters as well as fish has been suggested as one of the reasons why Soviet fishing fleets have appeared off north-east U.S.A., south-west Africa and other areas particularly sensitive to the Communist presence, while Soviet fishing vessels frequently get mixed up in manoeuvres carried out by western navies. Notwithstanding this aspect of fishing, the industry seems to have been seriously organized to provide an additional source of protein to offset the inadequate production of meat and other farm products at home.

The tonnage of fish and sea mammals caught by the U.S.S.R. was about 1,500,000 tons per year in the late 1930s, but after a slow recovery in the immediate postwar years, it passed 3 m. tons in 1959, 4 m. in 1962, 4·7 m. in 1963 and 5·2 m. in 1964. In 1963 figures are only available for Republics (*Nkh SSSR 1963*, p. 207) but it is evident that Black Sea ports only accounted for about 10 per cent of the catch and the Baltic Republics for rather more than 10 per cent. The remainder therefore was landed in the R.S.F.S.R., mainly in the Pacific ports, along the White Sea–Murmansk coast, and in the northern part of the Caspian. Distance from the main urban centres is a drawback for several of the main fishing ports, and the Far East in particular cans a considerable part of its catch, which includes crab.

Roughly a third of the total area of the U.S.S.R. is forested, somewhat less, presumably, than a few centuries ago before its reduction by clearance along the southern fringes of the main forest belt (see Figure 31b) for agriculture, and by cutting for wood without regrowth. The U.S.S.R. still has by far the largest reserves of softwood timber in the world. With the exception of some forest in the high mountain areas of the south, particularly in the Caucasus, and of relics in the southern part of European U.S.S.R., particularly in the Poles'ye, the forests west of the River Ob' lie mainly north of about 55°N, but they continue to the southern boundary of the country east of this. They thin out and disappear towards the Arctic coast as tundra replaces them, and are thin or absent in some mountain areas of East Siberia and the Far East as well as in considerable tracts in the West Siberian Lowland. Of the total forest areas, conifers occupy 78 per cent, broadleaf species

22 per cent. Of the coniferous species, larch (which is deciduous, but not broadleaf) occupies roughly 40 per cent of all the forest, occurring mainly east of the Yenisey. Pine, widely found but particularly common on sandy soils, occupies 16 per cent, the fir about 10 per cent. Of the broadleaf species the birch, a tree of somewhat limited commercial use, is by far the most widespread, occupying 13·5 per cent of all the forest. Many other species, both coniferous and broadleaf, are found more locally. In the early 1960s forest occupied altogether 6,800,000 sq. km., but at least another million sq. km. of former forest land remains without reafforestation in areas cut in the past, and currently some 30,000 sq. km. of forest (equal to the area of Belgium) is being cut each year, but only half of it replanted.

The proportion of forest to total area varies enormously among the economic regions of the country, being lowest in Kazakhstan and Central Asia and limited in the Ukraine, but very high in the North-west, Ural and much of Siberia. Several of the southern regions are deficient in timber resources and there is a great movement of timber southwards by rail and waterway throughout the western half of the country. Naturally a larger proportion of forest has been cut in European U.S.S.R., nearer both to the older industrial concentration and to exporting ports, than east of the Ural. In Siberia only the southern fringe has been seriously reduced as yet, although some of the best stands of timber occur in more remote areas, particularly in East Siberia. In 1963, the North-west accounted for over 25 per cent of the timber (*drevesina*) produced, the Ural region for over 20 per cent. The Siberian regions, with about two thirds of all the forest area, accounted for only about as much as the North-west, but this position is likely to change as attention is given to conserving and restoring the forest of European U.S.S.R. and as the demand for timber continues to rise in the developing zone between the Ural and Lake Baykal.

There has been much criticism of the wasteful way in which wood is used in the Soviet Union. A considerable proportion is still used for fuel, even in the smelting of iron ore, while only about one third of the timber cut actually ends up in finished products, and only 4 per cent becomes cellulose or paper, compared with 20 per cent in the U.S.A. Much of the saw-milling is now carried out in the forest belt itself (see Figure 31b) but previously logs were sent far south along the rivers in European U.S.S.R. for sawing. At the same time large new saw mills have been constructed in the east, and a large expansion of paper-making is proposed in Siberia. Some of the most recent railways built in the U.S.S.R. have been established to open up new areas of forest here, as for example the line from Achinsk to Abalakova and Maklakovo.

Chapter 9

INDUSTRY

I. EMPLOYMENT STRUCTURE

PERHAPS the most continuous single preoccupation of the Communists in the U.S.S.R. has been to transform their economy from a predominantly agricultural one to an industrial one based on modern technology and high productivity. The first great drive towards industrialization took place in the 1930s. The second, following rehabilitation after the Second World War, continues now. As industry grows, the other major productive sector, agriculture, continues to diminish in relative importance. Before the spatial aspects of industry in the U.S.S.R. are dealt with, changes in employment structure and industrial organization since 1950 will be reviewed briefly, to illustrate the kinds of development taking place.

Between 1950 and 1963 agricultural production in the Soviet Union grew by 57 per cent whereas industrial output, it was claimed, increased roughly four times. Between 1958 and 1963 there was no change in agricultural production, whereas industrial production increased by more than half. Changes in the contribution to gross national product made by these main branches of the economy are reflected in a changing class structure. For the Communist period three very broad classes have been distinguished: workers and office workers, collective farm workers and cooperative craftsmen, and private or self-employed persons. In the late 1920s, about 80 per cent of the total working population of the U.S.S.R. still occupied the third category. By the late 1930s this had largely been eliminated as a result of collectivization, and there were roughly equal proportions in the first two classes. So considerable has been the drift from collective farms, that in the early 1960s only about 25 per cent of the population was in class two and the remainder in class one.

The decline in employment in collective farms seems to have been particularly marked since the early 1950s. Around 1950 agriculture employed some 60 m. people out of a total labour force of 105 m., but many of the agricultural workers appear to have been women employed only part-time. In 1960 the figure for employment in agriculture was less than 40 m., which was however still a large number compared with less than 6 m. in the U.S.A. The actual number of *kolkhozniks* performing work on collective farms (as opposed to other people employed on collective farms but not performing agricultural work) was 27·3 m.,[1] whereas the corresponding figure for 1963 was only 19·2 m. Several million state farm workers must also be taken into account in the agricultural sector. The biggest decline in collective farm workers has taken place in the regions of the R.S.F.S.R., excluding two, the Blackearth Centre and the North Caucasus. In Kazakhstan the increase in agricultural workers has taken place in state farms rather than collective farms.

Turning to industry itself, the 1963 figure for persons employed in this branch of the economy was 25 m., but even of this total, only 83 per cent were employed in production work. It is remarkable that industry can provide nearly two thirds of the national income while employing less than 30 per cent of the total labour force of the country. This is to some extent the result of unusual definitions but it also reflects strikingly the low productivity of workers in agriculture. Moreover it appears that the great increase in industrial production claimed in the postwar period has largely been achieved thanks to greatly increased productivity of labour. For example it is claimed that productivity in industry increased by about 30 per cent between 1958 and 1963 alone, and elsewhere (*Pravda*, 6 January 1965) that planners are expecting 70 per cent of the increase in industrial production to be achieved by higher productivity in the next few years. This trend is consistent with development in many other countries. It seems clear that now most of the employment in industry is male and that in many areas in the U.S.S.R. in which heavy industry predominates, there is a need for female employment to absorb a potential female labour force.

II. BRANCHES OF INDUSTRY

The expansion of different branches of industry in the Soviet period has been very uneven. Almost throughout, the output of

1. *Nkh SSSR 1963*, p. 364.

capital goods (group A) have been increasing faster than that of consumer goods (group B). As a result, whereas consumer goods accounted for 65 per cent of all industrial production in 1913 they were a mere 25 per cent in 1963. Notwithstanding this relative decline, the volume of consumer goods produced in 1963 was still claimed to be eighteen times greater than that produced in 1913.

One view of the relative importance of different branches of the Soviet economy may be obtained from a consideration of basic funds available in January 1964. The fuel industry, electricity and thermal energy combined, had 29 per cent of all investment, metallurgical industries, metal-working and engineering another 30 per cent, at one extreme, light industry only 4·2 per cent and the food industry only 9·2 per cent at the other extreme. Since heavy industry tends to be more highly capitalized than light industry, the distribution of production workers (total 20·8 m. in 1963) was more even. Light industry and the food industry together claimed about 5·5 m. whereas extractive industries, and the metallurgical and chemicals branches, required only a relatively small labour force. By far the largest single branch of industry in terms of employment was engineering, which had about 6·9 m., or one third.

III. REGIONAL DISTRIBUTION OF INDUSTRY

A general idea of the regional distribution of employment in industry in 1950 and 1963 by Republics or groups of Republics is given in the following table. The table shows the number of workers and employees in thousands.

	1950	1963
U.S.S.R.	14,144	25,057
R.S.F.S.R.	10,051	16,763
Ukraine–Moldavia	2,350	4,720
Belorussia	300	670
Central Asia	370	820
Transcaucasia	390	730
Kazakhstan	340	680
Baltic Republics	350	760

SOURCE: *Nkh SSSR 1963*, p. 122.

1961 figures are available for the nineteen economic regions[1] and it is quite clear from these that in spite of the desire to make all regions equally highly industrialized, nothing of the sort has yet been achieved or is anywhere near. By measuring the number of people employed in industry in 1961 in each region against the total population of the region in the same year (total employed population figures are not available) it is possible to work out a rough index figure for industrialization. The mean for the U.S.S.R. was 107 industrial workers per thousand people. At the extremes, however, were the North-west with 180 per thousand and the Centre with 174, compared with Central Asia and Moldavia with a mere 45 per thousand. Other regions more highly industrialized on this basis than the country as a whole were the Donbass–Dnepr region and the Ural region. In contrast the western Ukraine, Belorussia and Kazakhstan were all under-represented industrially.

A study of growth rates in industry in different regions between 1958 and 1963 (see Figure 32) suggests that as a group the relatively weak regions are not improving their position. The rate of industrial growth over this period actually tended to be somewhat less in Transcaucasia and Central Asia than in the country as a whole, though it was considerably faster in Kazakhstan and Belorussia. A consideration of the allocation of total investment (excluding the allocation to collective farms) by regions in the period 1959 to 1963 also appears to confirm that no particular effort is being made to bring the less highly industrialized regions up to the level of the more advanced. Thus the five regions receiving the highest *per caput* investment in this period are the North-west, the three regions of Siberia, and Kazakhstan, all of which except the last are already more highly industrialized than the national average, while the lowest five, Moldavia, the South-west, Belorussia, Central Asia and the Blackearth Centre are among the least highly industrialized (see Figure 32b).

One marked trend in the location of industry over the last two or three decades has been the growing share of capacity and employment in the so-called eastern regions. These are the Ural region, the three regions of Siberia, Central Asia, Kazakhstan and part of the Volga region. Their share of production in selected important

1. *Nkh SSSR 1961*, pp. 131–2.

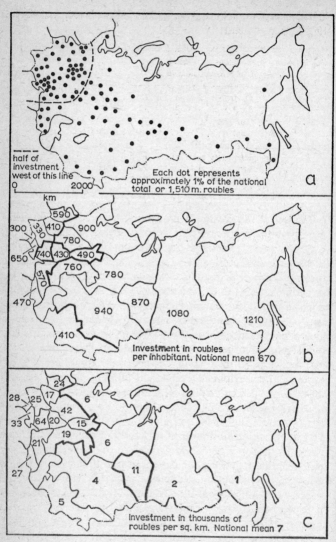

half of
investment
west of this line

0   2000

km

Each dot represents
approximately 1% of the national
total or 1,510 m. roubles

a

590
300 330 410 900
780
650 740 430 490
570 760 780
470 870
940 1080 1210
410

Investment in roubles
per inhabitant. National mean 670

b

24
28 25 17 6
42
33 64 20 15
21 19 6
27
11 2 1
4
5

Investment in thousands of
roubles per sq. km. National mean **7**

c

32. Distribution of capital investment in all branches of the Soviet national
economy except collective farms during 1959–63. The dots have been placed
in the top map on the basis of data for the economic regions.

branches of heavy industry changed as follows between 1940 and 1963 (in percentages):

Percentage of total U.S.S.R. production	1940	1963
Pig iron	28	37
Steel	32	42
Iron ore	9	46·5
Coal	36	49·5
Gas (natural)	1	8
Electricity capacity	23·5	42
Electricity generated	22	41
Fertilizers	31·5	38

SOURCE: *Nkh SSSR 1963*, pp.130–31.

The rest of this chapter is an attempt to summarize the main features of the distribution of various branches of industry in the U.S.S.R., industry in this context including mining and processing as well as manufacturing. How well this can be done depends on the availability of Soviet data. This is unfortunately very poor for some branches. It is of particular interest to distinguish which branches of industry are evenly spread out over the national area, tending towards a considerable degree of regional self-sufficiency, and which branches are concentrated in one or a few regions. Once this degree of concentration or dispersal has been calculated it becomes possible to work out, if only very approximately, the expected inter-regional movement of goods. An example will illustrate the procedure. The Ukraine has roughly 20 per cent of the total population of the U.S.S.R. but accounts for about 50 per cent of the total pig iron output of the country. It seems improbable that it consumes all this pig iron, and a certain proportion, though not necessarily of course the difference between its share of population and of pig iron production, presumably finds its way into other regions, mainly neighbouring ones. Similarly the central region, with only about 12 per cent of the total population, produces about 74 per cent of the cotton textile manufactures. It is inconceivable that all these could be consumed in the region itself, and a very large surplus must therefore be sent elsewhere in the country. An index of concentration and localization is discussed in Chapter 12, Section 2.

IV. THE FUEL INDUSTRY

The relative importance of different sources of energy in the U.S.S.R. is constantly changing as new reserves of different kinds are being found and improvements in technology change production costs. Expressed in terms of conventional units of fuel at 7,000 calories per unit, it is possible to compare the relative contribution of the various sources of fuel (hydro-electricity is not included here) in different years. In 1963 coal only contributed 46 per cent of the total fuel balance and oil and gas together 47 per cent, while the rest was contributed by wood, peat and oil shales. The position was strikingly different even around 1950, when coal accounted for 66 per cent of the total, oil and natural gas for less than 20 per cent. Over a longer period, back to 1913, the following trends may be discerned. The consumption of wood as a fuel has declined relatively almost throughout. Even so, the absolute amount actually used is much greater now than in 1913, though somewhat less than a decade ago. The relative importance of oil, high before the First World War when Russia was one of the leading producing countries, declined in the inter-war period, but for about the last ten years now great efforts have been made to expand this industry as rapidly as possible. Compare a production of 38 m. tons of oil in 1950 with 204 m. in 1963 and 224 m. in 1964. The natural gas industry, which was only of slight importance in 1950, has shown an even greater rate of increase, from 6,000 m. cu. m. in 1950 to 110,200 m. in 1963. The increase in coal production has, by comparison, been very slow indeed in the last few years.

The last word has not of course been said on the relative importance of these main sources of energy by Soviet planners, and recently the discovery of easily accessible, very thick coal seams in central Siberia has helped to reaffirm the future of the coal industry. One source anticipates at least a doubling of coal production over the period 1960 and 1980, but over the same period oil production is expected to increase by 400 or 500 per cent and natural gas production by about 1,200 per cent.

Since at least nine tenths of the energy reserves of the U.S.S.R. are in the form of coal, and very large reserves are available in the Kuzbass coalfield and in the more recently developed coal regions between the Kuzbass and Lake Baykal, it seems reasonable to expect that a great increase in coal production will take place here, using opencast methods, even if still bigger reserves in parts of Siberia to the north remain untouched for many decades.

In 1963, 532 m. tons of coal were extracted in the U.S.S.R., in 1964, 554 m. The coal produced varied greatly in thermal efficiency and in quality and amounted in 1963 to only 388,007,000 calorific units, or 466 m. tons of hard coal equivalent. Of the tonnage of coal extracted, 137 m. tons was lignite (brown coal), 76 m. tons was anthracite, the highest grade coal, and 318 m. tons other types of coal.

The main producing Republics of the country in 1963 were the R.S.F.S.R., which accounted for 302 m. tons, much of it lignite, the Ukraine, 180 m. tons, almost all hard coal, and Kazakhstan, 39 m. tons, mostly hard coal. The principal coalfields are shown in Figure 33. Coking coal, the type used for smelting in the iron and steel industry, amounted to 127 m. tons in 1963 and of this the Ukraine produced no less than 72 m. while Kazakhstan (mainly from the Karaganda field) produced 10 m., and the R.S.F.S.R. 44 m.

The trend in the last few years has been for the limited increase in coal output to come mainly from new opencast mines, and in 1963 121 m. tons were extracted by opencast methods. Some of the new areas in northern Kazakhstan and central Siberia, particularly Ekibastuz and Kansk–Achinsk, offer the possibilities of exploiting very large coal reserves with capital costs per unit of coal produced 6–12 times lower than those in European U.S.S.R. and with a productivity per miner 10–20 times higher. At some sites it will be possible to extract 10,000 tons of coal per hour and up to 45 m. tons of coal per year and to feed this to nearby thermal-electric power stations, themselves very large and therefore benefiting from economies of large scale. Since oil and gas reserves, though adequate for a large increase over the next decade or two, are very limited in extent compared with coal reserves, it seems sensible to start planning at once to use these promising coal reserves and to retreat somewhat from the very great emphasis placed on oil and gas in the late 1950s.

Optimism about the future of the oil and gas industry in the U.S.S.R. appears to be based partly on the many reserves recently

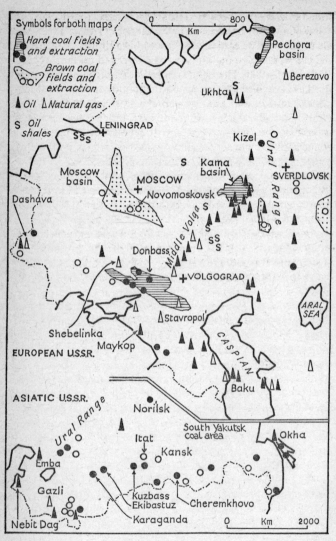

33. Extraction of energy minerals.

found in new areas both in European U.S.S.R. (particularly the Ukraine and North Caucasus) and in Siberia (Tyumen' oblast) and Central Asia. The earliest area from which oil was extracted was the Caspian, where the first oil was discovered on the Apsheron Peninsula in 1871. The Baku area and other early oilfields on the northern side of the Caucasus were for a time among the leading oilfields of the world, but they were rapidly eclipsed by the Volga–Ural region after the Second World War. Production started here as long ago as the early 1930s at Ishimbay, but it was not until about 1950 that more was being produced here than in Azerbaijan. The contribution to the total oil output of 206 m. tons in 1963 was made up as follows: 169 m. from the R.S.F.S.R. (probably at least 150 m. of this from the Volga–Ural fields), about 20 m. tons from Azerbaijan and 9 m. from the Republics of Central Asia, particularly Turkmenistan.

The production of natural gas is less a monopoly of the R.S.F.S.R., which in 1963 contributed 48,000 m. of the total of 90,000 m., compared with 32,000 m. from the Ukraine. Azerbaijan 6,600 m. and Uzbekistan 3,000 m. were the other major contributors.[1] The North Caucasus region appears to be the principal producer among the regions of the R.S.F.S.R.

So many new important deposits of oil and gas have been discovered in recent years that it is difficult to keep track of them and to differentiate between large and small deposits. Some are indicated in Figure 34. Attention must be drawn in particular to new oil discoveries in West Siberia since about 1960 (see Figure 34a), to the discovery for the first time of oil in the Lena valley in East Siberia, and to new discoveries in Kamchatka, Central Asia and at Mangyshlak to the east of the Caspian. The view, apparently long held, that oil would not be found in Siberia, has now been completely shattered and the usefulness of the oil pipeline from Tuymazy to Irkutsk, the longest single pipeline in the world, put in doubt. Even though the cost of moving oil along this pipeline from the Volga–Ural field is claimed to be six to seven times less than it is by rail, it would seem more economical in the long run to divert East and West Siberian oil into Kazakhstan and central Siberia, and to concentrate on sending the Volga–Ural oil westwards rather than east into Siberia.

1. *Nkh SSSR 1963*, p. 156.

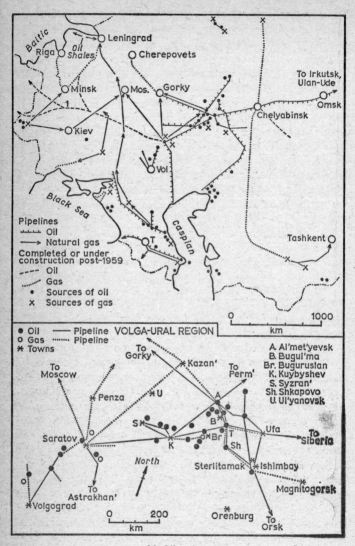

34. Oil and gas.

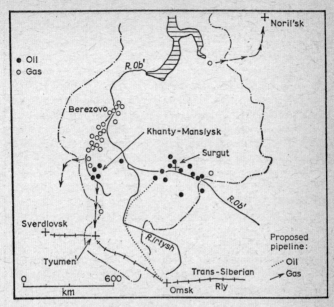

34a. Oil and gas in Tyumen' oblast.

It has been calculated that at the moment the cost of producing oil is three times lower than that of producing an equivalent amount of coal, though of course the cost of producing both oil and coal themselves varies enormously from one field to another. As well as being indispensable to some kinds of transportation, oil can easily be used in thermal-electric power stations, is being used increasingly as a raw material in the chemicals industry, and finally, unlike Soviet coal, can find an outlet in Western markets when this is desired. The recent great expansion of the oil and gas industry has been accompanied by the establishment of a pipeline system which is many times more extensive than the few pipelines of the inter-war period (see Figure 34). The trend now seems to be towards moving crude oil by pipeline from the oilfields to refineries located near markets, particularly, of course, near the main industrial concentrations. Many new oil refineries in European U.S.S.R. and in the four northern Communist countries of East

Europe are now dependent on this new pipeline system and the Volga–Ural fields. Oil refineries will be discussed in a later section in this chapter.

Natural gas appears to be an even cheaper source of fuel than oil, the cost of its extraction being only about one twelfth of that of extracting an equivalent amount of coal. Some natural gas has been extracted for a long time now, particularly in Azerbaijan and more recently in the Volga–Ural field, but only from about 1955 did the share of natural gas in the total energy balance begin to rise appreciably: from 2·4 per cent in 1955 to nearly 8 per cent in 1960 and 12·4 per cent in 1963. In general the natural gas industry was not well organized until the mid-1950s although for some time considerable quantities had been piped from Saratov on the Volga to Moscow.

Initially many of the natural gas deposits were encountered during the exploration for oil, but more recently many new gas deposits have been discovered away from the traditional oil-producing areas, and many are particularly attractive on account of their reasonable proximity to the great energy deficient area of the country, the regions of European U.S.S.R. lying north of the Ukraine. Thus (see Figure 33) Dashava in the western Ukraine, Shebelinka in the middle Ukraine, Saratov and many other places in the Volga region, and even Stavropol' in the North Caucasus, are now sending gas by pipeline to the Centre and to other regions in this part of European U.S.S.R. Moreover, a second energy-deficient region, the Ural, is also beginning now to draw on deposits of gas found within the last few years. These include Berezovo in the West Siberian Lowland and the Bukhara area in Central Asia. What is claimed to be the longest gas pipeline in the world was completed in 1964 between Gazli in Central Asia and Chelyabinsk in the Ural region. It is almost 2,000 km. in length, not counting branches serving other towns in the Ural region. The capacity is about 7,000 m. cu. m. of gas per year, equivalent to about 9 m. tons of coal. It is planned to duplicate this pipeline eventually.

Even more ambitious is the project to build a gas pipeline from Central Asia to the Moscow area by 1967. The reserves of gas in Central Asia are claimed to be twice as large as those of the Ukraine, North Caucasus and Transcaucasia combined, and would be capable eventually of supplying some 30,000 m. cu. m. of gas in three pipelines to the central part of European U.S.S.R. The length of each pipeline would be about 2,500 km. Given the low cost of moving natural gas compared with that of moving coal, it seems reasonable to make it the main source of energy in coal-deficient regions such as the central and western parts of European U.S.S.R., the Ural region, Transcaucasia and Central Asia itself. In this way, however, Central Asia loses the advantage of having the best deposits of natural gas in the country.

Compared with coal, oil and natural gas, the other sources of energy in the U.S.S.R., apart from hydro-electricity, which will be dealt with in the next section, are clearly of limited importance. Wood, which still supplies 3·6 per cent of the fuel, should not be used for this purpose any more except in areas where it is impossible to obtain other sources, since it is of growing usefulness as a raw material in the chemicals industry. Similarly peat, which supplies 2·5 per cent of the fuel consumed, is very costly to cut and prepare for consumption in thermal-electric power stations and if cut at all could better be used in agriculture. Oil shales, which are extracted mainly in Estonia and the adjoining part of the North-west region, account for less than 1 per cent of the total fuel consumption and are inconvenient because they need heavy processing.

v. ELECTRICITY

Electricity is both a prime source of energy when generated in hydro-electric power stations, and a means of transmitting energy, whether that generated by hydro-electric stations themselves or that generated in thermal stations by other sources of fuel such as coal or natural gas. The fuels used in the generation of thermal electricity have been discussed in the last section. The Communists have had almost an obsession about electricity from the very beginning, stressing its ability to bring modern life to Russian villages, its cheapness when produced by hydro-electric stations, its flexibility as a source of power in industry, and its usefulness, given an appropriate transmission system, in smoothing out regional differences in energy supply and demand. Moreover, although it does not employ much labour, the electricity industry takes a large share of all capital investment. It also presents Soviet planners and technologists with perhaps their greatest single challenge, the need to generate much of the electricity in Siberia and at the same time to supply the great market of European U.S.S.R. and East Europe. In view of the great interest in electricity and its fundamental importance to the Soviet economy, the industry will be covered in some detail in this section. Many of its spatial problems are in fact similar to those of other branches of industry in the country.

In 1963, about 22 per cent of all electricity generating capacity was in hydro-electric stations, the remainder in thermal stations. In that year however only 18 per cent of the electricity generated came from the hydro-stations, since these, for reasons both of climate and organization, do not usually run so continuously as the main thermal stations. The total amount of electricity generated in 1963, 412,418 m. kilowatt-hours (kwh.), was equivalent to about one third of all energy consumed in the U.S.S.R., or in other words about one third of all energy consumed in the country was consumed in the form of electricity. Since hydro-electricity was less than a fifth of this third, the relative unimportance of hydro-electricity as a source of energy in the U.S.S.R., contributing as it did only 6–7 per cent of the total, can be appreciated. For various reasons, however, the much advertised hydro-electric stations of the country, as well as being associated with navigation and irrigation schemes, and the flood control of rivers, are expected to be particularly useful in the future to supply electricity at peak periods, since water in the reservoirs behind them can be regulated and therefore conveniently passed through to generate electricity when needed. On the other hand, it is inconvenient to regulate thermal-electric stations in this way. They are most efficient when running continuously, regardless of demand. This special use of hydro-electric stations presupposes the establishment of an all-Union electricity grid.

The supposed cheapness of hydro-electricity has been seriously questioned recently in the U.S.S.R. So much capital has been needed to build most of the older hydro-electric stations that the apparently low-cost product may not make up for this investment for a very long time. In fact, the cheapness of construction of the latest hydro-electric stations, assessed by the cost of installing, say, a kilowatt of generating capacity, is much lower than that in older stations, thanks both to the improved technology of construction, and to the choice of sites in which dams are smaller in relation to the head of water produced. The following table compares the capacity of five famous power stations, representing four 'generations' in the evolution of hydro-electricity.

Date established		kw.
1921–6	Volkhov near Leningrad	56,000
1927–32	Dneproges, Zaporozh'ye on the Dnepr	now 650,000, but less when first completed
1958	Zhigulevsk near Kuybyshev	2,300,000
1960	Volgograd	2,530,000
1964	Bratsk (Angara)	3,600,000

The Bratsk power station, completed in 1964, is the largest in the world, but was completed much more quickly than its two giant predecessors on the Volga. Its ingredients included 4,700,000 cubic metres of concrete, 16 million tons of earth and 200,000 tons of metal. The plant is located in a relatively remote part of Siberia with long very cold winters. It is not even certain that this project was a sensible use of investment.

It has been estimated that the capital outlay on one kilowatt of capacity in sites on the Angara and Yenisey is only 80–100 roubles compared with 200–220 in the Volga stations and 300 in the Dnepr stations. The difference in the cost of generating 10 kwh. of electricity is even wider; compare 1·2 kopeks on the Volga with 0·3 to 0·5 in East Siberia and as little as 0·25 kopeks at the proposed Sayan station near Abakan on the upper Yenisey.

There are many small hydro-electric power stations in European U.S.S.R., especially in the North-west and in the Caucasus area, but the Dnepr is the first river, travelling eastwards across Europe, with an impressive 'cascade' of stations. Six stations, Kakhovka, Zaporozh'ye (the original Dneproges), Dneprodzerzhinsk, Kremenchug, Komev and Kiev, will eventually have a generating capacity of 3·5 m. kw. This, however, is only equal to the capacity of Bratsk alone. Navigation on the Dnepr has been improved and the possibilities of irrigation along the lower valley extended, but there is some question about the adequacy of the water in the river.

The Volga system, with thirteen major power stations completed or projected, should eventually have a capacity about four times that of the Dnepr, or some 14 m. kw. installed. Of this capacity, 6·2 m. kw. had been installed in seven stations by 1962. Evaporation from the reservoirs has become a cause of concern, however, since the Volga is the main feeder of the Caspian Sea.

The part of the U.S.S.R. with the most favourable sites and greatest hydro-electric potential is East Siberia and the Far East, and this is now the major area of construction in terms of capacity being installed, though some stations (e.g. Novosibirsk) have also been built in the Ob'–Irtysh basin. With the Bratsk station on the Angara now complete, attention has shifted to the even larger station at Divnogorsk on the Yenisey near Krasnoyarsk. This should be completed in 1966 and will have a capacity of 5 m. kw., roughly a hundred times that of the Volkhov station and ten times that of Dneproges. The generating capacity of both Bratsk and Divnogorsk could eventually be substantially increased.

As yet, the Lena basin has only been contemplated by planners from a distance, though one small station has been built to serve the diamond mines in the Vilyuy valley. The whole basin has a potential capable of generating some 250,000 m. kwh. of electricity, which is more than the amount generated by all the power stations in the country, hydro- and thermal, in 1958. One site very near the mouth could have a capacity of 20 m. kw. In passing, it may be noted that the Mamakansk station on the Vilyuy, mentioned above, was constructed in an extremely inaccessible locality, and cement and steel consumption had to be kept to a minimum, while extreme temperatures dropped as low as − 70°C. Such is the environment throughout the Lena basin. Moreover the usefulness of any new stations here depends on the development of very long distance transmission

Since thermal electricity provides over 80 per cent of all the electricity generated, and is expected to retain this share for a long time to come, the distribution of thermal stations is also of great interest to the geographer and planner. Although not restricted in their location to certain favourable localities on the larger rivers, thermal stations are by no means indiscriminately distributed about the national area. Many of the larger ones are in the immediate vicinity of the sources of fuel they use, though in some cases fuel is transported over considerable distances to feed thermal stations near large urban centres. Several large coal-fired stations are situated in the Donbass coalfield, for example, while others burn lignite or peat where these are extracted in the Centre region. A large new thermal station nearing completion in Estonia will use oil shales obtained there. Some new stations burning oil or gas, however, are being placed in the areas in which their electricity is to be consumed, rather than where the fuel is derived, for the loss in transmission of electricity in the latter case is much greater than the cost of sending the fuel along a pipeline. An example of a large new oil-fired thermal station far from the source of oil is at Konakov, between Moscow and Kalinin.

The current aim in the Soviet electricity industry, as in those of the West European industrial countries, is to extend to the limit the possibilities of bringing down the cost of generating electricity by benefiting from economies of large scale. Recently thermal stations of $1 \cdot 2$ m., $2 \cdot 4$ m., and even 4 m. kw. have been completed or started. These sizes are multiples of generating units of 200, 300, 500 or 800 kw. now being produced in the U.S.S.R. Electricity from such giant stations is estimated to be five to six times cheaper than that from medium plants. Indeed, an absurd situation is revealed by data for 1960, which showed that a limited number of large regional power stations were producing nine tenths of the electricity in the country, while the remainder was coming from 170,000 small ones, in which production costs were ten to fifteen times higher. The cheapness of the fuel fed into the station is of course also a consideration. Gas, in some circumstances oil, and in certain areas, particularly the Kansk–Achinsk basin in central Siberia, opencast coal, are regarded as the most favourable fuels.

With its vast reserves of conventional fuel and its enormous hydro-electric potential, the U.S.S.R. has shown less urgency in developing nuclear power than West Europe. Nevertheless, great progress has been made in nuclear research, and one of the earliest nuclear power stations in the world, generating however only a token quantity of electricity, was opened near Moscow in the mid-1950s. In 1964 the first 100,000 kw. block of the Beloyarsk nuclear station in the Ural region began generating electricity, but even this capacity is negligible in relation to the national total (about

$\frac{1}{1000}$). Nuclear energy is also used directly for propulsion. The nuclear propelled ice-breaker *Lenin* has already proved useful in the Arctic, keeping the Northern Sea Route open longer than previously. Small mobile nuclear power stations of 1,500 kw. capacity and weighing 350 tons, moving on caterpillar tracks, have been useful in oil drilling in West Siberia.

The possibility of using geothermal heat to generate electricity has not been overlooked. This source is used both in Italy and in New Zealand, and interest in this possibility has led to the study and mapping of temperatures below the surface of the ground. Areas in which these are relatively high near the surface are found in the North Caucasus and in Kamchatka.

Transmission technology is as vital as fuel and power station technology, for although a country could derive its electricity from a very large number of small power stations, each transmitting its electricity over a short distance to nearby consumers, it is far more advantageous to have a few large stations serving some consumer at considerable distances, and still better to link as many stations as possible to a single transmission network. The basic problem in transmission technology is the fact that electricity is lost during transmission, so that there is a limit, both ultimate and commercial, to the distance over which it can be transmitted. The commercial distance over which it can be transmitted depends on the voltage of the line and the method of transmission, direct or alternating. Since the beginning of this century, when experiments were being carried out in several countries in the local and then regional movement of electricity, enormous progress has been made in inter-regional transmission, to such an extent, indeed, that in a country the size of Sweden or France it is feasible to cover the required distances of up to several hundred kilometres. To achieve a unified national electricity grid in the U.S.S.R., however, distances of 2–3,000 kilometres would have to be covered in some cases. Understandably, the U.S.S.R. is now one of the pioneers in the development of very long distance transmission, and, given the determination of Soviet planners eventually to transform most energy into electricity and to move it about the country in this form, the geography of electricity transmission is of extreme importance.

From the very early days of electricity transmission until very recently alternating current was the form used. In the last few years, however, direct current has been successfully adapted to long-distance transmission. Even before the Second World War electricity was being transmitted using alternating current at 220–330 kilovolts, and by 1958 the U.S.S.R. had 2,700 km. of 400–500 kilovolts, including a line linking the Volga power station near Kuybyshev with Moscow. The most recent advance has been to construct an 800 kilovolt line between the Volga station near Volgograd, and the Donbass system (474 km.), though the line Volgograd to Moscow, which is 1,000 km. in length, uses only 500 kilovolts. Even this is able to transmit each year 7–8,000 m. kwh. each year, an amount that would need 5 m. tons of coal if produced in a thermal station.

While the task of linking up all the power stations in individual regions is still incomplete, the long-distance lines mentioned above may be considered the first inter-regional links in an all-Union grid, with the regulation of supply achieved through the regional exchange of current on a grand scale. For example, in the summer, when the Volga is full, electricity can be sent from Volgograd both to the Donbass and to Moscow, whereas in winter, when output is reduced, electricity generated from Donbass coal can be sent from the Donbass via Volgograd to Moscow. The key to the successful inter-regional movement of electricity is a further increase in the voltage of direct current. Fortunately direct-current transmission lines at 800 kilovolts are only half as costly as alternating current at 750 kilovolts, and direct-current lines with a voltage of as much as 1,500 kilovolts are considered feasible and commercially useful.

So far, three principal regions in the U.S.S.R. have the beginnings of a coordinated grid system (see Figure 35): firstly the triangle between Moscow, the Donbass and the Ural region, with the Volga in the centre; secondly, the extreme western part of the Ukraine with the other members of COMECON, and thirdly, the Kuzbass–Baykal area, where the great complex of new thermal and hydro-stations is being integrated. At some stage in the not too distant future it is hoped both to link these three regional systems and to bring in peripheral areas such as Transcaucasia.

For this system to work on a national basis, it is not expected literally to transmit electricity from one end of the country to another, say from the Angara to Czechoslovakia, but rather to

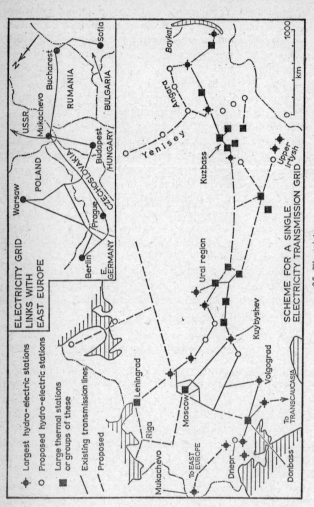

Large thermal stations
Largest hydro-electric stations
Proposed hydro-electric stations
or groups of these
Existing transmission lines
Proposed

ELECTRICITY GRID
LINKS WITH
EAST EUROPE

Warsaw

POLAND

Berlin
E. GERMANY

Prague
CZECHOSLOVAKIA

Budapest
(HUNGARY)

Mukachevo

U.S.S.R.

RUMANIA

Bucharest

Sofia

BULGARIA

N

Leningrad

Riga

Moscow

To EAST
EUROPE

Mukachevo

Dnepr

Donbass

To TRANSCAUCASIA

Volgograd

Kuybyshev

Ural region

Yenisey

Kuzbass

Angara

Baykal

Upper
Irtysh

1000
km

SCHEME FOR A SINGLE
ELECTRICITY TRANSMISSION GRID

35. Electricity.

direct it westwards in stages, from the Kuzbass to the Ural, from the Volga to Moscow, from the Donbass to East Europe.

The Angara and Yenisey stations, which, in spite of their location in a cold area, can operate all the year, could use their reservoirs as regulators and generate electricity at peak periods, letting water through the generators from the reservoirs as needed. To fulfil this role it would be best to have about 25 per cent of all electricity produced in hydro-stations. Altogether by 1980 it should be possible to use the electricity grid to carry the equivalent of some 400,000 m. ton-km., roughly the amount of all kinds of fuel carried by rail in 1960. Put in another way, the grid system would convey the equivalent of 200 m. tons of coal 2,000 km. on average. The economic feasibility of the operation of sending 15–20 per cent of the East Siberian electricity westwards to the Ural and beyond is based on the calculation that although the transmission of a given amount of electricity 2,000 km. by direct current increases its cost threefold, East Siberian electricity would still be 6–8 times cheaper than electricity generated in the Ural region and therefore advantageous. Another benefit of the all-Union grid results from the great east–west extent of the U.S.S.R. and the fact that the peak-hour consumption of electricity occurs at different times in say Prague, Moscow, Sverdlovsk and Novosibirsk. Changes in the direction of flow of electricity can therefore be made to follow the busiest periods across (or round) the U.S.S.R.

VI. METALLURGICAL INDUSTRIES

The metallurgical industries, which are concerned with the smelting or refining and initial processing of metals, may be divided into two main branches, those connected with the iron and steel industry and those handling non-ferrous metals. The lack of information on non-ferrous metals makes it impossible to assess the relative importance of different regions. It is only possible to indicate where the processing of these metals takes place without giving any indication of the quantity involved (see Figure 37). For the most part processing takes place near to the source of the ore from which the metal is obtained. Thus copper ore is smelted in the desert of Kazakhstan at Dzhezkazgan and Balkhash, lead and zinc near the upper River Irtysh. The non-ferrous metals industry apparently employs about a million workers, is heavily capitalized, and for some metals is a large consumer of energy.

More data are available for the iron and steel industry, though even here the regional breakdown of production has in the 1960s been confined to Republic data. The following figures for 1963 for selected Republics show the main features of the distribution of pig iron and steel in the U.S.S.R.

| | Millions of tons produced in 1963 | |
	Pig iron	Steel
U.S.S.R.	58·7	80·2
R.S.F.S.R.	26·9	44·5
Ukraine	29·6	32·6
Kazakhstan	1·4	0·4
Georgia	0·8	1·3

SOURCE: *Nkh SSSR 1963*, pp.145–6.

The strong position of the R.S.F.S.R. and the Ukraine is clear. The remaining Republics, with some 25 per cent of the total population, produced only 3–4 per cent of the pig iron and 5 per cent of the steel. Most of the R.S.F.S.R. total came from the Ural region in the late 1950s and this region accounted for about one third each of the total Soviet pig iron and steel output, while the Kuzbass and Moscow areas provided most of the remainder. The principal centres associated with the industry are shown in Figure 37.

The industry employs roughly a million workers, but no regional breakdown is readily available. Although there has been roughly a twentyfold increase in steel production between 1913 and 1964 (see Figure 36), the iron industry of the U.S.S.R. has a long history before the Revolution. The changing fortunes of the main iron-smelting and iron-working areas over the last three centuries are of great interest. Here it must suffice to point out that the oldest area, around Moscow and Tula, has long suffered from a poverty or absence of raw materials and fuel, while the Ural region, outstanding in the eighteenth century, but eclipsed by the Ukraine in 1880–1900, has been revived in the 1930s. The large iron and steel industry of the Ukraine is relatively modern, dating from the rail-

way age, the 1870s and 1880s. The various works scattered over
the rest of the U.S.S.R., such as the large integrated works in the
Kuzbass or the small steelworks in Central Asia and the Far East,
are virtually all post-1917. The latest area of new development is
the so-called third metallurgical base of northern Kazakhstan and
central Siberia.

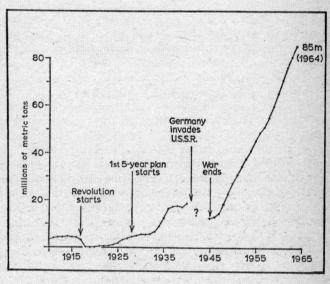

36. Soviet steel output 1910–64.

The iron and steel industry, like the electricity industry already
described, derives benefits from economies of large scale by carrying out at one site in large plants all the processes needed to convert iron ore into rolled steel. But the iron and steel industry
requires a greater variety of ingredients than the electricity industry, the bulkiest being coking coal and iron ore for the production
of pig iron, some limestone, and large quantities of water. Little
pig iron is used directly for manufacturing purposes since almost
all is now transformed into steel. Steel may be made in works that
produce no pig iron but use pig iron from elsewhere or simply scrap

metal collected locally; in these all the energy needed may be obtained from electricity. Ferro-alloys, particularly manganese, but also chrome, nickel and other metals, are used in the manufacture of various types of steel.

As in all the leading industrial countries, the basis of the iron and steel industry in the Soviet Union is provided by a limited number of integrated works using all the items listed above, and carrying out various processes from the manufacture of coke, the smelting of iron ore and the production of steel, to the preparation of items such as rails and girders, or sheets for the metal-working and engineering industries. On the whole, production costs are much lower in the U.S.S.R. in those works producing 2–3 m. tons of steel a year than in smaller ones. In recent years, for example, production costs have been lowest at the Magnitogorsk works, which has a capacity of about 8 m. tons and a proposed future capacity of 12–13 m. tons. Production costs are also affected by the age and equipment of works and the cost of the raw materials used.

Iron ore is now known to exist in so many localities that its widespread nature, together with modern possibilities for enriching ore before transporting it from the iron ore field to the iron works, ties the industry less than previously to restricted localities. Coking coal is much less widely available, and long hauls of this, as from the Kuzbass and Karaganda to the Ural region (see Figure 37) or from the Pechora field to Cherepovets near Moscow, have been a feature of the industry and a burden on the railways. Again, however, new technology allows much of the energy in a modern iron and steel works to be in the form of electricity or natural gas. Other ingredients such as limestone and ferro-alloys are secondary considerations in location. On the other hand, it is sometimes attractive to have an iron and steel works near a large market for its products, even if all the ingredients have to come a long way. This seems to be the reason why efforts have been made to produce some steel in the Moscow area.

A Soviet study[1] of production costs in the industry in the mid 1950s and other Soviet sources[2] bring out very marked differences in regional production costs for pig iron and steel. Clearly there-

1. R. S. Livshits, *Razmeshcheniye chernoy metallurgii SSSR*, Moscow, 1958.

2. e.g. *Pravda*, 11 September 1958.

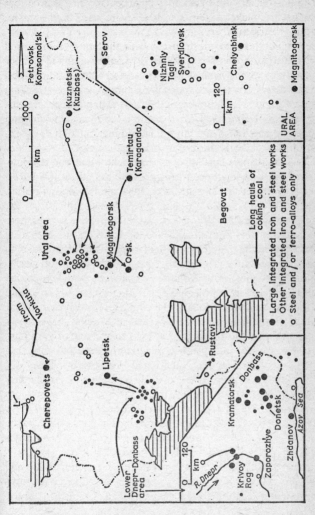

37. Iron and steel industry.

fore certain areas are much more advantageous than others for further expansion of the industry. If production costs in each area are measured against the lowest of all in the U.S.S.R., those at the very large, integrated works at Magnitogorsk in the Ural region, then costs at other main works in the Ural region tend to be up to 50 per cent higher, while costs in the Ukraine works are about 100 per cent more and those of Rustavi in Georgia and Cherepovets near Moscow 3 or 4 times greater. On the other hand, the Novo-kuznetsk works, established in the 1930s like Magnitogorsk itself, is almost as profitable as Magnitogorsk, while Temirtau near Karaganda appears to have production costs even lower than those at Magnitogorsk thanks to the presence of good iron ore only 360 km. away, limestone 110 km. away and coking coal virtually on the spot. Production started at Temirtau in 1963. Other sites chosen for large new works, such as Barnaul, a new Kuzbass ('West Siberian') works, and Tayshet, also offer very low production costs.

Of course if steel from Magnitogorsk is moved a long distance by rail, freight charges reduce its initial low cost, but even when rail-haul charges are added, Magnitogorsk steel is still theoretically cheaper in the Donbass than local steel, and far cheaper in Moscow than Cherepovets steel. In general terms, the problem facing Soviet planners in the iron and steel industry is very similar to that for electricity. Excellent reserves of coking coal and iron ore exist in the eastern or central part of the country but the bulk of the population is still in the extreme west. Obviously some steel must still be produced in European U.S.S.R. and some works, such as Krivoy Rog and Lipetsk, are even being expanded in the 1960s, yet it is absurd to embark on major expansion here when production costs are only half as high in the newer areas to the east. The answer seems to be to organize the westward movement of steel from the new areas as efficiently as possible. If, however, the U.S.S.R. is hoping to sell its steel in foreign markets on a strictly competitive basis, then its low-cost steel is as inconveniently placed as it could be, with a location as far as possible from the seaports of the country.

VII. CHEMICALS INDUSTRY

The chemicals industry is very complex in the range of its raw materials and products and in its technology. While in general the U.S.S.R. has made great strides since its first Five Year Plan in the establishment of energy, metallurgical and engineering branches, the chemicals industry has lagged behind. One basic reason suggested is simply the question of organization. Such a diversified industry is more difficult to plan and offers less obvious targets to aim for than, say, an increase of so many million tons of coal or of steel. Whatever the reasons, it is certain that the chemicals industry was relatively far less important in the U.S.S.R. in the late 1950s than in West Europe or the U.S.A. This backwardness and small capacity could not be attributed to a lack of the raw materials needed, for in this respect the U.S.S.R. is far more fortunate than West Europe.

In 1958 the chemicals, resins and asbestos industry of the U.S.S.R. only employed 500,000 production workers, but by 1963 the total was already 800,000. In the last few years there has been a great drive to expand the industry, and in December 1963, many ideas on the subject crystallized. Some notion of the expansion hoped for is conveyed by the following targets (in tons):

	1960	1970	1980
Plastic materials	330,000	5·3 m.	20 m.
Synthetic fibres	210,000	1,350,000	3·25 m.
Mineral fertilizers	14 m.	77 m.	130 m.

SOURCE: *Vedishchev*, p. 84.

Even given the apparently abundant reserves of various raw materials for the industry, including oil and natural gas, lignite and fertilizer minerals, the 1980 production levels would put great pressure on resources. A more immediate drawback has been the weak development of that side of engineering producing equipment for the chemicals industry. A general lack of know-how, too, has obviously caused problems, but western research work can be drawn on.

There are three important relatively new products from the chemicals industry of particular interest to Soviet planners: plastics, synthetic fibres and synthetic rubber, all of which have of course been produced in the country for some time. The attraction of synthetic materials is that for many purposes they can replace several times their weight in metals, and are cheaper to produce. Likewise, synthetic fibres are cheaper to produce than cotton, and their production can be planned more easily than the production of raw cotton, which is affected by unpredictable fluctuations of the weather. Synthetic rubber can free the U.S.S.R. from imports from areas such as Malaya. Vegetable products such as potatoes have been used as raw materials in the chemicals industry, but oil and gas seem the principal source in the future, and the petrochemicals industry is likely to expand rapidly, while products from coking processes also provide a major raw material for some branches of the industry. In spite of the obvious need to expand the chemicals industry, and the enormous amount of propaganda on the subject, there have been signs of misgivings at least since 1963, and items of news have appeared about the failure to complete new plant to schedule. A large amount of investment is needed to get the expansion under way, while construction and chemical-engineering techniques have been criticized (e.g. *Pravda*, 14 August 1964, 23 September 1964).

In view of the widely scattered nature of the many raw materials for the chemicals industry and the ease with which crude oil and natural gas can be piped over considerable distances, the industry is widely dispersed among the regions of the U.S.S.R., with a tendency for some of the older branches to be most prominent in the coalfield areas, and for the newer petrochemicals establishments to favour the oilfields, especially the Volga–Ural field. Some major chemicals factories are in remote parts of the country, as for example the apatite processing plants, one of which is currently being greatly expanded, in the Kola Peninsula. In attempting to characterize the location of the chemicals industry one is faced with a bewildering list of centres, some so new that they do not even appear in recent Soviet atlases. What follows (see also Figure 38) is merely a summary drawing attention particularly to some of the latest developments.

With the great increase in oil production the refining capacity of

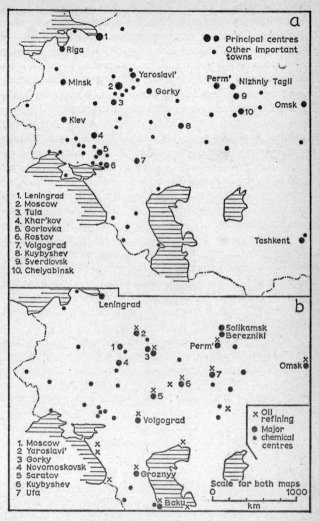

38 a. Engineering. b. Chemicals.

the U.S.S.R. has had to be increased rapidly as well. The desirable standard capacity for an oil refinery has been considered to be a throughput of about 6 m. tons of crude oil per year, but capacities of 12 m. and 18 m. tons are being considered in some cases. In fact many of the existing refineries have a capacity of much less than 6 m. and therefore presumably have high operating costs. Several of the oldest refineries are in the Caucasus area (e.g. Baku, Groznyy), but since the 1930s there has been a new generation in the Volga–Ural region (e.g. Salavat, Syzran'). The latest trend is to transport crude oil from the oilfields to markets and to establish refineries there (e.g. Ryazan', Gorky in the central industrial area, Angarsk in East Siberia, Polotsk in Belorussia, which will have the largest refinery in the country).

One aim is to keep oil and oil products off the railways. The Volga system is useful for carrying oil in certain directions, but pipelines are more flexible in general. These can carry crude oil much more conveniently than various refined products, which obviously cannot use a pipeline simultaneously.

The location of petrochemicals plants is to a considerable extent determined by the distribution of oil refineries. The new trend towards locating oil refineries in energy-deficient regions appears to be emphasizing the already strong position of the central industrial region of European U.S.S.R. in the production of plastics, synthetic fibres and rubber. This region already accounts for about half of the national output, although its raw materials come largely from other regions, much of its output leaves the region, and energy is costly. Much of the expansion of petro-chemicals in the last few years appears to have been in a few large new establishments (see regional maps in Chapter 10). These include Sterlitamak (synthetic rubbers), Salavat (various), Kazan', Stavropol' on the Volga[1] (rubber), Nevinnomyssk in the North Caucasus, Kirovakan in Transcaucasia, all on or near oilfields, and Moscow, Yaroslavl', and Omsk (rubber) away from the oilfields. Future development of petrochemicals is anticipated in West Siberia on the basis of oil from the fields of the West Siberian Lowland.

1. This Stavropol' should not be confused with Stavropol' in the North Caucasus. The Volga Stavropol' has now been renamed Tol'yatti after the former Italian Communist Party Leader.

One of the most vital branches of the chemicals industry as far as agriculture is concerned is the production of fertilizers.[1] The output of some 19·9 m. tons in 1963, 25·6 m. in 1964 (contrast 5·5 m. in 1950 and 12·4 m. in 1958) is regarded as still far below the amount needed. In this case a rough idea of the regional distribution of production can be gained from Republic figures (*Nkh S S S R* 1963, p. 141). The R.S.F.S.R. has roughly the same share of fertilizer output as it has of population, the Ukraine is somewhat over-represented, but most of the other Republics have a considerable industry in view of their population: Central Asia and Kazakhstan produce over 2 m. tons, Transcaucasia 600,000 tons and the Baltic Republics 900,000 tons. But until lately much of the production came from the coalfield areas, particularly the Donbass and Kuzbass, or from certain mineral deposits found some time ago and developed intensively in the Soviet period, as for example the potash of the upper Kama valley in the Ural and the apatite of the Kola Peninsula. New plant is now being established both in association with oil and gas (e.g. Volzhsk) and near new deposits (e.g. phosphate deposits in the Bashkir A.S.S.R., a silvinite deposit yielding potassium at Soligorsk in Belorussia, and the phosphorite deposits of Karatau (Central Asia), which are claimed to contain one third of the total reserves of the world).

It is considered undesirable to have the production of fertilizers concentrated in a few regions, with consequent long hauls of the products to consuming areas. The ideal would be to have a system of fertilizer-producing complexes each serving a region of appropriate size and turning out the particular types of fertilizer needed in the region served, since different types of soil and different crops have their own particular requirements. This new situation would, of course, involve the movement of raw materials over considerable distances in many cases.

VIII. OTHER BRANCHES OF INDUSTRY

In terms of numbers of persons employed, metal-working and engineering is the predominant branch of industry in the U.S.S.R. since it employed about 7 m. production workers in 1963.

1. The figures quoted below are for factory output and are appreciably larger than those quoted in Chapter 8, Section 2, for deliveries to farmers.

T–H

Quantitative data on the regional distribution of production of different branches of engineering are difficult to obtain, but some very broad features can be discerned in atlases. Given the very wide range of products from the industry and the additional service function it performs in maintaining and repairing machinery, it is understandably very dispersed. According to Soviet atlases, every self-respecting town with over about 50,000 inhabitants has some engineering.

At the moment it is clear that heavy engineering in general is found particularly in the eastern Ukraine (e.g. Gorlovka, Khar′-kov) and in the Ural region (e.g. Chelyabinsk, Sverdlovsk) and indeed rolled products such as rails and girders come directly from steelworks themselves. In contrast, those branches of the engineering that are more complex, or tend to require a large amount of skilled labour, congregate in and around Moscow, Leningrad and Gorky. Electrical equipment, precision instruments and motor vehicles are characteristic products. In neither case do these areas have a monopoly of the types of item mentioned, for there has been strong pressure to decentralize engineering, and heavy engineering has been encouraged to move eastwards to such areas as the Kuzbass, while light engineering is regarded as a useful cure for the backwardness and under-industrialization of such areas as Belorussia and Transcaucasia. Many specialized items are of course produced in areas in which they are likely to be needed, for example oil drilling equipment in Transcaucasia, cotton ginning machinery in Central Asia and so on.

Light manufacturing altogether only employs about $3\frac{1}{2}$ m. production workers. The manufacture of textiles is one of its principal branches. This branch is characterized by the very uneven distribution of its productive capacity. There was already a large textile industry in the Centre region before the Revolution and skills here seem to have been useful for subsequent growth. This is certainly one reason why there is still a great concentration here. But Soviet economic theory stresses the need to put each branch of manufacturing where its raw materials are produced (this is an oversimplified and almost old-fashioned concept now) and to industrialize the ex-colonial areas such as Central Asia. It is therefore surprising that this region was still only producing about 5 per cent of the Soviet cotton cloth in the early 1960s, compared with about 75 per cent from the Centre region. The predominance of the Centre is clearly shown by the fact that it has less than 12 per cent of the total population of the country but produced in 1963 74 per cent of the cotton cloth, 54 per cent of the woollen cloth, 66 per cent of the linen and 70 per cent of the silk. Nor has Central Asia improved its position in the postwar period.

There have lately been signs of decentralization in the textile industry with a rise in the relative importance of the Baltic Republics, Transcaucasia, the Ukraine and West Siberia. The growing importance of synthetic fibres, produced in many areas hitherto without textile manufacturing, may further change the pattern, but it seems difficult to reduce the concentration in the Moscow area where, however, it is admitted that many of the textile mills are out-of-date. To do so would deprive this region of one of the few branches of productive activity from which it has an obvious surplus. In contrast to the textile industry, the manufacture of clothing and footwear is spread over the regions roughly according to population, but even here the Moscow and Leningrad areas show some concentration of extra capacity. As yet much of the clothing industry appears to be in small workshops rather than in factories, and in these circumstances it would be difficult to concentrate it in a few centres.

Lack of data for the regions of the R.S.F.S.R. makes it difficult to say much about other industries, but for comparison with those already discussed, two other branches may be referred to briefly. The production of cement, which has shown remarkable increase between 1950 and 1964 (from 10 m. to 65 m. tons) is an industry corresponding closely in its regional distribution to the distribution of total population; indeed, some is produced in all the Republics. There is some extra capacity and a surplus in the Volga region. One reason for this even spread of capacity is the wide availability of limestone. The manufacture of paper, in contrast, is very much restricted to a belt of country along the southern fringe of the coniferous forest, and in 1963 the R.S.F.S.R. produced well over 80 per cent of the national total.

Little precise can be said, unfortunately, about the geography of service activities in the U.S.S.R. Certainly these differ in the number of people employed in them and in their quality between regions and between town and country. There seems no doubt that

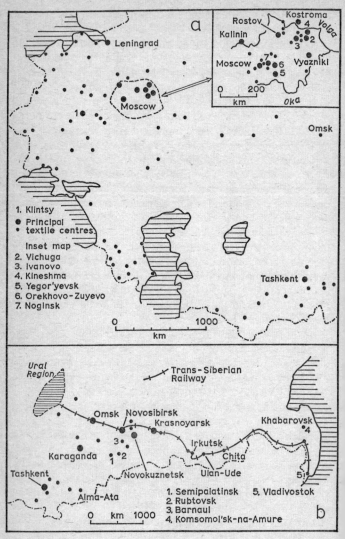

39 a. Textiles. b. Selected industrial centres in Asiatic U.S.S.R.

rural areas are generally very badly provided with services. For example a comparison of the degree of urbanization and the availability of doctors and of hospital beds (per 100,000 people) among the regions indicates a strong positive correlation between urbanization and good health services (see Chapter 12, Section I).

Moscow, of course, employs a large number of people in central government administration, and also handles many of the cultural activities of the country including publishing and higher education. Other regional centres such as Leningrad, Kiev, Kazan' and Novosibirsk also stand out as educational centres. Local administrative activities are of course centred on oblast capitals. The tourist industry is one of the main reasons for the existence of a string of resorts on the Black Sea coast of the Crimea (e.g. Yalta) and Caucasus (e.g. Sochi), while a number of inland resorts (e.g. Mineralnyye Vody) are situated on the northern flanks of the Caucasus.

Chapter 10

REGIONS OF THE U.S.S.R.

I. INTRODUCTION TO THE REGIONS

IT will have become clear in preceding chapters that resources, population and production are spread very unevenly over the surface of the U.S.S.R. At the same time, it is obvious that some parts, such as the Far East, Central Asia and Transcaucasia, are fairly distinct entities in terms of remote location and/or characteristic environment and products. Some parts, moreover, such as West Siberia with its minerals, seem extremely well endowed with resources, while other areas such as the North-west are lacking. In some regions there is a relatively dense concentration of population, while others are empty.

Clearly, then, it is desirable to reconsider the geography of the U.S.S.R. in terms of smaller regions, both for a better geographical appreciation and in order to organize regional planning. In this chapter, therefore, the relationship of various distributions will be reconsidered within major regions of the U.S.S.R. It must be borne in mind, however, that often the actual boundary separating two regions is quite arbitrary and artificial.

Much time is spent by geographers in deciding which set of regions is most meaningful, and much energy goes into justifying a particular set as opposed to other possible sets. Taking the case of the U.S.S.R., it is possible either to study this as one unit of area or to split it into compartments. If it is split, then the number of useful compartments can be anything from two to *at least* several thousand. Moreover, there is not just one way of dividing the U.S.S.R. into a given number of regions, say twenty, but an infinite number of different networks of different shape, each with twenty compartments, that could be devised to do this. The criterion or criteria chosen for defining the regions are also numerous. Some regions, such as politico-administrative ones (e.g. oblasts) are clearly defined, though they may not necessarily be the most convenient administrative units for the area they serve. Other regions can be mapped with reasonable precision as, for example, regions more than 1,000 metres above sea-level (though nothing special happens precisely at 1,000 metres all over the U.S.S.R.). Many regions, however, are destined to be vague from the start. What, for example, is the Volga region or the Soviet Far East? The only precise Volga region might be the water surface of the river itself, with or without all its tributaries; once land is brought in, then one can argue for ever as to how far each side of the river itself the Volga region extends. Nevertheless it is useful to be able to refer in general terms to the Volga region, the Ural region, the Caucasus, and so on. Moreover, as already shown in Chapter 6, Soviet planners have never stopped their vain search for the optimum set of economic regions.

The six main regions into which the U.S.S.R. has been divided for the purposes of this chapter have merely been chosen for convenience. They are used for a regional description of the U.S.S.R. because there have been such profound changes in the official system of economic regions in the last few years that the system of fifteen or so regions used in several recent Soviet geography textbooks is losing its meaning and usefulness especially since the most recent data is being given for nineteen new ones. Some key data for these nineteen economic regions are given in Chapter 12, but no attempt has been made to describe each of them.

In this chapter the six regions chosen (see Figure 40) are used to summarize basic features and problems of the U.S.S.R. connected with its population/resource balance. The theme in each case is the balance between population, resources and actual production. It is hoped to bring out convincingly that contrasts are so great between the regions that it would be extremely difficult to fulfil one of the main aims of Communism, namely to achieve a uniform level of productivity and prosperity everywhere in the national area.

It must be appreciated that there is no sudden change from one side to the other of the limits of the six regions chosen and indeed that as changes take place over time the limits of the regions should themselves be modified. For example two or three decades ago one might have put the Baykal area into 'empty' U.S.S.R., but with recent developments, it has qualified in the view of the author to become the eastern end of the region of great expansion. In devising the six regions, it was necessary in places to violate some divisions by splitting them (e.g. Tyumen', Krasnoyarsk), but this has been avoided as far as possible so that data for the nineteen regions, and where possible the next level of administrative divisions, could be used. Figure 40 shows the main regions proposed, and subdivisions of these for more detailed description where appropriate.

The six main regions chosen differ greatly in area, number of inhabitants, and resource inventory, and this makes precise comparison difficult. The main concern is to bring out the differences between the first four (I–IV). A fairly uniform approach has been applied to the description of the regions, with particular emphasis on the resources and products in which they are deficient or have a surplus. Place-names have been kept to a minimum in the text, but the regional maps have been designed to show the location of a considerable number of places, with a view to including all that can be considered 'important'. This lengthy preamble is intended to point out the difficulties of dividing the U.S.S.R. into regions rather than to serve as a justification of the six chosen.

For convenience, short titles have been given to each region. The numbers I–VI are referred to in the rest of this chapter as shown below. They should not be confused with the numbering of the sections in the chapter. More precise titles are also given.

I North-west: roughly the northern two thirds of European U.S.S.R. Not to be confused with the smaller North-west economic region of the R.S.F.S.R.

II South-west: roughly the southern third of European U.S.S.R. excluding Transcaucasia. Not to be confused with the South-west economic region of the Ukraine.

III Middle belt: an area with many new developments extending from the Volga to Lake Baykal.

IV Southern: Transcaucasia and the more densely settled parts of Central Asia and southern Kazakhstan.

V Dry: the residue lying between regions III and IV, consisting of the more thinly settled parts of arid U.S.S.R.

VI Empty: Siberia lying north of the Trans-Siberian Railway and east of the Ural Range.

In this chapter a section is devoted to most of these regions and a subsection to each of the sub-regions shown by letters in Figure 40. A preliminary view of the main features of the regions can be

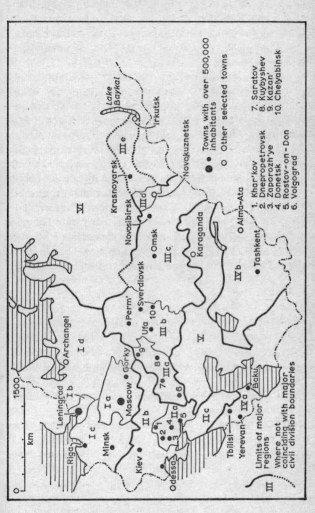

40. Regions of the U.S.S.R. and towns with over 500,000 inhabitants in 1964. These regions have been worked out to serve as the basis for regional description of the U.S.S.R. in Chapter 10.

Towns with over 500,000 inhabitants
Other selected towns

1. Khar'kov
2. Dnepropetrovsk
3. Zaporozh'ye
4. Donetsk
5. Rostov-on-Don
6. Volgograd
7. Saratov
8. Kuybyshev
9. Kazan'
10. Chelyabinsk

Limits of major regions
Where not coinciding with major civil division boundaries

obtained by considering the table below. In this table it is possible to compare the share each region has of total national area and total population with the share it has of some key branches of production and of other features. If more data were available it would be interesting to state also the share of actual resources. An approximate idea of this can be obtained in Chapter 5, but the regions here are a little different. In the table below surpluses and deficits can be detected. Thus, for example, region IV, Trans-caucasia and most of Central Asia, has about 12·5 per cent of the total population of the U.S.S.R. but only 4 per cent of the sown area and of energy production, and 3 per cent of the steel production. These figures suggest therefore that it is very weak both in agriculture and in heavy industry. Region III, however, has a share (percentage) of production greatly in excess of its 21·5 per cent of population, except in cotton textiles (and light manufacturing in general). From this one might be led to conclude that either region III is more prosperous than region IV or that region III gives more to other regions than it receives from them. Data is insufficient to show precisely which of these is happening, but vague and oblique references to such a situation in Soviet publications allow some tentative conclusions to be drawn.

II. NORTH-WEST U.S.S.R.

This region consists of Belorussia, Lithuania, Latvia and Estonia, the North-west, the Centre, and the Volga–Vyatka region excluding its two most southerly divisions, the Mordov and Chuvash A.S.S.R.s. It is referred to for convenience (see Figure 40) as region I. The region is characterized in the view of the author by its unfavourable population/resource balance, at least by Soviet standards, and by high production costs in many branches of the economy. It has to be decided firstly whether or not population is to be made or encouraged to move on a large scale into other regions, and if not, what new employment can be introduced for the growing population of the area.

Region I has about one eighth of the national area, but over a quarter of the population. Essentially it is that part of European U.S.S.R. lying in the forest zone north of the best agricultural lands, which are associated with forest steppe and steppe. It is for the most part lowland or hill country, but climatic and soil conditions have limited the possibilities of cultivation, and the proportion of arable land to total area diminishes from around 50 per cent in the most favourable southern fringe to virtually nothing north of about 65°N. The large extent of forest is some compen-

*Figures represent the approximate percentage of
the national total contained in each region*

	Area	Population Total	Population Urban	Sown area	Energy production	Steel production	Cement production	Cotton textiles	Basic Investment
I North-west U.S.S.R.	12·5	26·5	30·5	16	10	7	22	82	28
II South-west	5·5	32·5	28·5	29	25	43	26	3	24
III Middle belt	14	21·5	23·5	49	55	47	38	6	34
IV Southern	7·5	12·5	10	4	4	3	10	9	7
V Dry	8·5	2·5	2·5	1	4	*	1	*	2
VI Empty U.S.S.R.	52	4·5	5	1	2	*	3	*	5

*Negligible.

SOURCE: All figures are calculated from appropriate tables in *NkhSSSR 1963* and are for 1963 or as near as possible to 1963. Basic investment is for the period 1959–63.

sation for the lack of agricultural land, but much of the most accessible stands of timber have been used already. A further major drawback is the lack of mineral resources of all kinds. The coal (Pechora) and oil (Ukhta) are limited and remote, the lignite near Moscow costly to extract, iron ore of only moderate grade, and even the apatite (for phosphate fertilizers) distant from markets. With over 25 per cent of the population of the country but only

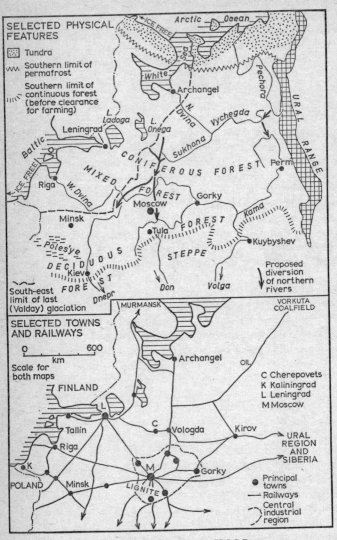

SELECTED PHYSICAL FEATURES

Tundra
Southern limit of permafrost
Southern limit of continuous forest (before clearance for farming)

ICE FREE
Arctic Ocean
URAL RANGE
White Sea
Archangel
Pechora
N. Dvina
Vychegda
L. Ladoga
L. Onega
Sukhona
Leningrad
Perm
Baltic
CONIFEROUS FOREST
W. Dvina
MIXED FOREST
Riga
Gorky
Moscow
Kama
Minsk
Tula
FOREST
Kuybyshev
Polesye
STEPPE
DECIDUOUS FOREST
Kiev
Don
Volga
Proposed diversion of northern rivers
South-east limit of last (Valday) glaciation
Dnepr

SELECTED TOWNS AND RAILWAYS

MURMANSK
VORKUTA COALFIELD
OIL
0   600
km
Scale for both maps

Archangel

C Cherepovets
K Kaliningrad
L Leningrad
M Moscow

FINLAND
L
Tallin
C
Vologda
Kirov
Riga
URAL REGION AND SIBERIA
K
M
Gorky
POLAND
Minsk
LIGNITE

Principal towns
Railways
Central industrial region

41. Region I: North-west U.S.S.R.

about 15 per cent of total agricultural output, 10 per cent of the
energy output, and limited raw materials, the region as a whole
understandably draws on other parts of the U.S.S.R. for many
items, including chemicals and heavy machinery as well as food,
fuel and raw materials.

Region I includes the oldest area of Russian settlement of the
post-Kiev period and the oldest parts of the Russian State. Farming has always been a struggle in this environment and has long
been supplemented by forest products and crafts, while trade with
other regions has been characteristic. From the seventeenth century on, there has been a movement of Russians out of the area,
both south and east, and from the eighteenth century, if not before,
some degree of specialization in manufacturing (textiles, clothing,
wooden articles, metal goods) for other parts of the Russian
Empire. These generalizations apply less to the western part of
region I, notably Belorussia, which has remained predominantly
agricultural up to the present century, and the Baltic Republics
which have led a separate existence, or in the nineteenth century
served as outlets for the Russian Empire.

Clearly the idea of bringing food and raw materials into the
region is not a new one, and even applies now to Belorussia and the
Baltic as well. The problem is to decide which branches of industry
can best be expanded and which raw materials, therefore, should
be brought in. Much development has taken place in light industry,
including branches of engineering producing consumer goods, as
well as in electrical and precision engineering, which do not generally require large quantities of raw materials. But at the same time
reference is often made to the need for a large iron and steel
industry (e.g. the Centre only provides 20 per cent of its
rolled steel needs), and also a chemicals industry, based, of course,
on oil and gas from other regions. As usual, Soviet planners are
trying to reconcile two mutually exclusive possibilities for the
industries of this region: specialization in certain branches, and a
complete industrial base, heavy and light.

The 55 m. inhabitants of the region are distributed very unevenly
over the total area, with about 20 per cent in Greater Moscow (8
m.) and Leningrad (over 3 m.) alone and about another 20 per cent
in the central industrial region situated around and particularly to
the east of Moscow. There are only a few million people in that

part of the region north of about 60°N, but even this number gives a much higher density of population than is found at comparable latitudes east of the Ural Range. The remainder of the population in region I, about half of the total, lives in a few large and fairly highly industrialized centres (Riga, Minsk, Tallin) or in smaller, often stagnating towns, and in rural areas. Some of the latter are shown by Soviet figures for collective farm family income to be among the poorest in the U.S.S.R.[1] The high level of development of the industrial areas, and the high standard of living of Moscow in particular, contrast with the standards in the unpromising rural areas of this part of the U.S.S.R. and have not, as yet, reached them through industrial decentralization. The rural areas appear to have suffered through neglect in the Second World War and impatience at their apparent lack of efficiency compared with that in the new lands much further east. Indeed, almost throughout the present century there appears to have been a net loss of population from these rural areas and some have fewer people than before the Revolution.

In view of the many unfavourable features of region I that have been outlined, it is surprising to find that both the Centre and the North-west are receiving a share of investment greater in *per caput* terms than the national average, though less than some areas further east (see Figure 32). This suggests either that there are some branches of the economy that are worth expanding or that, in spite of high production costs, industrial expansion is being maintained and the region in a sense subsidized. One should not however overlook certain features of region I that may in fact favour it in comparison with newer areas. These include the satisfactory infra-structure of railways and various services, the long tradition of manufacturing, with availability of skilled labour and know-how in precision engineering largely lacking elsewhere in the U.S.S.R., and the advantage of having a large market on the spot, at least for new industries established anywhere near Moscow. Many higher educational and research centres associated with science and technology are found in and around Moscow. Indeed, with only 12 per cent of the total population, the Centre has 18 per cent of the industrial workers.

A further feature of the region is that at least the western part

1. See *Nkh RSFSR 1963*, pp. 316–18.

lies between the rest of the U.S.S.R. and the northern and most highly developed COMECON partners, while both the Baltic Republics and the White Sea–Kola Peninsula areas are not dead ends but have major Soviet seaports, the importance of which has undoubtedly increased since the mid 1950s with the growth of Soviet foreign trade. If the region does not pay its way in total, it does nevertheless provide many goods and services for other parts of the country, including textiles and clothing, electrical, machine-tool, precision and transport engineering products, items of household equipment such as television sets, and many services, not least those provided by central government administration.

Region I has been subdivided somewhat arbitrarily into four parts for further description.

	Population 1964 (thousands)		Percentage urban	Area (thousand sq. km.)	Density persons per sq. km.
	Total	Urban			
Ia Moscow area	26,200	17,480	67	451	58
Ib Leningrad oblast	4,790	4,210	88	86	56
Ic West	19,540	8,130	42	592	33
Id North	7,320	3,880	53	1,610	5

Ia *Moscow and the Central Industrial Area.* This area consists of Moscow town and oblast together with nine adjoining or nearby oblasts.[1] It contains some 26 m. people but is nearly as large in extent as France, which has 46 m. One third of the population is still classed as rural, but even in the less highly industrialized oblasts non-agricultural activities are now dominant. Agriculture has to some extent become influenced by the great industrial concentration, for dairying, the raising of pigs and poultry, and the cultivation of vegetables have been encouraged in the vicinity of the major urban centres. Areas remain in which improvements could be made to allow a further expansion of this kind of farming (e.g. the Meshchera Lowland), but there is no question of the area satisfying its own needs in agricultural products. Flax is the only important raw material grown here, while grain, sugar, fruit and meat come from other parts of the country, as well as raw materials

1. Kalinin, Yaroslavl', Kostroma, Vladimir, Gorky, Ryazan', Tula, Kaluga, Ivanovo.

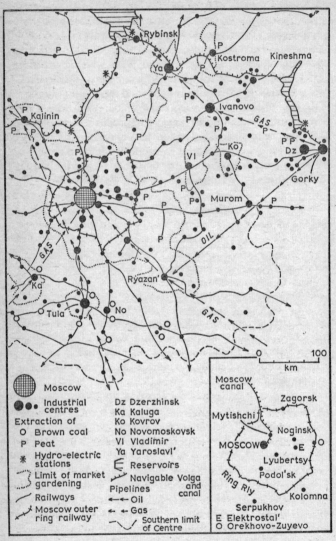

42. Region Ia: The central industrial area.

for industry, such as wool, cotton and oils. While in many ways the similarity is superficial, one can to some extent compare this area, deficient in fuel, raw materials and food, with the metropolitan countries of the former sea empires of West Europe.

The Moscow area is even more deficient in fuel, metals and other minerals than in agricultural products, and there is now even talk of a water deficiency. Lignite is mined south of Moscow and now serves both to generate electricity and as a raw material in the chemicals industry, but its share of the regional fuel balance of the Centre has dropped from one third in 1960 to one fifth in 1965. Some power stations are fired with peat, while a limited amount of power comes from stations on the Volga, the largest and newest being just above Gorky. Other items have to be brought in. Until recently coal was the heaviest single item, but this is being replaced to some extent by oil and natural gas and by hydro-electric energy from the middle Volga. The pipeline system carrying the oil and gas to Moscow and places near by is seen in Figure 42. The new system of pipelines and electricity transmission lines relieves the railways of coal traffic, especially the two lines north from the Donbass to Moscow. Eventually it is hoped to make available electricity from central Siberia. The Volga, together with certain tributaries and canals, has long proved a useful means of bringing bulky materials into the area. Moscow itself is reached by the Moscow Canal from the upper Volga to the Moscow river, and has two port areas. There is access via the Volga to the Black and Caspian Seas, and northwards via the newly improved Volgobalt, to the Baltic and White Seas.

More complete than either the waterway or pipeline systems is the railway network, the pattern of which gives a clue to the importance of Moscow. It is evident that in the last century the first consideration in this part of Russia was to link St Petersburg, the administrative capital, and Moscow, the principal industrial centre, as directly as possible with other major towns or regions. Eleven main railways radiate from Moscow, and most parts of European U.S.S.R. can be reached reasonably directly from it, whereas journeys in many other directions are usually by no means so direct. There are also two ring railways round Moscow, one within the town itself, a few kilometres from the centre and another 50–100 km. out. Compared with most other parts even of

European U.S.S.R. the railway network in the central industrial area is very dense, and several of the radial lines as well as many suburban lines near Moscow are electrified.

The Centre region accounts for about 25 per cent of all Soviet engineering production and 75 per cent of the cotton and linen textiles, as well as much of the clothing and footwear. Machine tools, instruments, motor vehicles, rolling stock, energy equipment and light industrial equipment are outstanding in engineering. Within the area itself, several sub-regions may be distinguished. The approximate area of Moscow town and Moscow oblast, which contains $11\frac{1}{2}$ m. people, is naturally profoundly influenced by the capital. It can be considered in terms of a spider's web layout of both roads and railways, with roughly concentric circles at increasing distances from the centre. Moscow itself is now contained by a remarkable ring road, and within this are distinguishable a central area with largely non-residential functions, and surrounding residential and industrial zones, as well as exhibitions, the university and other large users of land. Housing in Moscow is typically in the form of large blocks of flats, five storeys being the optimum in terms of building costs, but ten to fifteen storeys saving land. Beyond the ring road, many suburbs are located on the radial railways, but attempts are being made to retain a green belt of forest and farmland. Beyond this, a rapid expansion of population is now taking place, both in newly established satellite towns and in existing centres on convenient roads and railways. In the early 1960s there were already seventeen official satellite towns with a million inhabitants altogether, and thirteen more are planned. Even by the late 1950s over 400,000 commuters travelled into Moscow to work, some as much as 50 km. Further out there are several sizable towns, particularly on the eastern side of Moscow, for example Zagorsk, Elektrostal' and Serpukhov.

Like London and Paris, Moscow and its nearby towns have a very wide variety of industries, with heavy industry represented by the manufacture of steel (Elektrostal') and chemicals (various places, with a new oil refinery at Moscow itself), motor vehicles (Moscow), locomotives (Kolomna), textiles, both woollen and cotton (to the north-east in particular). Indeed the diversity has been criticized, and a narrowing of interests recommended, with emphasis on precision engineering, electronics, complex chemicals and textiles, and greater specialization within factories to allow automation.

Further out, at distances of 150 to 250 km. from Moscow, are many other industrial centres or clusters of centres, forming an outer ring. The main textile centre is Ivanovo and many smaller towns around specialize almost entirely in this branch. Yaroslavl' has varied industries, including chemicals and the manufacture of motor tyres. To the south of Moscow, Tula with metal-working and Novomoskovsk (formerly Stalinogorsk) with chemicals are the principal centres in the heavy industrial belt of the lignite field. The iron and steel industry is found here but not on a scale comparable with that of the Donbass or Ural. To the north-west and south-east of Moscow respectively are Kalinin (textiles) and Ryazan' (new oil refinery and chemicals), both sizable industrial centres.

Gorky, which is a major regional centre in its own right, might be considered to mark the eastern end of the central industrial area. With its suburbs and the nearby town of Dzerzhinsk it has well over a million people. Its rail and water connexions with the forest to the north and the Volga to the east and south-east make it well placed to assemble raw materials. Engineering and wood each employ about 30 per cent of the manufacturing population. Paper and wood products, leather and fur and chemicals are manufactured in the area, but Gorky is outstanding as the home of motor vehicle manufacturing. At one time it produced almost all the motor vehicles in the U.S.S.R., but with decentralization it is relatively less prominent now. Many motor vehicle parts are in fact produced in other centres, particularly between Gorky and Moscow, for assembly at Gorky.

Ib *Leningrad*. Although Moscow and Leningrad differ in many ways, in a national context they have basic problems in common. Trends in the Soviet period have however tended to strengthen the position of Moscow greatly while Leningrad has stagnated. To an outward-looking Russia depending on western countries for many imports, for technicians and so on, St Petersburg was a satisfactory outlet, even if its site was inconvenient and its access to the sea hampered by ice for several months. After the Revolution the national capital was moved back to Moscow, foreign trade was cut to a minimum, and security was a consideration behind

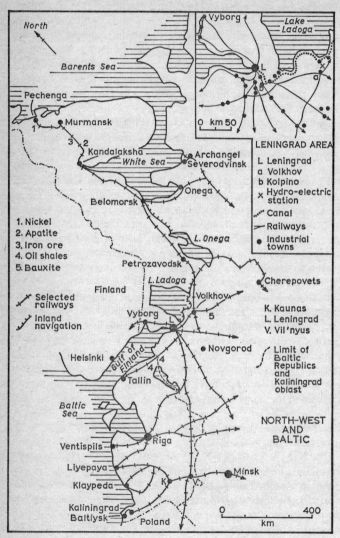

North

Barents Sea

Pechenga

1

Murmansk

3 2

Kandalaksha

White Sea

Archangel
Severodvinsk

Onega

Belomorsk

1. Nickel
2. Apatite
3. Iron ore
4. Oil shales
5. Bauxite

L. Onega

Petrozavodsk

Cherepovets

Finland

L. Ladoga

Volkhov

Selected
railways

Inland
navigation

Vyborg

L

5

K. Kaunas
L. Leningrad
V. Vil'nyus

Helsinki

Gulf of Finland

4

4

Novgorod

Limit of
Baltic
Republics
and
Kaliningrad
oblast

Tallin

Baltic
Sea

NORTH-WEST
AND
BALTIC

Riga

Ventispils

Liyepaya

Minsk

Klaypeda

K.

V.

Kaliningrad
Baltiysk

Poland

0   400
km

LENINGRAD AREA

Vyborg

Lake
Ladoga

L

a

b

x

0   km 50

L. Leningrad
a. Volkhov
b. Kolpino
× Hydro-electric
  station
---- Canal
⊢⊣ Railways
● Industrial
  towns

43. Region Ib, c and d: Leningrad, the North-west and the Baltic.

planning. Leningrad therefore tended to be left stranded, and the siege in the Second World War, which caused depopulation and damage to buildings, was a further setback. Good agricultural land is very limited in the vicinity of Leningrad and rural population is very thinly scattered. The main sources of energy are the oil shales near by in Estonia, peat and limited hydro-electric power, all of which are costly to exploit. Natural gas is to be piped across European U.S.S.R. from Stavropol' in the North Caucasus to make up the energy deficiency. Some timber and minerals (bauxite) are available locally and imported raw materials could easily reach Leningrad by sea, but dependence on other countries for these has been avoided.

The position of Leningrad is unfavourable in relation to the national and even to a regional market. Connexions with the great developing regions of the U.S.S.R. pass through or close to Moscow, underlining the superior position of the latter. Nevertheless, in Leningrad town and oblast there are $4\frac{1}{2}$ m. urban dwellers, depending basically on industrial activities, and one can only attribute the propensity of Leningrad to survive, and even expand, to its long tradition as a manufacturing centre. The range of industries is less diverse than in Moscow and revolves more round engineering, with electrical and shipbuilding branches in particular, as well as machine tools and precision instruments. It can hardly be convenient, however, to continue producing electricity-generating equipment of ever growing size for installation in Siberia. While Leningrad, like Moscow, has radial lines leaving for important places at least on its southern side, there is virtually a vacuum to the north, with Lake Ladoga, the Gulf of Finland and Finland itself. Nor have any large industrial suburbs or more distant towns grown up as they have around Moscow. Leningrad itself has 3,600,000 inhabitants.

Ic *The Baltic Republics, Belorussia and Adjoining Parts of the R.S.F.S.R.* This part of the U.S.S.R. lies west of Moscow and north of the Poles'ye. Although there are considerable variations within the area, it has many features in common in a national context. There are altogether twenty million inhabitants, but virtually no mineral resources of more than local importance. Agricultural land is for the most part of poor to moderate quality, needing frequent liming; fortunately rainfall is abundant. The forests do not match up even to those in the northern part of European U.S.S.R. Belorussia and the R.S.F.S.R. oblasts west of Moscow (Novgorod, Pskov, Smolensk and Bryansk) are among the least progressive in the U.S.S.R., with little industry, very low collective farm incomes and, apart from Minsk, no large urban centre in association with which new industries could be established. In the Baltic Republics, particularly Latvia and Estonia, conditions seem to be superior, and much has been done since the war to promote the development of light manufacturing, producing items such as telephones, radios and television sets, calculating machines and medical apparatus.

If Latvia and Estonia, perhaps through the efforts of their peoples, perhaps through greater development in the past, are managing to advance with the U.S.S.R. in general, the rest of the area seems to be lagging behind. One drawback, the lack of an energy base, is to some extent being remedied by the introduction of gas from the Ukraine and oil from the Volga. Even after transport, the gas still only costs one third as much as the local peat. The establishment of new fertilizer factories should gradually benefit agriculture.

Traffic between the rest of the U.S.S.R. and Poland, as well as the Baltic ports, even in passing through the area, should stimulate improvements in the transportation system. The lack of raw materials remains a problem, and the exploitation of costly oil shales in Estonia, the utilization of a hydro-electric potential of limited capacity, the sparing use of timber for high-value products such as paper and furniture, and even the exploitation of potash deposits, cannot form a local resource base for twenty million people.

The region as a whole does not appear to have an appreciable surplus of farm products, but with its good conditions for the cultivation of fodder crops and vegetables it could specialize more than it does in dairying and the raising of beef cattle, pigs and poultry, as well as market gardening. Industrial crops produced include flax, hemp and sugar-beet, but the high latitude and short growing season discourage the cultivation of several useful crops grown farther south in the Ukraine.

Of the ports, Riga is the largest in population, but Kaliningrad (formerly Koenigsberg) is more attractive since it is ice-free all the year. There are several other ports as well (see Figure 43) including Tallin, capital of Estonia. Inland centres such as Kaunas, Vil'nyus, Smolensk and Bryansk have some manufacturing, but the greatest effort has been put into making Minsk a growth-centre and it already produces most of the heavy lorries in the U.S.S.R., as well as tractors and cycles. New industrial 'knots' are expected to emerge at Starobinsk (potash) and Polotsk (petrochemicals). The southern part of Belorussia awaits long talked of improvements expected from further drainage of the Poles'ye. Over one third of the Republic is considered to need drainage of some kind, and large areas are susceptible to spring flooding. Such land if improved should largely be devoted to fodder crops.

Id *The Northern Part of European U.S.S.R.* The North-west region of the R.S.F.S.R., excluding Leningrad oblast, lies between the Moscow industrial area and the Arctic, and extends from Finland in the west to the Ural Range in the east. It consists either of undulating coniferous forest, with sizable patches cleared for cultivation only along the southern fringe, and with extensive marshes, or of the tundra in the extreme north. It is much less densely populated than the area just described, having some seven million people in an area nearly three times as large. It is deficient in agricultural products, since the area under cultivation is extremely limited and cereal cultivation difficult. Dairying seems to be the most promising branch of farming to develop. The timber reserves, on the other hand, are large by West European standards, but the limited extent of the railway system and the poor quality of roads leave many areas of forest difficult to reach.

The mineral reserves, also, are considerable, and mining is being expanded in some areas. The Pechora coalfield, the chief mining centre of which is Vorkuta, is still being exploited in spite of its high production costs and remote location, and is considered a 'local' fuel base for Leningrad, Moscow and the Cherepovets iron and steel works. Oil and gas have been found near Ukhta, but not on the scale of the new deposits in the West Siberian Lowlands east of the Ural Range. Several economic minerals are found and exploited in the Kola Peninsula, including nickel ore (at Nikel'), iron ore (Olenegorsk), now sent to Cherepovets, and apatite (Kirovsk), while small hydro-electric power stations form one source of energy. In no way, however, is the scale of exploitation of the forest, mineral and hydro-electric resources comparable with that envisaged in Siberia. Only the greater proximity of this area to Leningrad and Moscow has made it worth while to put an above average amount of investment (in *per caput* terms) into the area in the last few years.

The area is highly urbanized, since there is little dispersed agricultural population. Murmansk and Archangel, with various industries, are among the leading seaports of the U.S.S.R. The fish catch landed at the Barents Sea ports is increasing rapidly, as more distant seas are fished by Soviet fleets. Murmansk handles about 20 per cent of the Soviet total. Petrozavodsk, Cherepovets (iron and steel), Vologda (glass) and Kotlas, are considerable industrial centres. Engineering is found in many centres, but sawmilling, and the manufacture of wood and paper products, is the most widespread branch of all. The railway system consists simply of three trunk lines north to Murmansk, Archangel and Vorkuta, with links in the south to centres such as Kirov, Moscow and Leningrad.

III. SOUTH-WEST U.S.S.R.

Region II consists of the Ukraine, Moldavia, the Blackearth Centre, the North Caucasus and three small administrative units from the Volga–Vyatka and Volga regions.[1] Conventionally Soviet geography books and even planners consider the Blackearth Centre and North Caucasus as separate from the Ukraine, but they are included here to stress the many similarities they have in common with it. Altogether region II as defined here contains some 72 m. inhabitants, or over 30 per cent of the total population of the U.S.S.R., but only occupies between 5 and 6 per cent of the total national area. It contains one major industrial complex, the Donbass–Dnepr area, which includes for the purposes of this book the five eastern oblasts of the Ukraine[2] and the Rostov oblast in the North Caucasus. This complex has some $17\frac{1}{2}$ m. people, almost 75 per cent of which are urban dwellers. It accounts for about 12 per cent of the total industrial output of the U.S.S.R. The rest of the area is predominantly rural, with urban percentages ranging mainly between 25 and 45 per cent.

1. Chuvash and Mordov A.S.S.R.s and Penza oblast.
2. Dnepropetrovsk, Zaporozh'ye, Donetsk, Lugansk and Khar'kov.

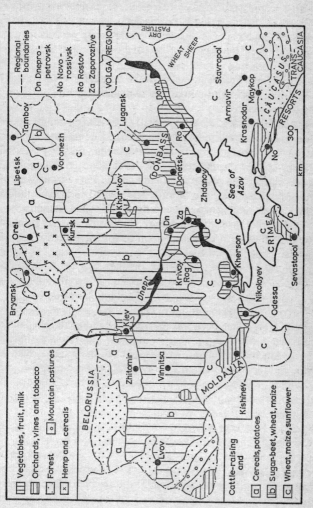

44. Region II: South-west U.S.S.R.

Legend (top-left box):

⊞ Vegetables, fruit, milk
▥ Orchards, vines and tobacco
⣿ Forest
⊙ Mountain pastures
× Hemp and cereals

Legend (bottom box):

Cattle-raising and
a Cereals, potatoes
b Sugar-beet, wheat, maize
c Wheat, maize, sunflower

Legend (top-right box):
— — — Regional boundaries
Dn Dnepropetrovsk
No Novorossiysk
Ro Rostov
Za Zaporozhye

Labels on map:

VOLGA REGION
DRY PASTURE
WHEAT SHEEP
Tambov
Lipetsk
Voronezh
Orel
Bryansk
BELORUSSIA
Kursk
Khar'kov
Lugansk
DONBASS
Donetsk
Ro
Don
Stavropol
Armavir
Maykop
Krasnodar
CAUCASUS
TRANS-CAUCASIA
No RESORTS
Zhdanov
Sea of Azov
CRIMEA
Sevastopol
Kherson
Nikolayev
Odessa
Dn
Za
Krivoy Rog
Dnepr
Kiev
Zhitomir
Vinnitsa
MOLDAVIA
Kishinev
Lvov

300 km

The most striking feature of the region as a whole, perhaps, is the large proportion of the total area used for arable farming. This admittedly falls off along the fringes, as in the Poles'ye, Carpathians, Caucasus, and eastern semi-desert extremities of the North Caucasus. But it reaches 70–80 per cent of total land surface in some places, and is fortunate in having excellent blackearth or associated soils. Two drawbacks that are a cause of great concern are gullying, and the limited and unpredictable rainfall in the growing season.

Region II still exchanges products with other regions of the country, but its traditional surpluses, coal, iron and steel, grain, oils and fats, meat and sugar, are sent less than formerly into the deficient area of European U.S.S.R. to the north, tending to be needed more in the region itself, and also in East Europe and in other foreign markets. In relation to the Soviet Union as a whole it is therefore becoming more balanced and self-sufficient than previously, and the population/resource balance is superior in most ways to that of region I, described in the previous section. It has much larger deposits of coal, oil, gas and iron ore, as well as better agricultural conditions, but in one respect it is less favourably placed, for it has only limited forest reserves, while industry is threatened with a water shortage if consumption continues to rise. In terms of production, rather than resources, its industry is very one-sided, for it has been starved of light manufacturing. This is surprising because, as pointed out in Soviet publications, there is a large potential supply of female labour in the heavy industrial areas, and there are areas in the western Ukraine almost without industry, but with an infra-structure as good as that in Belorussia and the Baltic Republics, where, as already noted, light manufacturing is being encouraged.

Region II is generally favourable physically. It consists of a succession from west to east of hill country and lowlands, with flanking mountains in places and almost dead flat coastal plains by the Sea of Azov. The hill country rarely exceeds three hundred metres, but in places, including the Donbass coalfield, can be very dissected, with steep slopes. Several rivers, which are large by European standards, cross the region, the Dnestr and Dnepr in the Ukraine, and the Lower Don in Rostov oblast being the outstanding ones. Mean annual precipitation is relatively high in the north-west of the Ukraine (over 60 cm.) and along the northern foothills of the Caucasus as well as on the Carpathian, Crimean and Caucasus Ranges themselves, but is low (below 40 cm.) in the southern Ukraine and again towards the Caspian. A forest vegetation, much of it now cleared, covered the mountains, the north-western part of the Ukraine and parts of the Blackearth Centre, but elsewhere a grassland vegetation predominated.

Soil and temperature conditions favour agriculture widely, but in years with a precipitation much below average in the growing season yields suffer badly. Many warm temperate crops are grown but there is specialization in particular groups of crops in different parts. From potatoes, flax, fodder crops and rye in the western Ukraine one passes south-eastwards through the sugar beet belt, which runs south-west–north-east through Kiev, and through an area of very varied farming, to the drier parts by the Black Sea and towards the Volga, where wheat and the sunflower are widely grown. The cultivation of maize has spread throughout the area in the last decade and much of the grain maize of the U.S.S.R. comes from the Ukraine and North Caucasus. More locally, hemp, vines, rice, vegetables, fruit and tobacco are cultivated. Cattle and pigs are widely raised in the area in conjunction with arable farming, and the relative importance of livestock farming has grown in comparison with arable, with the contraction of the wheat area in the face of 'competition' from the new lands. Dairy farming and pig raising would seem the best line for the future in the more humid northern and western fringes and possibly in the humid Kuban valley.

In spite of this apparently flourishing agriculture, the region has one major drawback, too large a rural population. For reasons of its relatively long settlement it has accumulated a high density of rural population by Soviet standards. Even in recent decades this has continued to increase. There is a contrast therefore both with areas to the north, where rural population has been diminishing sharply, and with the new lands of Kazakhstan and Siberia where there is a shortage of farm workers. In general, collective farm incomes are low, farms inefficient, whether on account of size or for other reasons, and output of farm products per worker disappointing considering the opportunities of the region. Some agricultural surplus still goes to the Moscow area, especially from the

Blackearth Centre, but not so much as might be hoped. Nevertheless, now that the new lands of the east have been occupied and exploited, the best prospects for expanding agricultural production still further in the U.S.S.R. seem to lie in improving region II.

The energy and other mineral resources of the region appear to be good and exploration is clearly far from complete, for in the last decade many oil and gas deposits have been found, as well as much greater coal deposits in the Donbass area than had hitherto been known, new iron ore at Kremenchug and at Belozersk near Zoporozh'ye, and manganese ore at Bol'she-Tokmaksk. The so-called Greater Donbass coalfield actually extends from Kiev to Volgograd, covering an area 1,500 km. by 700 km., but seams are far below the surface in places. Nevertheless it is considered possible to open new deep mines at the western and eastern extremities of the present mining area. Among recent finds are gas at Stavropol' in the North Caucasus and at Shebelinka, and oil and gas at Mirgorod, in the Ukraine. Altogether two hundred gas-producing sites have been discovered, especially around Poltava. Minerals already known and exploited for some time include some oil and gas around Dashava on the western Ukraine, the iron ore of Krivoy Rog and the manganese ore of Nikopol', salt, mercury and other minerals in the Donbass coalfield, and oil (Maykop, Groznyy) and non-ferrous metals (Ordzhonikidze) in the North Caucasus. The only sizeable hydro-electric potential is on the Dnepr; this is in course of being developed. The very large iron ore deposits at Kursk have been contemplated for a long time but, being in the Blackearth Centre, are counted as part of the iron ore resources of the Centre. As they lie midway between Moscow and the Donbass, however, the fact that a major politico-administrative boundary cuts them off from the Ukraine, with the Donbass coalfield, seems a weak reason for not developing them with Donbass coal. The Kursk deposits consist of two underground iron ore ranges some 600 km. in length and near enough to the surface in places to be mined by opencast methods. There are reserves of 30,000 m. tons with an iron content of over 50 per cent, and virtually inexhaustible reserves with a 30 per cent content.

In spite of its favourable mineral resources, however, region II is not providing the surplus that might be expected, for in total it is deficient in oil, is using most of its coal locally, and could no doubt use more of its gas if this were not regarded as a new cheap source of energy for areas lying to the north, particularly, of course, Moscow. Although almost as much coal is now produced in the Donbass coalfield as in the whole of the U.K., many of the mines, of which there are over five hundred, are small and uneconomical. Nor is the industrial balance as much in favour of the region as it might be, even though in 1960 over 50 per cent of the Soviet pig iron and 40 per cent of the steel came from here.

The impressive coal, iron and steel and chemicals industry of the eastern Ukraine and lower Don has failed to produce a super-structure of more complex manufactures. The metal-working and engineering industries are the main users of the products of the basic industries, but the engineering products, such as mining machinery (e.g. Gorlovka), equipment for the iron and steel industry itself and for chemical plants, girders, rails, ships (Niko-layev), diesel locomotives (Lugansk), turbines and so on, are dis-tinguished more for the quantity of steel in them than for their complexity. New branches of engineering such as the manufacture of motor vehicles parts at Melitopol' are only beginning to appear. Nor does the region produce much high-grade steel, for this is largely a monopoly of the Ural region.

Similarly the chemicals industry is based on the coal and metal-lurgical by-products rather than on oil and natural gas, and high-value chemicals products do not seem to originate from the region, though in the North Caucasus some modern petrochemical plants (e.g. Nevinnomyssk) are being introduced. Nevertheless, the importance of the Donbass and associated heavily industrial centres is still very great. Their propensity to expand in the wake of devastating wartime destruction and generally high production costs gives rise to speculation about the soundness of investment priorities in the U.S.S.R.

For the purposes of further description, region II has been sub-divided into the heavy industrial area (six oblasts), a western and northern belt extending from Moldavia through the Ukraine and Blackearth Centre towards the Volga, and the south-eastern residue, the North Caucasus without Rostov oblast. The heavily industrialized region, which is characterized by its large towns and industries, has agricultural conditions transitional between those of the second and third areas.

	Population (thousands)		Percentage urban	Area in thousands of sq. km.	Density of population in persons per sq. km.
	Total	Urban			
IIa Donbass /Dnepr and Rostov	17,500	12,850	74	246	71
IIa Moldavia, Ukraine, Blackearth Centre, etc.	45,000	15,150	34	769	59
IIc North Caucasus	9,000	3,550	39	240	38

IIa *Lower Dnepr – Donbass – Rostov.* The heavy industrial region of the Dnepr and Donbass extends about 500 km. from west to east (Krivoy Rog to Shakhty), roughly the distance between London and Tyneside. Without the close interdependence between the metallic minerals in the west and the coal in the east it might be considered as two separate parts, with a largely rural agricultural belt in between.

The western part consists of a ring of towns (see Figure 45) on the iron ore deposits of Krivoy Rog and the manganese at Nikopol' or on the banks of the Dnepr itself. Krivoy Rog is expected to be able to produce iron ore equivalent to 50 m. tons of iron content for a good time to come, but the ore is now being extracted from depths of 500–600 metres in places, and much of the production goes to East Europe. Coal is brought by rail into this area to supply iron and steel works, several of which are among the largest in the U.S.S.R. They are Krivoy Rog itself, Dnepropetrovsk, Dneprodzerzhinsk, and Zoporozh'ye, which also produces non-ferrous metals, including aluminium.

The eastern part is based on the Donbass coalfield, which has now been exploited on modern lines for nearly a century. The coking coal of this field was used initially to smelt iron ore found locally, but soon a rail link made it possible to bring in Krivoy Rog ore. There are two main types of centre, those on the coalfield itself and those some distance away. The former include many coal-mining centres, several with iron and steel works (e.g. Donetsk-Makeyevka, Konstantinovka), and chemicals centres. The western end of the coalfield consists of clusters of towns with

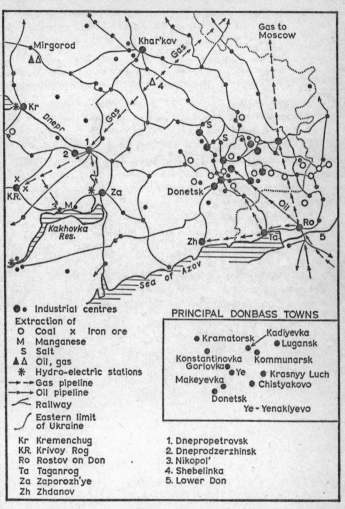

45. Region II: The Dnepr–Donets–Don industrial area.

settlement strung out along the valleys in continuous belts for great distances. The centres off the coalfield include Lugansk, an engineering centre to the north, and Rostov-on-Don, Taganrog and Zhdanov, all ports, to the south. Zhdanov uses iron ore from the Crimea (Kerch′) and has one of the largest iron and steel works in the country (Azovstal′). Further away still is Khar′kov, which is an engineering centre drawing its raw materials from the Donbass and likely to become the centre of a new industrial district based on the oil and gas recently found near by.

The whole area described is deficient in food, and presumably draws on nearby oblasts in the agricultural Ukraine and North Caucasus. Grain, sugar beet, sunflower oil, beans and meat are produced, but there is a tendency for areas around the main urban centres to specialize in market gardening and dairying.

The area is served by a close railway network, but in the absence of a large single centre like Moscow in the Centre region, there is no obvious focus of routes. Connexions are good northwards towards the Centre and westwards to places in the Ukraine, but good direct rail links with the Volga and places further east are not evident, although it is of course possible to move in this direction by devious routes. The opening of the Volga–Don Canal in 1953 improved this position considerably, giving waterway access to the Volga region and western Ural.

IIb *Moldavia – Ukraine – Blackearth Centre*. The western and northern parts of region II contain a large agricultural population but few very large urban centres and no large industrial complexes. The Poles′ye in the Ukraine awaits further improvements for, as in Belorussia, much of the surface is still forested or marsh. The Carpathian and Crimean Ranges consist of high mountain pastures and flanking forests, those of the Carpathians being extensive enough to provide local industries with timber. The rest of the area is for the most part devoted to arable farming, with only local unfavourable tracts left in forest, and only river flood plains and steep slopes uncultivated. The sown area covers more than 80 per cent of the surface of many rayons in Kirovograd in the centre of the Ukraine, and again around Lipetsk in the Blackearth Centre, and most rayons have over 60 per cent of their area sown.

Perhaps the most characteristic crop of the area is sugar beet. This occupies around 10 per cent of the total sown area in many rayons in a belt extending from Lvov to the middle Dnepr, and again in the southern part of the Blackearth Centre. It rarely occupies more than this proportion, and disappears rapidly both south and north of the belt. The more precise distribution of its cultivation is to some extent tied to the distribution of sugar factories, which process the beet, and as these have to be reasonably large to be efficient, and it is inconvenient to move the beet far, it is essential to have a considerable production in the vicinity. Where there are no sugar factories, there is no point in cultivating the plant at all. Wheat and maize are widely grown throughout the belt, but grain maize seems to have found the hotter though drier south-eastern side of the area more favourable. This applies even more to the sunflower, which is cultivated particularly in the south-eastern part of the Ukraine. More locally there are areas of specialization in the cultivation of the vine, other fruits and tobacco in the small lowland area beyond the Carpathians, in central Moldavia and in the Crimea, and of hemp in the Blackearth Centre.

Most towns in the area are of small to medium size. Some of them, like Zhitomir and Chernigov in the Ukraine, and Belgorod and Saransk (Mordov A.S.S.R.) in the Centre, have not grown appreciably in the Soviet period. Thanks to the presence of local mineral resources, or to their location on busy through railways, some oblast capitals have been able to attract industry, particularly places like Kursk, Lipetsk (new iron and steel works) and Tambov between Moscow and the Donbass, or Nikolayev (shipbuilding) and Kherson on the Black Sea coast. Places of more than local importance include Lvov, Kiev and Odessa in the Ukraine and Voronezh in the Blackearth Centre. The western part of the Ukraine, including Lvov, only became part of the Soviet Union in 1939, and this fact, coupled with the peripheral nature of the area, may have contributed to hold back development here, for low collective farm incomes suggest stagnation in agriculture, and heavy industry is virtually non-existent. There are however gas, oil and coal deposits in the vicinity, but most of the manufacturing is confined to Lvov itself.

Kiev is the capital of the Ukraine and now has well over a million inhabitants. There are no mineral resources near by but the energy base of the town, which until recently has depended on Donbass coal, has been improved by the supply of gas from Dashava near Lvov. Kiev has a considerable range of industries including food, textiles and engineering. The experience of Odessa is to some extent parallel to that of Leningrad. As foreign trade became less important in the Soviet period, the functions of the town as a port declined. The size of Odessa has not changed greatly since before the Revolution. Though clearly one of the major Soviet Black Sea ports, it is somewhat less accessible from the industrialized eastern Ukraine even than Nikolayev and Kherson. Novorossiysk in the North Caucasus is considerably nearer than this group of ports to the Volga region and the areas of new development to the east of this. Voronezh, like Kursk, is roughly midway between Moscow and the Donbass, on one of the main north–south railways. Its industries are varied, but are connected particularly with food processing and agricultural machinery.

IIc *North Caucasus.* Though similar in many ways to the previous region, the North Caucasus, excluding Rostov oblast, is smaller and more distinct. Most of the population is found along the foreland to the north of the Great Caucasus range and particularly in the Kuban valley in the west. The density of population falls off sharply both south into the mountain area and north-eastwards into the desert. In contrast to Transcaucasia, the North Caucasus is largely an area of Slav settlement, though non-Slav peoples do remain, especially in the mountain valleys. Some continuity is given to the region by the railway that runs the whole length of it from Rostov to the Caspian Sea, with branches to the coast (Novorossiysk, Tuapse), into the mountains, and into the desert.

The high mountain area provides timber, limited pastures, hydro-electric power and some minerals (especially lead, silver and zinc). The hill country and lowland to the north have most of the sown land as well as many small oilfields. The actual proportion of sown to total area diminishes eastwards, and the cultivation of rice, maize, wheat and the sunflower gives way to dry wheat cultivation and lowland sheep pastures, or to orchards and vines on the foothills of the eastern Caucasus. There is scope for improving and extending the irrigation systems, since the Caucasus Range provides a considerable and reliable supply of water in several rivers. To the north-east, semi-desert and even desert conditions with blown sand and little vegetation are soon reached towards the Caspian. Industries in the area consist mainly of oil refining, food processing, cement production and light engineering. The fairly recent discovery of large deposits of natural gas at Izobil´noye near Stavropol´ is the most notable recent development. Part of the gas is being piped to various places in other regions to the north including Moscow itself, part will be used in local petrochemicals industries. Apart from Rostov which is near the eastern extremity of the Donbass, there are no major centres and no obvious potential industrial complexes of national importance, for Krasnodar and Groznyy are concerned largely with agricultural and oil processing respectively. In general the area seems more prosperous than both the non-industrial Ukraine and Transcaucasia, thanks to its high productivity per farm worker and its surplus of many items. Although there is probably now little oil over after regional needs have been satisfied, natural gas and petrochemical products are sent north. Many agricultural items, including grain, sunflower oil, fruits, meat and wool are also sent out of the North Caucasus.

IV. THE MIDDLE BELT OF THE U.S.S.R.

The possibilities of economic development east of the Volga and Ural Range have been appreciated by the Russians for some time but until the 1930s very little use was made of this part of the Empire. What is even more important to appreciate is that even now only a small part of the total area has more than a token number of inhabitants. The subject of this section is a belt of country some 4,000 km. from west to east, extending from the middle Volga to Lake Baykal, and varying in width from about 800 to 1,500 km.[1] This belt includes not only the main eastern areas of economic growth but also the Volga and Ural regions,

1. Region III consists of the Volga economic region excluding Penza (to region I) and Astrakhan´ (to region V), the Ural region excluding the northern thinly peopled part of Tyumen´ oblast, West Siberia including Tomsk oblast, the northern part of Kazakhstan, and parts of Krasnoyarsk and Irkutsk oblasts from East Siberia.

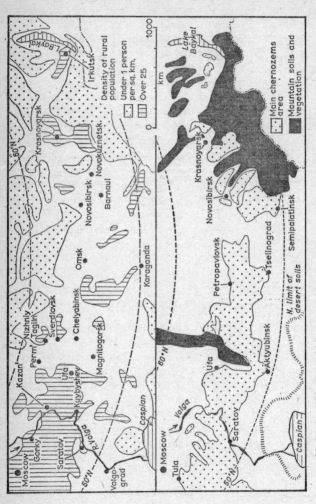

46. Region III: The middle belt of the U.S.S.R. a. Density of rural population. b. Selected physical features.

Density of rural population

Under 1 person per sq. km.

Over 25

Main chernozems area

Mountain soils and vegetation

L. Baykal
Irkutsk
Krasnoyarsk
Novokuznetsk
Barnaul
Novosibirsk
Omsk
Chelyabinsk
Magnitogorsk
Sverdlovsk
Nizhniy Tagil
Perm'
Ufa
Kazan'
Kuybyshev
Gorky
Saratov
Moscow
R.Volga
Volgograd
Caspian
Karaganda

Lake Baykal
Krasnoyarsk
Novosibirsk
Semipalatinsk
Tselinograd
Petropavlovsk
Aktyubinsk
N. limit of desert soils
Ufa
Volga
Saratov
Moscow
Tula
Caspian
60°N
50°N
1000
km
0

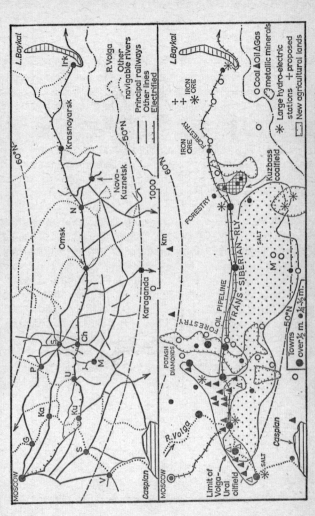

a

MOSCOW
L. Baykal
Irk
60°N
Krasnoyarsk
50°N
Novo-Kuznetsk
N
Omsk
S
Ch
U
M
P
Ka
Ku
G
S
V
Karaganda
1000
Km

R. Volga
Other
navigable rivers
Principal railways
Other lines
Electrified

b

MOSCOW
L. Baykal
IRON ORE
FORESTRY
60°N
Kuzbass coalfield
TRANS-SIBERIAN RLY
OIL PIPELINE
FORESTRY
50°N
SALT
SALT
POTASH
DIAMONDS
Limit of
Volga-
Ural
oilfield
R. Volga
Caspian
Caspian

+ + IRON
      ORE
✳ metallic minerals
○ coal ▲ oil △ gas
✳ Large hydro-electric
      stations + proposed
✳ New agricultural lands

● Towns   ● over ½ m. ½-½ m.   ○

47. Region III: a. Railways and navigable waterways. b. Productive activities.

both of which were held by the Russians for a long time, but have only been developed seriously since the early 1930s in the case of the Volga, and revived at this time from stagnation in the case of the Ural.

The middle belt is far from being a unit with homogeneous conditions, or with regional consciousness among its inhabitants, and it cannot be defined precisely. Rather its limits can be considered to be the frontiers in which new development is currently the prominent feature. Such a region is felt to exist by Soviet writers and has been the subject of investigation by D. J. M. Hooson.[1] Altogether the region has about 47·5 m. inhabitants or 21·5 per cent of the total population of the U.S.S.R. but it occupies only 14 per cent of the total national area. Outstanding features of the region include its great east–west extent, its enormous natural resources, many so well placed that they offer the lowest production costs in their exploitation in the whole country, and a rate of growth of both investment and urban population much faster than that in the country as a whole over the last thirty years. The region is well endowed with or has a surplus of all the important energy minerals, as well as a great hydro-electric potential, most other key minerals, timber, iron and steel and chemicals. The physical background to agriculture is less favourable and reliable on the whole than in region II, but thanks to the limited rural population and the smaller demand on the land it has been easier to extend the area of cultivation, to go over to a state farm system, and to achieve high productivity per agricultural worker. In both the Ural region and Siberia east of the Kuzbass, however, arable land is not extensive enough to prevent local deficiencies in food products.

A question that concerns the whole region is whether to move far more people into it, or to send the surpluses to deficient regions to the west. Policy before the Second World War and during the War itself helped to get people to move east of the Volga at all costs. The urban population of the area has roughly doubled between 1939 and 1959 and this could have been achieved only by a large influx of people from other regions. But if the U.S.S.R. intends to trade much more with the rest of the world, then it is

1. See D. J. M. Hooson, *A New Soviet Heartland?* (Searchlight Book No. 21), Princeton, Van Nostrand, 1964.

not likely to place too much of its new investment in the interior of the country. Apart from the Volga region, region III is far from seaports.

Agriculturally, region III is characterized by the large amount of sown area in relation to its population rather than by high yields. Although the main chernozem area extends east of the Volga, it is less continuous than to the west, being interrupted by the Ural Range, fragmented east of Omsk, and very reduced beyond Krasnoyarsk. To the north, the equivalent of the forest steppe in the Ukraine is very narrow, and the forests, marshes and podzols of the West Siberian Lowlands are soon reached. Southwards the quality of soils deteriorates rapidly towards the desert of Central Asia, and precipitation diminishes. The whole area has long, cold winters, and cereals have to be sown in spring. The growing season is short and the whole farming process largely confined to a few months in the year. There have been many cereal and dairy farms along the Trans-Siberian Railway for some time, but only since 1953 has a serious attempt been made to convert the southern fringe of the chernozems and the even drier areas to the south into an almost continuous arable belt from the middle Volga through northern Kazakhstan to the Altay Mountains (see Figure 46). At all events, there has been an increasing surplus of grain and livestock products from parts of region III and some of the surplus has been sent to places west of the Volga. The haste with which arable farming has been extended has meant that in years of good harvest much grain has been lost through lack of harvesting facilities, storage buildings and road and rail feeders to the main railway lines.

The mineral and hydro-electric resources seem more promising in the long run than the extensive farmlands of the region. Although the largest coal reserves of all in the U.S.S.R. lie in East Siberia and the Far East, to the north and east of region III, several coalfields in the region have reserves sufficient to last several centuries even at the ambitious rates of exploitation envisaged for 1980. These are mainly in northern Kazakhstan, the Kuzbass, and along the Trans-Siberian Railway from Krasnoyarsk to Irkutsk (Kansk–Achinsk and Cheremkhovo). Though Karaganda has been included in dry U.S.S.R., much of the coal from here is in fact sent to the Ural region, but the Karaganda reserves, while useful for their coking properties, are relatively small. The Volga and Ural regions are deficient in coal compared with the rest of region III. They, on the other hand, have some of the largest and most cheaply exploited sites for hydro-electric stations.

As these energy resources are exploited more and more, the westward movement of surpluses will become the main direction of inter-regional movement of energy in the country. This movement started in the 1930s with the transportation of oil west from the Volga region and the movement of Kuzbass coal to the Ural region. It is strange, therefore, that this east–west trend should have been contradicted by the construction of a pipeline from the Volga–Ural oilfields east to Novosibirsk and the Baykal area, intended to take crude oil into Siberia. The discovery of oil and gas in the West Siberian Lowland and even in East Siberia threatens to make this superfluous. Certainly the flow of electricity will be in an east to west direction. As well as having a surplus of energy, mineral raw materials and food, the region has to the north of it enormous reserves of timber.

In addition to movements of raw materials, food and manufactured goods within the region itself, there is an outward movement to other regions – including the Far East, Central Asia and southern Kazakhstan, and the northern and central parts of European U.S.S.R. in particular – of coal, oil, gas, pig iron and steel, timber and grain, as well as various other metals, chemicals and machinery originating particularly in the Ural region. In contrast, light manufacturing, and the production of sophisticated engineering items, are little developed. Although there is not much direct evidence to show this conclusively, it seems that region III and region II (the Ukraine, North Caucasus) do not exchange many goods, apart from a movement between the Volga region and adjoining parts of the Ukraine and North Caucasus stimulated by the opening of the Volga–Don Canal and the railway from Volgograd to Novorossiysk. This may partly be due to the lack of good direct railways between the two regions, partly to the barrier of the Caspian Sea and desert to the north, and partly also to the fact that the two regions have surpluses and deficiencies of many of the same things.

Unlike regions I and II, region III is an area that has inherited little from the past in the form of large agricultural communities, established crop specializations or traditional manufactures. The main exception is the Ural region which already had iron and other mineral workings and metal production in the eighteenth century. New railways and towns have been built generally in areas that were virtually uninhabited at the beginning of this century, and in some cases only a decade or two ago. One of the major problems, indeed, has been to attract new settlers and to build up an industrial society from almost nothing. Features that merit study are the concentration of much of the urban population in a limited number of relatively large centres, for example Kuybyshev, Chelyabinsk, Omsk, Novosibirsk, Krasnoyarsk, and, away from the oil and coalfield areas, the lack of smaller centres. This is a feature of other areas that have grown almost from nothing in the railway era, for example much of western North America, southern South America and Australia.

For the purposes of this book, region III has been divided into five parts. These do not coincide with traditional Soviet economic planning regions but in the view of the author they are reasonably distinct, and a brief description of each will be sufficient to show how varied the region really is. The first area, referred to as the Volga, consists of the series of oil and gas fields stretching north-east from around Volgograd to the western flanks of the Ural Range. Here the Volga and its tributaries, with their power stations and possibilities for navigation, are an important part of the economic background. The second area consists of the Ural Range and its immediate foothills and adjoining lowlands. This area is characterized above all by its great variety of minerals, both metallic and non-metallic. The third area is the great expanse of new agricultural land flanking the southern part of the Ural and extending east to the Altay Mountains. Here many new minerals have been discovered, but at the moment there are few large industrial establishments. The fourth area is that associated with the Kuzbass coalfield, while the fifth extends roughly between the Yenisey and Lake Baykal. The general area between Novosibirsk and Lake Baykal is now frequently referred to as central Siberia but this term has been avoided since it contains parts of the official economic regions of both West and East Siberia. The following figures point to considerable contrasts between the five areas:

	Population in thousands		Percentage urban	Area in sq. km. (thousands)	Density of population persons per sq. km.
	Total	Urban			
IIIa Volga	11,030	5,800	53	373	30
IIIb Ural	17,290	10,720	62	754	23
IIIc New lands	13,130	5,460	42	1,530	9
IIId Kuzbass	2,950	2,340	79	96	31
IIIe Yenisey–Baykal[1]	3,000	2,000	67	400	7·5

1. Estimated figures.

IIIa *The Volga Region.* The first of the five areas into which region III has been divided is the Volga. This economic region has changed shape many times in the Soviet period but has always included the stretch of the Volga between Kazan' and Volgograd and never the Upper Volga. Recently the official Volga region was extended further east to include most of the oilfields that formerly belonged to the Ural region. The Volga region is central in relation to population in the U.S.S.R. and is also situated within the triangle formed by the three greatest industrial concentrations in the country, the Centre, the Donbass and the Ural.

Some continuity is given to the region by the presence of the Volga river, which serves both as a major waterway and as a source of hydro-electric power. Most of the larger towns in the region are also on the Volga and some, like Saratov and Kazan', are at places that the Russians have used for centuries for crossing the river. In a sense, however, the Volga is also something of a frontier, for while the lands to the west of it filled with rural population in the seventeenth and eighteenth centuries, there was little settlement beyond the river in the area facing the semi-desert of Turkestan.

The outstanding function of the Volga region at the moment is to send its energy surplus, in the form of oil, gas and hydro-electric power, widely over European U.S.S.R. and to foreign markets. The region has the lowest production costs for both oil and hydro-electric power in European U.S.S.R. The oil is 5–7 times cheaper than that produced in Transcaucasia, and electricity 4–5 times cheaper than that produced in the Centre. The future of industry

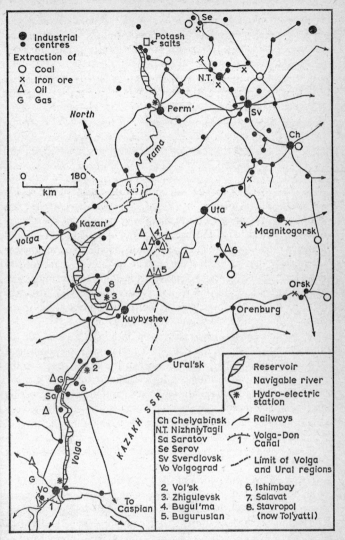

Industrial centres
- ● Industrial centres
- ● (smaller dot)

Extraction of
- O Coal
- × Iron ore
- △ Oil
- G Gas

North

Potash salts

N.T.

Se

Perm'

Sv

Ch

Kama

0 ____ 180
km

Kazan'

Volga

Ufa

Magnitogorsk

△ 4
△ △
△
△ △ 5
7 △ 6

8
✳ 3
△

Kuybyshev

Orsk

Orenburg

Ural'sk

KAZAKH SSR

✳ 2

△ G
Sa
G

△

Volga

G
Vo
✳

1

To Caspian

Legend:
- ⟋ Reservoir
- ∿ Navigable river
- ✳ Hydro-electric station
- ⌒ Railways
- —1— Volga-Don Canal
- ---- Limit of Volga and Ural regions

Ch Chelyabinsk
N.T. NizhniyTagil
Sa Saratov
Se Serov
Sv Sverdlovsk
Vo Volgograd

2. Vol'sk
3. Zhigulevsk
4. Bugul'ma
5. Buguruslan
6. Ishimbay
7. Salavat
8. Stavropol (now Tol'yatti)

48. Region III: The Volga-Ural region.

appears to revolve largely round the establishment of petro-chemicals and the production of various kinds of fertilizers, plastics and so on, but engineering is also developing. Some surplus of grain and livestock products may be expected in most years.

Physically much of the region is favourable for agriculture. The western side of the Volga is more hilly and has a somewhat higher precipitation than the corresponding area on the eastern side. Agriculture is based largely on the cultivation of wheat, the sunflower, and fodder crops for cattle, pigs and sheep. On the eastern side, wheat is the principal arable crop and beef cattle and sheep are raised. The sheep depend largely on natural pastures, especially in the southern semi-desert area by the lower course of the River Volga. The flood plain of the Volga between Volgograd and Astrakhan' already grows vegetables and melons, but could be improved considerably if the flood plain were properly drained. North of the latitude of Kuybyshev a considerable part of the total area is forested and farming is more diversified. The region as a whole does not produce many industrial crops.

Oil occurs in some sixty different oilfields of varying size, and natural gas is found in association with it in many cases. The general area of the oilfield extends from near Volgograd in the south-west to Perm' in the north-east. Much of the oil comes from places in the vicinity of Saratov, Kuybyshev, Bugul'ma, Tuymazy and Sterlitamak. The last two are in the Bashkir A.S.S.R. (capital Ufa) which has recently been transferred to the Volga region. In addition to the older oil refineries on the Volga itself (e.g. Volgograd, Syzran') new oil refineries have been built, particularly in the Bashkir A.S.S.R. (e.g. Salavat). The pipeline system connected with oil and gas production is shown in Figure 34. Several large new petrochemicals works are being constructed in the region including Stavropol' (renamed Tol'yatti) and Salavat.

Much of the urban population of the Volga region is found in several large centres, notably Volgograd, Saratov, Kuybyshev, Kazan' and Ufa. In their different ways each of these forms the centre of an industrial knot. In all of them oil, petrochemicals, and engineering are represented, but there is little light industry. The largest complex of all is at and to the west of Kuybyshev where hydro-electric power from the large station at Zhigulevsk provides a local source of cheap electricity.

Weaknesses of the Volga region include the absence of an integrated iron and steel industry, although some steel is produced at Volgograd, and the possibility that the large reservoirs behind the power stations will reduce the flow of water in the Volga. The project to bring water from rivers (notably the Pechora and Vychegda) that flow into the Arctic has been mentioned in Chapter 6 and is illustrated in Figure 20.

IIIb *The Ural Region.* The Ural region has changed shape several times in the Soviet period, but the Ural Range has remained as its core and varying amounts of adjoining hill country and lowland upon either side have also been included. The region started to make a serious contribution to the Russian economy in the seventeenth and eighteenth centuries first as a source of furs, timber and minerals, then as a source of iron, which could easily be smelted thanks to charcoal from the widespread forests and to numerous small iron ore deposits. Some very old iron works are still in use and even use charcoal for smelting, but the region was developed and modernized from 1930 on and is less complicated than the Moscow area or the Donbass by relics of earlier industrialization. The north-to-south Ural Range is narrow but high for most of its length but lower and easy to cross at about 55°N. Several railways converge on a gap about 200 km. wide from north to south. Further south the range splays out in several ridges and is higher and inconvenient to cross from west to east.

The region has never been associated with a surplus of agricultural products and in northern and central oblasts the sown area is only a small part of the total area, but the lowlands around the southern part of the range are extensively cultivated, though the variety of crops is limited. Considerable areas in the south have been brought into cultivation in the new lands project but it still seems doubtful if the region as a whole is self-sufficient in food.

It is for the production of minerals that the Ural region has achieved most distinction in the national economy. Most of the metallic minerals are found in the north-to-south core of the range and include various precious metals, non-ferrous metals and ferro-alloys. Most of the non-metallic minerals including potash (Solikamsk), oil and natural gas, lignite and some coal are found to the east and west of the range. Very little of the coal is suitable

for coking, but some use is made from that extracted around
Kizel. Iron ore is found in many deposits, but none of these are
large compared with those of Krivoy Rog and Kursk or with new
deposits found further east. Moreover some of the ore used in the
iron and steel industry is not of high grade – for example, the ore
from Kachkanar, which is enriched. It is expected that the famous
deposit of high-grade iron ore on which the Magnitogorsk iron
and steel works was based in the early 1930s will be used up by
1975 and ore may be brought in from other regions. The plan at
the moment is to supply the southern part of the Ural region with
iron ore from the Kustanay basin in Kazakhstan, where there are
twenty thousand million tons of good ore, and opencast methods
can be used.

The Ural region accounts for about 10 per cent of all Soviet
industrial production. Its industry is based largely on the processing and refining of minerals, on timber and its products, and on
the production of iron and steel. From the iron and steel industry,
which produces most of the high-grade steel of the country, and
from the production of non-ferrous metals, has developed the
manufacturing of heavy machinery, such as mining and electrical
equipment, as well as machine tools and motor vehicles, including
tractors and cars. More recently the manufacture of chemicals has
been encouraged. The region also has sufficient timber to support
the manufacture of paper and cellulose on a large scale. All these
items form part of the surplus of the region.

It is disturbing to find that while the Ural region consumes over
15 per cent of the energy used in the U.S.S.R. it has only 0·5 per
cent of the energy reserves, and also that although it produces
something like 40 per cent of the pig iron, its iron ore reserves are
very limited. It has been suggested therefore that it would be unwise
to expand the iron and steel industry here, and better to concentrate more on engineering and also chemicals, drawing on oil and
gas supplies from the Volga region to the south-west and from
West Siberia and Central Asia. To make the raw materials base of
the region appear better for planning purposes, much of the northern part of West Siberia has now been transferred to the Ural
region, greatly improving the appearance of the energy and timber
situation.

Other problems of the Ural include the possibility that water supplies will become inadequate in some of the industrial centres, and the fact that much of the population is becoming concentrated in several large centres, whereas, given the widespread nature of the minerals in the region, it would be advantageous to have more processing and manufacturing in medium-sized towns. Sverdlovsk is the major centre in a regional and cultural sense, but Chelyabinsk is almost as large. Both towns have a wide variety of industries. Perm′ (chemicals), Nizhniy Tagil and Magnitogorsk are somewhat smaller and more specialized.

IIIc *The New Lands*. This area has been distinguished from the more highly industrial parts of region III because it is characterized by a simultaneous rapid growth of both agriculture and industry, a feature not found elsewhere in the U.S.S.R. The two branches are not complementary at this stage, for at the moment each is being developed to supply food or raw materials to other parts of the country.

The area in question stretches through northern Kazakhstan and the southern part of West Siberia from the oilfields of the Bashkir A.S.S.R. to the Altay Mountains. It contains more than a third of the sown land in the U.S.S.R., and, depending on climatic conditions, has recently produced each year between about 20 and 30 per cent of total Soviet farm output. Agriculture is somewhat precarious on account of the low precipitation of most of the area and the short growing season. Certain parts of the area have been developed less intensively than others, and in one area, the Tselinnyy *kray*, it is still hoped to increase grain production two or threefold. The whole area is characterized by modern, reasonably well equipped, state farms geared to the production of wheat, but this monoculture is unsatisfactory and the farm economy is to be diversified by the wider introduction of cattle and sheep. There is a labour problem in the area due to the seasonal nature of work on the state farms and this is one reason why it is desirable to introduce manufacturing.

In recent years a large number of new mineral deposits have been found in northern Kazakhstan and West Siberia, including iron ore, coal and various non-ferrous metals and ferro-alloys. Coal and iron ore are sent to other regions but there are also major heavy industrial developments in the area itself. The expansion of production of iron and steel, cement, fertilizers and agricultural machinery may be noted. Although it seems certain that the costs of producing fuel, electricity, many ores and metals, grain, wheat and wool, are lower than for the same items in European U.S.S.R., the problem of transporting these items two or three thousand kilometres to the west remains. Goods moved out of the region include coal, non-ferrous metals, chemicals, timber, certain kinds of machines, and meat and wool, as well, of course, as grain. This has also been the area in which the greatest amount of new route has been added to the Soviet railway system recently.

IIId *The Kuzbass Area.* The Kuzbass coalfield occupies a special place in the economy of Siberia since it was the first area of large-scale industrial development east of the Ural Range. The exposed coalfield is roughly equal in extent to that of the Donbass, but at the moment only about a third as much coal is produced and there are only about half as many people living on or near the Kuzbass as there are on the Donbass coalfield. Reserves are much larger, however, and production costs are only about a third as great. The development of the Kuzbass, which began in the first Five Year Plan period, was to provide coal for the iron and steel industry of the Ural region, but at the same time it was considered useful to establish a large integrated iron and steel works in the Kuzbass itself, initially using iron ore from the Ural region. The iron and steel industry in the Kuzbass, which is to grow with the opening of a large new works, the West Siberian (ZAPSIB) at Novokuznetsk, close to the earlier works, is to obtain its iron ore from places in the vicinity (e.g. Tashtagol). In addition to coalmining and metallurgical industries, both chemical and engineering industries have grown up on and near the coalfield. There tends to be specialization in iron and steel at the southern end of the coalfield and chemicals and paper at the northern end, and in towns to the north. Novosibirsk, a great regional and cultural centre, with a wide range of industries, and Barnaul, are to some extent dependent on the coalfield, but are also related to the new lands to the west and south.

IIIe *The Krasnoyarsk and Baykal Area.* Between the Kuzbass and Lake Baykal is an area of recent but particularly rapid development. It occupies a zone along the Trans-Siberian Railway and

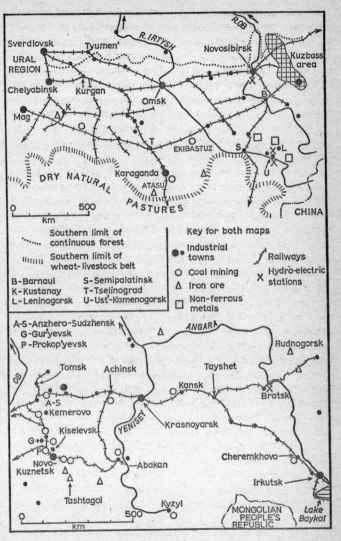

49. Region III: Parts of West and East Siberia and northern Kazakhstan.

along certain branch roads and railways penetrating from this into the forests to the north and mountains to the south. This mid-Siberian area, in which good agricultural land is very restricted, but timber, hydro-electricity and many minerals are abundant, is currently receiving a much larger share of investment than would be expected given the size of its population. Production costs of coal, iron ore, hydro-electricity and timber are claimed to be among the lowest in the country.

Some of the principal centres and resources are shown in Figure 49 and Figure 58 and three main development 'knots' and some secondary ones are suggested in Figure 20. Krasnoyarsk is both a commercial and manufacturing centre, likely to expand its engineering branches with the growth of iron and steel production in Tayshet to the east and to benefit from the harnessing of the great hydro-electric potential in the Yenisey valley above the town. The Bratsk area, again with hydro-electricity, timber and iron ore, is expected to develop the manufacture of aluminium as well as paper and other wood products. The Irkutsk–Cherem-khovo complex should become a major district for the chemicals industry. Further expansion of industry may also be expected to the north of the Krasnoyarsk–Tayshet–Bratsk axis as new roads and railways are built. Here, more perhaps than anywhere else in the Soviet Union at the moment, is the pioneer frontier. The shape of the present politico-administrative and economic planning units is quite out of step with the distribution of towns and economic activities, and the creation of some new major economic region here may soon take place, giving recognition to the rapid changes.

V. THE SOUTHERN AND EASTERN REGIONS

The rest of the U.S.S.R. has been divided into three parts (see Figure 40). Region IV consists of the southern part of the country and has special features and problems connected with its warm conditions and ability to grow plants which cannot be cultivated elsewhere in the U.S.S.R. Further, its population is essentially non-Slav and non-European. Region V is the dry area between III and IV, and is still relatively empty, although new developments in irrigation and mineral exploration are taking place. Region VI is the empty part of the country lying east of the Ural Range and north of region III. The following figures show population; region IV is subdivided into Transcaucasia and Central Asia.

	Population in thousands		Percentage urban	Area in thousands of sq.km.	Density of population persons per sq.km.
	Total	Urban			
IVa Transcaucasia	10,340	4,980	48	187	55
IVb Central Asia	17,150	6,380	37	1,505	11·5
V Dry U.S.S.R.	5,740	3,070	53	1,911	3
VI Empty U.S.S.R.	9,660	5,840	61	11,528	0·8

IVa *Transcaucasia*. For the purposes of comparison with the other major regions of the U.S.S.R., Transcaucasia and Central Asia have been placed together to form region IV. They have certain features in common, including their southern latitude, the presence of high mountain and desert areas, a basically non-Russian population, a shortage of arable land, and a level of industrialization and investment below the national average. The figures in the previous section show however that there are differences in the number of inhabitants, degree of urbanization and, most of all, territorial extent. Central Asia here refers to three of the four Central Asian republics (Kirgizia, Tadjikistan and Uzbekistan) as well as to certain oblasts of southern Kazakhstan, which are very similar.

As one of the economic regions of the U.S.S.R., Transcaucasia is of considerable interest, since at first sight it is apparently largely self-contained, even having its own iron and steel industry, yet at the same time it is highly specialized, producing a surplus of tea, citrus fruits, wine and tobacco, and including along its Black Sea resort coast places visited by people from all over European U.S.S.R. Moreover, there are great contrasts between the three Republics, particularly between Georgia and Armenia. A closer look reveals, however, that Transcaucasia is deficient in most food products and manufactured items, and even the favourable balance in oil production has come to an end; indeed a pipeline is to be built across the Greater Caucasus Range to carry natural gas across from the North Caucasus region.

Transcaucasia falls into three fairly distinct zones based on

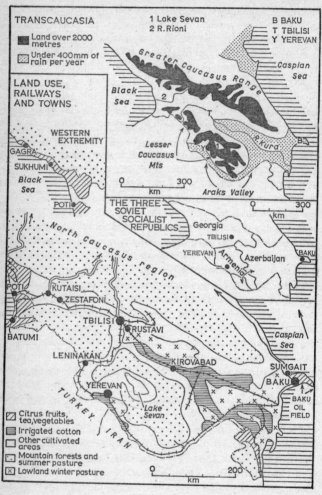

TRANSCAUCASIA

■ Land over 2000 metres

▨ Under 400mm of rain per year

1 Lake Sevan
2 R.Rioni

B BAKU
T TBILISI
Y YEREVAN

Greater Caucasus Range

Black Sea

Caspian Sea

Lesser Caucasus Mts

R.Kura

B

Araks Valley

0   300
km

LAND USE, RAILWAYS AND TOWNS

WESTERN EXTREMITY

GAGRA

SUKHUMI

Black Sea

POTI

North Caucasus region

THE THREE SOVIET SOCIALIST REPUBLICS

Georgia

TBILISI

YEREVAN

Armenia

Azerbaijan

BAKU

0   300
km

POTI

KUTAISI

ZESTAFONI

TBILISI

RUSTAVI

BATUMI

LENINAKAN

KIROVABAD

Caspian Sea

YEREVAN

Lake Sevan

SUMGAIT

BAKU

BAKU OIL FIELD

TURKEY

IRAN

▨ Citrus fruits, tea, vegetables
▤ Irrigated cotton
☐ Other cultivated areas
⬚ Mountain forests and summer pasture
☒ Lowland winter pasture

0   200
km

50. Region IV: Western part: Transcaucasia.

relief: the Greater Caucasus Range in the north, the ranges and plateaux of the Lesser Caucasus to the south, and between these a depression widening eastwards in the Kura lowlands. Arable land is in short supply both in the more rugged parts, on account of steep slope, and in the drier parts of the eastern lowland where irrigation is necessary. The amount of land under forest is limited and much of the area is classed as natural pasture.

Although a number of minerals are available and worth exploiting, these do not compare with deposits of similar minerals in many other parts of the country. The extraction of oil in the Baku area is becoming more and more costly, while the coal and iron ore deposits mined to supply the iron and steel industry at Rustavi are small. Manganese ore (Chiatura) and non-ferrous metals are sent to other regions of the country. The lack of oil, coal and natural gas has to some extent been supplemented by the construction of hydro-electric power stations, but most of these are small in capacity. With nearly 5 per cent of the total population of the U.S.S.R., Transcaucasia has only 3 per cent of the national industry. Much of this is concerned with processing rather than manufacturing, but there is a textile industry, while engineering serves the needs of the oil industry.

The problems of Transcaucasia are complex, and the best lines for future development are uncertain, for although the region is more highly developed than neighbouring parts of Turkey and Iran, it is still underdeveloped by Soviet standards, depending heavily on agriculture and the 'export' of raw materials to more industrialized parts of the country. The root of the problem lies both in the small size of the area and in the lack of raw materials, and in these circumstances all-round development and self-sufficiency are out of the question. Since oil and gas reserves are of limited size it does not seem desirable to establish a chemicals industry of national importance in Transcaucasia. Another problem of the region is the fact that much of the industry is concentrated in a few large cities. In Azerbaijan 80 per cent of the industry is in and around Baku, and in Georgia 40 per cent is in Tbilisi. In many small and medium-sized towns it should be possible to place labour-intensive industries.

To some extent the future of Transcaucasia is inevitably related to the crops in which it is able to specialize on account of its particular climatic conditions. Tea, citrus fruits and the vine are the most promising, but there is a lack of machinery to process these and prepare them for delivery to other regions. As in Belorussia and the Baltic Republics, light engineering has also been suggested as one of the remedies, but in contrast to these other regions, Transcaucasia is remote from such large regional markets as the Moscow area and the eastern Ukraine.

IVb *Central Asia and Southern Kazakhstan*.[1] The total population of Central Asia and southern Kazakhstan is about 17 million, of which 13 million is in the three Republics of Central Asia (the fourth, Turkmenistan, is included in dry U.S.S.R., region V). The area is much less highly urbanized than most parts of the U.S.S.R. The natural rate of increase of population appears to be considerably higher than the national average. There are two main contrasting types of environment, the high mountain ranges with their interior valleys, and the hill country and lowlands to the north and west of the mountain area (see Figure 51). Precipitation is considerable on the mountains, but low elsewhere. There is little forest vegetation even in the more humid parts, and much of the lowland and even the interior valley floors have desert or semi-desert conditions.

Like Transcaucasia, this area is essentially non-Russian, but it has been even less influenced by Europeans and for the most part has been in the Russian Empire for a shorter time. There are several distinct peoples with their own languages, and virtually the whole population has been Moslem. Though predominantly agricultural at least until two or three decades ago, the area has a very old civilization, with some towns (e.g. Samarkand and Bukhara) far older than any in Russia itself. The economy was largely agricultural until the 1930s, and was based on irrigated arable farming in

1. This region consists of the republics of Uzbekistan, Kirgizia and Tadjikistan together with that part of Kazakhstan, the south-east, closest to Central Asia. In 1961 this consisted of the oblast of Alma-Ata and the kray of South Kazakhstan; in 1963 the kray was broken up and the three former oblasts of Dzhambul, Kzyl-Orda and Chimkent reconstituted. One of the most absurd cases of splitting a region on account of a Republic boundary is the division between Kazakhstan on the one hand and Uzbekistan and Kirgizia on the other. This boundary runs through densely peopled oases and divides into two parts an area served by the same main railway.

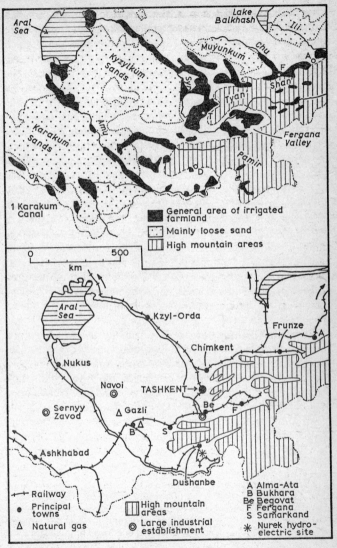

Lake Balkhash
Aral Sea
Ili
Muyunkum
Kyzylkum Sands
Syr
Chu
A
F
Tyan Shan
Karakum Sands
Amu
Pamir
Fergana Valley
D
A
1

■ General area of irrigated farmland
Mainly loose sand
High mountain areas

1 Karakum Canal

0   500
km

Aral Sea
Kzyl-Orda
Frunze
A
Chimkent
Nukus
Navoi
TASHKENT →
Sernyy Zavod
△ Gazli
Be
F
B
△
S
Ashkhabad

Dushanbe

A Alma-Ata
B Bukhara
Be Begovat
F Fergana
S Samarkand
✳ Nurek hydro-electric site

+—+ Railway
• Principal towns
△ Natural gas
⦾ Large industrial establishment
High mountain areas

51. Region IV: Eastern part: Central Asia and southern Kazakhstan.

the oases, and nomadic livestock farming practising transhumance in the adjoining desert and high mountain pastures. Herds of sheep horses and camels were moved seasonally in long circuits through the desert or from winter lowland pastures to high summer pastures. There was little interest in cattle or pig rearing.

Arable farming depends largely on irrigation, although cereals are grown in places where precipitation is sufficient in some lowland areas. There is a string of oases extending from the Caspian to the Chinese boundary. Many of the larger oases are in the Republic of Uzbekistan. The oases are either in interior valleys (e.g. Fergana) or at the foot of the mountains facing the desert lowlands (e.g. Tashkent) or extend along the valleys of rivers flowing out into the desert area (specially the Amu and Syr, which drain into the Aral Sea).

Only a small percentage of the total area is irrigated, but it is possible eventually to extend this considerably with new irrigation works, the ultimate aim theoretically being to use the water from all the rivers without it wasting in the desert or evaporating from the surface of the Aral Sea. Some further saving can be achieved by covering the irrigation canals to prevent evaporation. The irrigated land is already heavily fertilized and yields are high by Soviet standards, but more of the total irrigated area might be devoted to the most valuable industrial crops rather than to food crops. The principal agricultural products of the area at the moment are cotton (about 80 per cent of the Soviet total) and fruit of various kinds, as well as wheat, maize, rice and sugarbeet, and fodder crops (e.g. lucerne). Cereals are grown on non-irrigated land but yields here are generally low compared with those on irrigated land. Wool and meat are obtained from the natural pastures, karakul lamb skins being a special feature.

Central Asia and southern Kazakhstan are well endowed with energy and mineral resources. Central Asia is now estimated to have the second largest energy reserves (after East Siberia) of all the regions in the U.S.S.R.; Turkmenistan is included in this calculation. The mountain areas have the cheapest sites for large hydro-elcetric power stations in the whole of the U.S.S.R. on account of deep gorges (e.g. in the valleys of the Naryn and Vakhsh) and Central Asia has 13 per cent of the total Soviet hydro-electric potential. Reservoirs here would be useful both to generate electricity and to regulate the flow of water to the irrigation system. The region also has the lowest-cost gas in the whole of the U.S.S.R. and is third in terms of oil reserves. With these resources it should be possible to produce abundant cheap electricity, and a twenty-fold increase of electricity output between about 1960 and 1980 is considered desirable. Many non-ferrous metals are also available, while non-metallic minerals provide the basis for the developing chemicals industry. The region consumes about a fifth of the Soviet fertilizer output and large quantities have to be brought in from elsewhere. An eight to tenfold increase in the production of fertilizers is planned by 1970. This it is hoped will make it possible to raise the output of cotton from the present 4 to 5 m. tons per year to 10 to 11 m. tons by 1970.

Industry in the area is still largely devoted to the processing of food and minerals, and the only steel works (at Begovat) has a very small capacity. Engineering production is limited, and the whole engineering industry is unsatisfactory on account of the lack of collaboration between the several Republics in the area. The development of engineering is considered desirable however and it has been suggested that using iron and steel from central Kazakhstan it would be possible to introduce the manufacture of oil and natural gas equipment and of light-engineering products, such as refrigerators and air-conditioning equipment. The area is also considered to be remote enough and to have a large enough potential market to have a motor vehicles industry. The lack of industrial development so far may be one reason why the *per caput* income is only about 70 per cent of that of the Soviet average. It has also been noted that consumption of sugar, meat and fat is lower than in the U.S.S.R. as a whole and this reflects one of the fundamental problems, lack of arable land and good pasture, and specialization in 'export crops' for other regions of the country. Goods leaving the region include wool, cotton, karakul skins, silk, vegetables and fruits from the agricultural sector, non-ferrous metals and gas among minerals, and textiles, though only in limited quantities. On the other hand there is a deficit in most manufactured goods and in foodstuffs. Although Central Asia and southern Kazakhstan is clearly more advanced materially than comparable areas in Asia outside the U.S.S.R., it still has the very characteristics that are typical in Soviet eyes of a colonial economy, if a highly developed one.

V *Dry U.S.S.R.* This region has been distinguished to draw attention to the large part of the U.S.S.R. that is lacking in agricultural land and is thinly populated on account of dry conditions rather than cold conditions. Region V has about 8·5 per cent of the area of the U.S.S.R. but only 2·5 per cent of the population. In fact, however, it is less empty than region VI. The western and northern border is taken to be the southern fringe of arable farming, which runs roughly between mean annual isohyets of 30 and 40 cm., and also follows the zone in which soil conditions deteriorate towards the desert, and evaporation increases. The south-east limit of the area extends to the oases of Central Asia and southern Kazakhstan discussed in the previous section, but the Turkmen Republic has been put in region V. In fact, the frontiers of development are gradually converging towards the heart of this dry area, as cereal cultivation moves dangerously near the limits from the north and new irrigation products extend into the desert from the south.

The area is characterized by very patchy development, with some of the population clustered in small oases and some in mining and processing towns. The nomadic herdsmen have been discouraged from moving far with their herds and have been placed in permanent settlements. The area is crossed by several railways linking Central Asia with the rest of the U.S.S.R. These are the east–west line to the Caspian at Krasnovodsk crossing the Turkmen Republic, the line north-west from Tashkent towards European U.S.S.R., that passing the western end of Lake Balkhash, and the Turksib line. These lines have been built to link places outside the dry area rather than to serve places in it, but several lines branch from them to important mineral deposits in the desert.

Region V has no major concentration of population, and only Karaganda, which is becoming a major industrial complex, can be considered a regional centre though even it serves only a limited part of the area. Further development in agriculture awaits the completion of irrigation projects such as the Karakum Canal, which will carry water westwards from the river Amu. There are ambitious plans to bring in water from the Siberian rivers to the north. In 1964 work started on the construction of a canal from

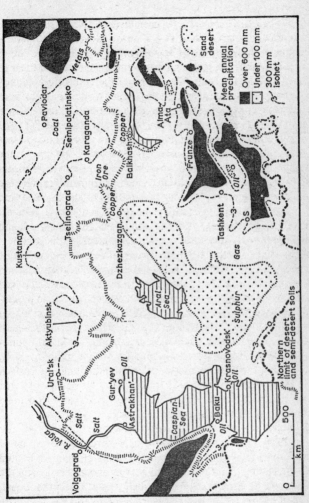

52. Region V: Dry U.S.S.R.

Volgograd
R. Volga
salt
salt
Ural'sk
Aktyubinsk
Kustanay
o Pavlodar
Metals
Coal
Semipalatinsko
Tselinograd
Karaganda
Iron Ore
Copper
Copper
Dzhezkazgan
Balkhash
Almā
Ata
Frunze
Oil
Tashkent
Gas
Sulphur
Aral
Sea
Gur'yev
Oil
Astrakhan'
Caspian
Sea
Krasnovodsk
Oil
Baku
Oil
Sand
desert

Over 600 mm
Under 100 mm
Mean annual
precipitation
300 mm
isohet

Northern
limit of desert
and semi-desert soils

0   500
km

the Irtysh to Ekibastuz and Karaganda. This is primarily to serve industrial needs at the moment but it may be possible in the future to divert much more water from the upper Ob'–Irtysh drainage basin towards the interior drainage area of central Kazakhstan.

Many mineral deposits have been discovered in the dry area, including the older copper deposits of Dzhezkazgan and Balkhash and, more recently, oil and gas in the Caspian Lowlands and at Mangyshlak. There are also several coal and iron ore deposits, but Karaganda was the only coalfield exploited before the Second World War, and the Karaganda area is still the only large concentration of manufacturing. The Temirtau integrated iron and steel works near Karaganda started production in the early 1960s and has very low production costs.

VI *Empty U.S.S.R.* The area lying east of the Ural Range and north of the Trans-Siberian Railway, together with the whole of the Far East, covers about half of the total area of the U.S.S.R. but has only a small percentage of the total population. The general area is referred to as Siberia, but parts of the economic regions of West Siberia and East Siberia have been included in region III. Moreover the extreme southern part of the Far East is different from the rest but for convenience has been included in region VI. The whole region appears to suffer basically from its remoteness both from the main concentration of population in European U.S.S.R. and from the railway system of the country. Although resources are vast, a large initial capital outlay is necessary in the form of transportation facilities, energy supplies and buildings before resources can be exploited, while unpleasant climatic conditions make it difficult to attract people to settle here voluntarily, at least unless much higher wages are paid than elsewhere. It has been estimated that for each production worker, about six others are needed to provide the infra-structure. Obviously therefore a small but highly productive labour force is needed to develop the area.

The region already sends several products to other parts of the country. Timber is sent out both from the Arctic and Pacific coasts by sea, and from the southern fringes of the forest by road and rail; Salekhard and Igarka are two of the principal timber ports. Non-ferrous metals, including copper from Noril'sk and gold from the mines behind Magadan, furs and fish, are other 'exports'.

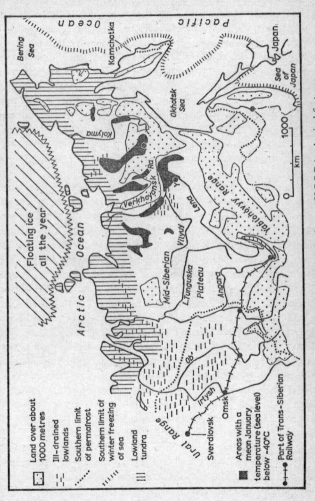

Key (legend):

- Land over about 1000 metres
- Ill-drained lowlands
- Southern limit of permafrost
- Southern limit of winter freezing of sea
- Lowland tundra
- Areas with a mean January temperature (sea level) below -40°C
- Part of Trans-Siberian Railway

Map labels:

Bering Sea

Kamchatka

Pacific Ocean

Floating ice all the year

Arctic Ocean

Okhotsk Sea

Kolyma

Sea of Japan

Japan

Verkhoyansk Ra.

Lena

Vilyuy

Yablonovyy Range

Mid-Siberian

L. Tunguska Plateau

Angara

Ob

Ural Range

Sverdlovsk

Irtysh

Omsk

0 1000 km

53. Region VI: Northern Asiatic U.S.S.R. (empty U.S.S.R.): physical features.

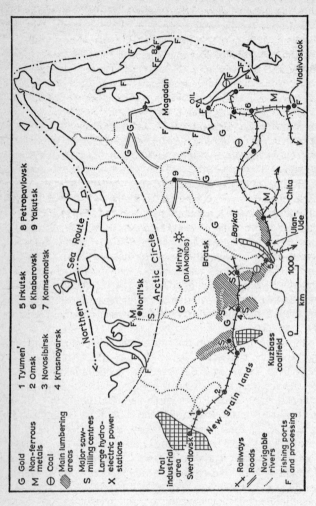

Legend (left side):

- G Gold
- M Non-ferrous metals
- ⊕ Coal
- ▽ Main lumbering areas
- S Major saw-milling centres
- ▨ Large hydro-electric power stations
- X

1 Tyumen'
2 Omsk
3 Novosibirsk
4 Krasnoyarsk

5 Irkutsk
6 Khabarovsk
7 Komsomol'sk

8 Petropavlovsk
9 Yakutsk

Ural industrial area

Sverdlovsk

New grain lands

Kuzbass coalfield

+-+ Railways
= Roads
···· Navigable rivers
F Fishing ports and processing

Northern Sea Route

Arctic Circle

Noril'sk

Mirny (DIAMONDS)

Bratsk

L. Baykal

Magadan

OIL

Vladivostok

Ulan-Ude

Chita

0   1000
km

54. Region VI: Northern Asiatic U.S.S.R.: economic activities.

The lowland area between the Ural Range and the River Yenisey, an area of some 3,000,000 sq. km., made virtually no contribution to the national economy until very recently, but has now become an area of great possibilities. It should be noted that this is the part of Siberia lying closest to the Ural region and European U.S.S.R. In *Pravda*, 24 July 1964, it was announced that there were some twenty oil deposits and the same number of natural gas deposits, including a very large oil deposit some 200 km. from Ust'-Balyka. Altogether the deposits are claimed to exceed those of the Volga–Ural oilfields. In the south the Bachkar deposit of iron ore (110,000 m. tons of ore) is said to equal that at Kursk. Other resources of the area include rare metals, timber, peat and fish.

In order to make development in the West Siberian Lowland possible, various railways are projected, including a line from Ivdel to the Ob' (400 km.) and from Tavda to Sitnik (180 km.). Helicopters are useful for exploration work and small mobile atomic-power stations with a capacity of 500 to 1,500 kilowatts can operate in areas where at this stage it is not possible to establish permanent thermal-power stations large enough to be worthwhile. Eventually pipelines would, of course, carry the oil and gas out of the area while the railways should be highly automated (as for example the line in Labrador, Canada, for the movement of iron ore).

To the east of the Yenisey the land is generally higher and more rugged than to the west of it, which, together with the added distance from European U.S.S.R., makes development here even more difficult than in the West Siberian Lowland. Considering together the empty parts of both East Siberia and the Far East, there is an area covering about a third of the U.S.S.R. with only about 1 per cent of the total population. Here, however, are about 80 per cent of all the coal resources of the country and 50 per cent of the hydro-electric potential, while recently oil was found in the middle Lena valley. The large-scale exploitation of these energy resources is not expected to take place for some decades. At the moment interest is concentrated on the production of gold, diamonds and other special minerals, and very little timber is moved out, although about half of the surface is forest-covered. At the same time attempts are being made to maintain the existing way of life of the peoples of the area, and reindeer herding is encouraged in the north, while there is some arable farming around Yakutsk. The beginnings of large-scale development, settlement and integration in the national economy could only come with the construction of new railways, either individual lines running north from the Trans-Siberian Railway to appropriate resources or, in the long run, more completely with the construction of a new west-to-east railway parallel to the present Trans-Siberian line.

A region of special interest and importance in the U.S.S.R. is the southern part of the Far East, what might be called the 'lesser' Far East, the Soviet window on the Pacific, lying roughly south of 55°N but having nearly all the population of the 'greater' Far East. This area has 4–5 m. people, which, of course, is in no sense comparable to the corresponding U.S. contingent on the Pacific coast of North America, now well over 20 m. in the three Pacific states alone. Even the relatively small number in the Soviet Far East is however about twice as great as it was in the 1930s, and it is estimated that about a million industrial workers and farmers have moved in during the last three decades.

There seem to be two main reasons why the southern part of the Soviet Far East has not progressed as hoped: firstly its great remoteness from the rest of the country and secondly its lack of agricultural land and a food supply base. The drawback of remoteness is difficult to assess precisely in quantitative terms but an idea of the high cost of moving goods between it and other parts of the country can be obtained from the fact that the cost of delivering one ton of goods by rail from Moscow to Khabarovsk (8,545 km.) is equivalent to four times the cost of producing one ton of coal. Clearly there is a case for greater regional self-sufficiency here than in other parts of the U.S.S.R., regardless of production costs. Moreover it is obvious that trade with Japan, Korea and North China, all of which are closer to the main centres of population in the Soviet Far East even than Lake Baykal is, could be beneficial all round. The role of the area as an outlet for Soviet trade with countries further afield in south-east Asia should also be borne in mind. It is best for the region therefore to send only items of high value such as gold, tin and canned fish to other parts of the U.S.S.R., and to export bulky products like timber, cellulose, coal and cement to foreign markets by sea. In fact, it appears that the more the region develops the more its economic life is likely to be associated with that of other Pacific powers. That Soviet planners intend to attract a larger population to the Pacific is shown by the fact that *per caput* investment in the Far East region in the period 1959–63 was double the national average, but much of this may in fact have gone towards the provision of an infra-structure rather than into production plants.

In spite of its relatively low latitude (about 45–55°N) the southern part of the Far East is less favourable for agriculture than might be expected, on account of its very long winter. On the other hand there is no lack of precipitation, and much of the rain comes during the growing season. The most serious drawback is lack of level or gently sloping land, for in spite of the severe winter, many useful crops can be grown, including maize, rice, soybean and sugar beet, where slope and soil permit. Only a small percentage of the total area is in fact arable but much of the total surface is forest covered. In addition to its agricultural land and timber, the area has deposits of several metallic minerals and of oil and coal, while the various seas off the coast, together with the north-western part of the Pacific Ocean, provide about a third of the total Soviet fishing catch. There are also sites suitable for the construction of hydro-electric power stations, but these are less favourable than · in East Siberia. About twenty-five dams and power stations would be needed along the course of the Amur to install a total capacity of about $7\frac{1}{2}$ m. kw. The relatively small size of these stations makes them unattractive commercially, while most of them would have to be built in collaboration with the Chinese, since the Amur forms the Sino-Soviet boundary for much of its length.

While regional self-sufficiency is desirable as far as possible, a population of about five million is not large enough to merit the establishment of large metallurgical and engineering plants. At the moment there is a small steel works at Khabarovsk, but it is estimated that an integrated iron and steel works with a capacity of seven to eight million tons a year might eventually be needed. Such a plant would be a liability for a long time unless it could depend on export markets in East Asia. The engineering industry and timber industry are both represented, and shipbuilding and the manufacture of paper are important branches of these. In practice, however, the region is deficient in many commodities, and

T–K

most machinery, as well as food and consumer goods, have to be brought in from places further west in the U.S.S.R.

The most southerly part is the hinterland of Vladivostok and of the newer port of Nakhodka, the principal outlets of the region. Here conditions are favourable for the cultivation of wheat, rice, sugar beet and fodder crops for dairying. The middle and lower Amur valley grows wheat and soybeans, and dairying is being encouraged here. The principal industrial centres are Khabarovsk and Komsomol'sk. The island of Sakhalin has been developed considerably in the last decade and a two to threefold increase achieved in oil production, the manufacture of paper and the fishing catch; coal is also mined. One cannot help feeling that this island could more usefully be linked economically to Japan, as it was for some time before the Second World War. Kamchatka is considered to offer considerable possibilities for development, though not of course of agriculture. Several minerals, including gold and oil, have been discovered lately, and no part of the peninsula is far from the coast.

Chapter 11

FOREIGN RELATIONS OF THE U.S.S.R.

I. FOREIGN TRADE

THIS section on the foreign trade of the U.S.S.R. is an attempt to answer briefly the three following questions: why does the U.S.S.R. trade at all, which are its chief partners, and what goods are exported and imported? Some general figures are available for 1963 but the breakdown of commodities by country was available at the time of writing only for 1962.[1]

It would be absurd to ask why the U.S.S.R. trades at all if it were not for the fact that for much of the inter-war period the country was trying to become and remain as self-sufficient as possible in every main commodity. It was of course hardly possible at all to do this in some cases. The U.S.S.R. was by its own definition the only socialist country at the time, and foreign trade was considered undesirable except where essential because planners did not want to be at the mercy of foreign powers that could suddenly deprive it of vital imports. This attitude still appears to be at the back of the minds of Soviet politicians and planners, even though the situation is very different now, and there was in reality a considerable trade in the inter-war period anyway.

Another possible reason why foreign trade has been frowned upon is that national economic planning is more difficult for a country that trades heavily than for one that is self-sufficient. The dependence of a country on foreign trade can be expressed approximately in terms of its export (or import) coefficient. This coefficient is the total value of exports and/or imports (with some further refinements possible) expressed as a percentage of total national income or some comparable measure. The larger the country, the less likely it is to have a high coefficient. In fact, the U.S.S.R., with one of around 2–3 per cent, has one of the lowest coefficients in the world. That of the U.S.A. is around 5 per cent, but in several West European countries it is 20–25 per cent. Moreover foreign trade tends to be disliked by central planners because it is difficult to

1. *Vneshnyaya torgovlya SSSR za 1962 godu, statisticheskiy obzor*, Vneshtorgizdat, Moscow, 1963.

organize, needing quick decisions and, sometimes, quick changes in policy. But for this objection to dependence on foreign goods, coastal regions of the U.S.S.R. might usefully have traded more. Why not, for example, establish an iron and steel works in Riga or Leningrad, using high-grade Swedish ore brought in very cheaply by sea? In fact very recently[1] there has been a move to allow the Far East region some freedom in its foreign trade, much of which is with countries like Japan, North Korea and China, far closer to it than Moscow is (see Chapter 10, Section V). In the postwar period, the U.S.S.R. has of course traded heavily with the East European countries and for a time with Communist China.

Since the mid-1950s there seems to have been more willingness on the part of the U.S.S.R. than previously to trade with non-Communist countries. Trade with them roughly doubled in value between 1958 and 1963 alone. Reasons for this probably include the growing need to obtain complex equipment, not produced in the Communist bloc, from Western industrial countries, and also the political advantages of establishing trade relations with as many neutral countries as possible. The reform of the rouble in 1961 may to some extent have been aimed at making trade with non-Communist countries easier from an organizational point of view. The idea that foreign trade may even be advantageous and not just a measure necessary from time to time is expressed by Vedishchev (p. 18): 'foreign trade helps to cheapen and speed the development of various branches of the economy'. In the long run, foreign trade is not only a complication that makes central planning more difficult, but is a further blow against regional self-sufficiency, and an admission of its usefulness amounts to an admission that there are places elsewhere in the world that produce certain goods more cheaply than they are produced anywhere in the U.S.S.R., even *after* transport costs to the U.S.S.R. have been added.

In practice there have been several obvious reasons why some foreign trade has always been necessary. Firstly the U.S.S.R. has had to obtain goods not produced at home either for climatic reasons or because reserves do not exist or have not been found, or because home industry is unable to produce them. Thus vital raw

1. *Pravda*, 7 February 1965.

materials such as natural rubber and industrial diamonds have
been imported over the last few decades, and also vital machinery,
such as equipment for the chemicals industry, not produced in the
U.S.S.R., luxury items such as tropical agricultural products
(coffee, cocoa beans), and emergency items such as grain during
1963 and 1964. To balance these imports, suitable commodities
are obtained for export from the Soviet economy, although
national plans do not usually appear to be geared to producing a
surplus of many things specifically for export to the Western
industrial countries.

The Soviet attitude to foreign trade seems to be improvised, and
trade is regarded at times as a means of getting rid of unexpected
surpluses. For example, at a given period there may be more pig
iron, oil or timber than can be absorbed at home. Occasionally
the U.S.S.R. even deals in re-exports. Recent examples have been
the re-export of refined metals from ores obtained from China
and processed in the U.S.S.R., and the re-export of cotton imported from Egypt.

It has frequently been suggested that Soviet foreign trade, or at
least that part of it with non-Communist countries, is carried on
in order to establish contacts with other countries, to establish
trading missions and diplomatic representation, to allow infil-
tration of technicians, or to show the Soviet way of life. There is
probably considerable truth in this last suggestion, but this need
not interfere with the basic economic motive behind foreign trade.
It has usually been possible for the Soviet Union to obtain commodities it has needed from those countries on which Soviet trade
could be expected to make the greatest political impact. For
example fish has been imported from Iceland rather than from
Norway, since the U.S.S.R. has been particularly interested in
Iceland for political and strategic reasons. Some measure of the
possible economic and political impact of Soviet foreign trade on
different countries can be obtained by assessing this in *per caput*
terms rather than absolute terms. For example, the total value of
Soviet trade with France is far greater than the value of its trade
with Iceland. But the value of the foreign trade between Iceland
and the U.S.S.R. is far greater in terms of roubles per inhabitant
of Iceland than the value of Franco-Soviet trade in terms of
roubles per inhabitant of France. From this it may be inferred

that the economy and even foreign policy of Iceland are therefore more easily influenced by Soviet policy than are those of France.

The following table shows the principal trading partners of the U.S.S.R. in 1962 in terms of their share of total value. Two thirds of all Soviet foreign trade was with other Communist countries but this proportion was considerably higher in the 1950s (75 to 80 per cent).

Principal trading partners *(socialist countries)*	Percentage of total Soviet foreign trade	Principal trading partners	Percentage of total Soviet foreign trade
East Germany	18·1	United Kingdom	2·4
Czechoslovakia	11·8	Italy	1·7
Poland	8·6	West Germany	2·5
Bulgaria	6·2	Finland	2·9
Hungary	5·9	France	1·8
Rumania	5·4	Sweden	1·0
	54·0		12·3
China	5·6	India	1·5
North Korea	1·3	Egypt	1·3
Mongolia	1·4	Malaya	1·2
Cuba	4·5	Japan	1·9

SOURCE: *Vneshnyaya torgovlya SSSR za 1962 god*, Moscow, 1963, p. 15.

Among the socialist countries the prominent position of East Germany should be noted, as well as the relatively small importance of China, particularly in view of the very large population of the latter country. It is remarkable indeed that by the early 1960s Soviet trade with Cuba was as great as that with China. Among the non-Communist countries, those of Europe occupy a prominent position, accounting for almost half of this sector of Soviet trade. The idea that the U.S.S.R. picks small countries for its trading partners in the non-Communist world is worth investigating, but it should not be overlooked that much of Soviet trade in Asia is with large countries such as India, Pakistan and Indonesia, while its principal trading partners in Latin America, apart of course from Cuba, have been Brazil and Argentina. The idea that it trades more heavily with countries that adjoin it is again worth considering. Certainly it trades relatively heavily with Finland and Afghanistan, but on the other hand its trade with Turkey and Iran has been small. Soviet trade with certain countries has been largely in one direction. For example, its imports from Malaya (of tin), and from Uruguay and Australia (of wool), have been much larger than its exports to these countries. On the other hand for a time its exports to Egypt greatly exceeded its imports.

Turning to the actual items involved in Soviet foreign trade, it is interesting to see the declining relative importance of raw materials on the one hand and the rise of semi-manufactured and manufactured goods on the other.

*Percentage of the value of Soviet foreign
trade made up of raw materials or other goods*

	1913	1950	1958	1963
EXPORTS				
Raw materials	64	39	40	35
Mf. and semi-mf. goods	36	61	60	65
IMPORTS				
Raw materials	44	40	36	26
Mf. and semi-mf. goods	56	60	64	74

SOURCE: *Nkh SSSR 1963*, pp. 551–2.

The diminishing relative importance of raw materials among both exports and imports seems to be a result of the increasing industrialization of the economy, while the fact that goods other than raw materials occupy a larger proportion of imports than of exports suggests that trade tends to be with countries that are more advanced industrially than the U.S.S.R. The following table shows some of the principal items exported and imported in 1963 (percentage of total value):

	Exports	Imports
Machinery and equipment	20	35
Crude oil and oil products	18	3
Agricultural raw materials	17	15
Ores and concentrates	4	4
Metals	5	2
Consumer goods	2	18
Rubber	—	3

SOURCE: *Nkh SSSR 1963*, pp. 551–2.

While there is obviously roughly a balance between the value of exports and imports in any one year (e.g. 1963 total trade 12,898 m. roubles, of which exports 6,545 m., imports 6,353 m.), there is a very great difference in the weight of exports and imports, which means that most ships and trains enter or return to the U.S.S.R. empty. In 1962 exports amounted to 117 m. tons, while imports were only 16 m. tons. The following were among the heaviest items exported in 1962 and 1963 (millions of tons):

	1962	1963
Crude oil	26	30
Oil products	19	21
Hard coal	19	21
Iron ore	19	21
Pig iron and rolled steel	6	6
Grain	8	6

SOURCE: *Nkh SSSR 1936*, p. 549.

Other items that were heavy and/or bulky included timber, both logs and sawn, manganese ore and some non-metallic minerals. In the early 1960s, Soviet foreign trade was carried in roughly equal quantities by rail and water (mostly by sea rather than by river), but in 1962, for the first time, some oil left by pipeline. Rail, inland waterway and pipeline trade is mainly with East Europe.

For its imports of machinery and equipment, the U.S.S.R. depends very heavily on East Germany and Czechoslovakia within COMECON and on the leading industrial countries of West Europe outside the bloc. On the other hand, its exports of machinery and equipment go mainly to the less developed partners of COMECON or to the under-developed countries outside. The coal and coke, iron ore, manganese ore, pig iron and rolled steel are bought almost exclusively by the COMECON partners, particularly East Germany (one third of the coal and coke), Poland and Czechoslovakia (especially the iron ore). Crude oil and refined products, on the other hand, reach many countries both in and outside COMECON. Large purchasers of Soviet oil in recent years have been East Germany, Poland and Czechoslovakia, none of which produces much oil, as well as Cuba, Italy and Sweden. One of the principal buyers of Soviet timber and products is the United Kingdom.

There have been some notable changes in the pattern of Soviet imports in recent years. For example, in 1961 and 1962 respectively over 3 m. and over 2 m. tons of raw sugar were imported from Cuba, and in 1964 (*Pravda*, 23 January 1964), the U.S.S.R. agreed to import in 1965 over 2 m. tons, in 1966 3 m., in 1967 4 m. and in 1968–70 5 m. each year, in order to shield Cuba from fluctuations in world sugar prices. This arrangement, if adhered to, may well have repercussions in the sugar beet growing areas of the U.S.S.R. There has also been an increase in the import of certain luxury items, including cocoa beans (fivefold between 1958 and 1965) and coffee (sevenfold), as well as imports of some consumer goods (e.g. knitwear, furniture).

One feature of Soviet foreign trade is the large number of items both imported and exported. To some extent this is done simply for political reasons. For example, the U.S.S.R. imported Egyptian cotton for a time to help Egypt dispose of a surplus, but at the same time it was exporting its own cotton to COMECON partners. To some extent, however, the paradox is a result of the great size of the U.S.S.R. Thus, for example, it is quite reasonable and convenient to export surplus wheat from the Ukraine to Czechoslovakia and at the same time to import wheat from Canada into the Far East region.

II. THE U.S.S.R. AND OTHER COMMUNIST COUNTRIES[1]

The influence of the U.S.S.R. increased greatly in east-central Europe after the Second World War as new régimes run by Communist parties or parties sympathetic to the Soviet Communist Party were established in various countries captured by the Russians from the Germans. The following table shows the countries concerned. Yugoslavia and Albania are put separately since they do not now cooperate economically to any great extent with the U.S.S.R. although they have Communist régimes.

1. See M. Kaser, *Comecon, Integration Problems of the Planned Economies*, Oxford University Press, 1965, and G. Ionescu, *The Break-up of the Soviet Empire in Eastern Europe*, Penguin Books, 1965

	Capital	Area in thousands of sq. km.	Population in thousands (1964 or nearest year)
East Germany[1]	Berlin	108	17,181
Poland	Warsaw	313	30,940
Czechoslovakia	Prague	128	14,004
Hungary	Budapest	93	10,104
Rumania	Bucharest	238	18,877
Bulgaria	Sofia	111	8,163
		991	99,269
Yugoslavia	Belgrade	256	19,177
Albania	Tirana	29	1,711

1 German Democratic Republic.

The first six countries listed are members, with the U.S.S.R., of the Council of Mutual Economic Aid (COMECON), and at the moment it looks very much as if their future is tied to that of the U.S.S.R. both economically and politically. The other two will not be discussed here since Yugoslavia occupies a very complicated position in world affairs and Albania is of slight importance economically, though politically potentially of considerable concern to the U.S.S.R.

The six COMECON partners of the U.S.S.R. have about a hundred million inhabitants, almost half as many as the U.S.S.R. itself, but they cover less than one million square kilometres and therefore occupy less than one twentieth the area of the U.S.S.R. Together they are therefore roughly equal in area only to the average size of one economic region of the U.S.S.R. Individually, they compare in area with the smaller Soviet Socialist Republics of the U.S.S.R. Though endowed with some good farming areas, several coalfields and a number of other resources, their population/resource balance is greatly inferior to that of the U.S.S.R., and far more like that of West European countries. Altogether COMECON contains about one tenth of the total population of the world.

During the postwar period the relationship between the U.S.S.R. and its so-called satellites of east-central Europe has changed. Initially military occupation was the main consideration and a large number of Soviet forces were based in the Soviet Zone of Germany. The second phase, which followed quickly in most cases, was the establishment of a pro-Soviet régime. This did not occur in Czechoslovakia until 1948, by which time Yugoslavia had already rejected Soviet domination. Military occupation, modified by the creation of alliances and a defence organization, political dominance, and a one-sided economic relationship whereby the U.S.S.R. benefited in its trade with these countries, characterized Soviet relations with its satellites until 1956. Until then the development of socialism in the satellite countries had followed the Soviet pattern of the inter-war period, with emphasis on the establishment of a heavy industrial base in each individual country and a minimum of dependence on foreign trade.

The Soviet attitude to its fellow Communist countries changed fairly quickly around 1956, and less emphasis was put on military and political dominance, while there was a new attitude towards economic development. On the economic side, the change in policy was away from self-sufficiency in each sovereign state to specialization in each on behalf of the Communist bloc, and consequent economic interdependence. In other words, a situation has emerged not unlike that created among certain countries of West Europe over the same period. Basically this attitude has remained unchanged, though there has been some doubt as to the amount of economic interdependence that should be introduced. For organizational reasons COMECON has been slow to get under way, but one cannot help feeling that since the late 1950s it has become more and more important to take into account the existence of COMECON in a study of the geography, or at least the economic geography, of the U.S.S.R.

The questions that have been asked at various points in this book about the system of economic regions in the U.S.S.R. and the resources and prospects of these could also be applied to the COMECON partners. These in fact vary considerably in their level of economic development. East Germany and Czechoslovakia are highly industrialized by any standards, while Bulgaria in particular is still heavily dependent on agriculture. They vary also in the nature and quantity of the resources they possess. For example East Germany has large brown-coal deposits, Poland and Czechoslovakia share the only large coalfield, while Rumania has the principal oil deposits. In total the six countries are deficient in fuel and raw materials and although they would like to be self-sufficient in food, the area can hardly hope to feed a hundred million people. The question has not been how to make each country self-sufficient economically, but whether to obtain raw materials and food by land from the U.S.S.R. or by sea from the rest of the world, and which branches of industry to concentrate on to provide the exports needed by the country or countries supplying the raw materials. The establishment of COMECON answers the question about the general direction of trade, but the specializations of each country have certainly not been fully decided yet.

Steps towards the economic integration of COMECON include the establishment in 1957 of a multilateral clearing system for trade instead of a bilateral one, in 1959 of a standard railway transit tariff in a standard currency, and in 1960 of a programme to co-ordinate agricultural production and to make agriculture more uniform. By 1960 decisions had already been made as to specialization by individual member countries in the manufacture of certain engineering products (e.g. Poland ships, Czechoslovakia and East Germany processing plant, Rumania oil-drilling equipment, and so on) and also products of the chemicals industry. In 1960 the U.S.S.R. signed long-term trade agreements with several partners, covering for example the export of Soviet iron and other metals to Czechoslovakia and of Czechoslovak uranium to the U.S.S.R. In other words, COMECON clearly exists, but whether it works or is mutually beneficial to its members is more difficult to decide.

One of the most convincing pieces of evidence of the serious intentions of COMECON has been the agreement of the four northern partners to receive most of their oil needs from the U.S.S.R. The 4,000 km. Druzhba (Friendship) pipeline is nearing completion (see Figure 55). It is to bring crude oil from the Volga–Ural field to four refineries, one in each country, and is intended eventually to convey 18 m. tons of oil annually. By early 1965 some 20 m. tons of oil had been pumped into East Europe along those parts of the system already built. Bratislava refinery in Czechoslovakia was the first to be served, receiving oil in 1962, while delivery to Poland began in 1963. Another feature of interdependence that would be difficult to undo in the future is the Mir (Peace) electricity transmission system connecting the western Ukraine and the six COMECON partners (see Figure 35).[1] This should eventually be linked to the all-Union grid of the U.S.S.R. to allow electricity from places further east to be sent to East Europe during periods of peak consumption.

By the early 1960s it was becoming clear that the integration of COMECON was not proceeding smoothly or quickly. Since COMECON has no executive powers, it can only make recommendations, and lacks the supra-national characteristics of the European Economic Community (the Common Market). The idea of division of labour among the member countries has long been accepted, but lack of realistic exchange rates, unwillingness to allow mobility of labour between countries and sheer reluctance to be submerged in a larger bloc, particularly on the part of Rumania, have slowed down progress. Even the coordination of national economic plans broke down after the U.S.S.R. abandoned its own 1956–60 Five Year Plan in 1957. Presumably plans will again be in step after 1965, and already at the end of 1962[2] it was proposed that they should be coordinated during the period 1965 to 1980, with the help of a clearing bank and the adjustment of major investment projects to improve financial organization.

COMECON has been complicated somewhat by the acceptance of Cuba as a genuine member of the 'socialist camp'. For the first time in its career the U.S.S.R. has found itself directly associated with a land in the tropics. The attitude of China to the U.S.S.R. and East Europe is another problem that must affect the success of COMECON. Nor is it clear whether in fact the U.S.S.R. (and Cuba) can provide everything that the other COMECON countries need. Clearly West Europe and North America can supply a bigger variety and often higher quality of machinery and equipment than the U.S.S.R.; and what is East Europe to do when the grain harvest fails in the U.S.S.R.? General de Gaulle has pointed out that Europe is one as far as the Ural Range. Certainly there is a continuous area of dense settlement here, and any major economic barrier through it would upset the spontaneous flow of goods that

1. *Pravda*, 6 November 1964.
2. *The Times*, 24 December 1962.

so often occurs between places near to one another in such a population cluster, even if these appear very similar in what they produce. In the view of the author, if any division had to exist in Europe it would do least harm by leaving East Europe and even parts of the U.S.S.R. to the west of it, with the rest of Europe; thus maritime-orientated Europe would be separated from the great belt of development in the U.S.S.R. extending from Moscow east to Lake Baykal. This idea is illustrated tentatively in Figure 55. As things are, it seems doubtful if the long rail haul of goods from Siberia to places in East Europe within a short distance of seaports is sensible at all, yet this is what is being produced by COMECON.

In addition to its partners in East Europe, the U.S.S.R. has four fellow Communist powers in Asia. The area and population figures of these countries are shown for comparison with COMECON countries.

	Capital	Area in thousands of sq. km.	Population in thousands
China	Peking	9,597	656,630 (1957)
North Korea	Pyongyang	121	11,568
North Vietnam	Hanoi	159	15,917
Mongolian People's Republic	Ulan Bator	1,565	984

China alone has about three times as many people as the U.S.S.R. and twice as many as COMECON, though it covers less than half the area. The Mongolian People's Republic lies between the U.S.S.R. and China, but until very recently was influenced much more by the U.S.S.R. than by China. The presence of Mongolians in China itself and the quiet alteration of the name of the Soviet Buryat-Mongol A.S.S.R. to Buryat A.S.S.R. suggests that the ultimate future of the Republic is with China itself. North Korea is associated with both the U.S.S.R. and China, but North Vietnam is largely a Chinese sphere of interest.

During the decade following the establishment of a Communist régime in mainland China in 1949 the U.S.S.R. provided China with equipment for heavy industrial establishments of various kinds, and sent technicians. Aid of various kinds came also from

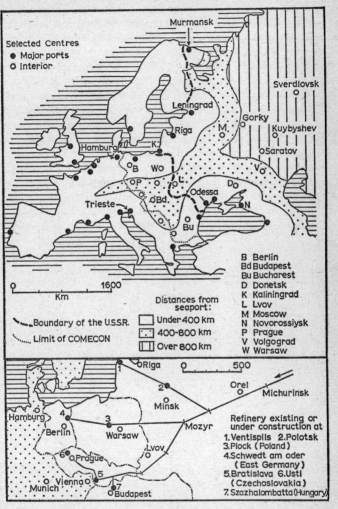

Murmansk

Sverdlovsk

Leningrad

Gorky
Kuybyshev

Riga
M.
Saratov

Hamburg
K.
B   Wo
V.

O   P
L.
Do

Bd.
Odessa

Trieste
N

Bu

Riga   1
                    0   500
        2   Orel
Minsk   Michurinsk

Hamburg   4
        3
Berlin   Warsaw   Mozyr

        Lvov
6 Prague
Vienna 5
Munich   7
Budapest

55. a. Maritime and interior Europe. b. The Friendship pipeline.

East Europe. This was done in spite of the fact that the U.S.S.R. was having to deliver over great distances by rail or sea precisely the goods (such as oil-drilling and steel-works equipment) needed for its own development. Even so, considering the size of the two countries, the value and volume of goods exchanged was surprisingly small. Since about 1960 there has been a diminution in trade, while China has been paying back previous Soviet assistance, sending to the U.S.S.R. a wide variety of items such as clothing and footwear, metals and food products, many of which could easily have been used at home. Potentially the two countries have many goods that they could usefully exchange, and in particular, the eastern part of the U.S.S.R. has reserves of timber and many minerals far in excess of its needs in the foreseeable future. But both for political reasons and on account of the inadequacy of transportation links between European U.S.S.R. and eastern China, the two countries are virtually independent in their economic lives.

Although the general pattern of Soviet trade has not changed greatly in the last few years, individual trading partners, apart from the faithful Communist countries of Eastern Europe, have come and gone quite suddenly. Who, a decade ago, would have thought that the value of Soviet foreign trade with Cuba would now be twice as great in value as Soviet trade with mainland China ? The favour of the Soviet Union has also fluctuated considerably over time *vis-à-vis* the neutral countries of Africa and Asia. In other words, the U.S.S.R. seems less willing or capable than most Western countries of forming trading links upon which it, and the partners at the other end, can rely.

Chapter 12

CONCLUSIONS

I. CORRELATIONS

ONE widely accepted function of geography has been to collect and map data about different parts of the world and to provide commentaries on the information thus presented. For example, in Figure 56 regional variations in income per collective farm family are mapped. These differences could be brought out visually on the maps by using appropriate kinds of shading for the nineteen regions. Collective farm incomes are listed in column O in Table 2.[1] It is becoming increasingly accepted, however, that a visual representation of distributions, and the intuitive and often biased conclusions drawn from this, may miss the underlying complexity of relationships of phenomena in area. The application of appropriate mathematical techniques[2] is one way of making greater use of geographical data. The reader may find them more difficult to follow than the rest of the book, particularly because several concepts and techniques new to him are introduced simultaneously and without full clarification. On the other hand, both geographers and non-geographers must face the prospect of methods more complicated than those used hitherto in the study of relationships in two-dimensional space, just as economists are using more and more sophisticated procedures to study time series and input–output matrices, and psychologists are grappling with n dimensional space. This section and the following section show briefly two relatively simple ways in which mathematical procedures can help to study spatial relationships in the U.S.S.R. The two studies use data for the nineteen economic regions of the early 1960s. These regions have been mapped in Figure 19, and have already been referred to frequently. They are also used in Figure 56.

1. The tables for this chapter are grouped together on p,301-7.
2. Referred to currently sometimes as statistical, sometimes as quantitative. The umbrella term mathematical is used here although statistics as a discipline is considered by some to be distinct from mathematics. One important recent example of the application of the use of factor analysis to interpret data for the sovereign states of the world is in the *Atlas of Economic Development* (Norton Ginsburg, Chicago, 1961), Part 8, by B. J. L. Berry.

Unfortunately there are drawbacks in using these regions: firstly, they differ greatly both in area and in number of inhabitants; secondly, much data that could be of interest is not available for them; and thirdly, it would be better to have at least fifty regions, rather than only nineteen. If data were available, a more satisfactory study could eventually be made based on the oblast–kray– A.S.S.R. level in the administrative hierarchy.

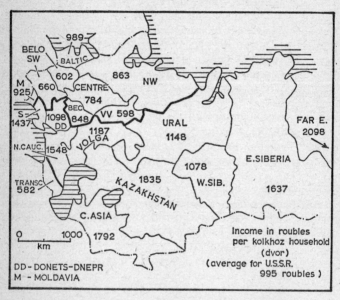

56. Regional variations in collective farm incomes in 1963.

Turning to the actual quantitative data for the nineteen regions, it is possible to display this in various ways, each of which has its particular advantages. Table 1 shows absolute figures for selected variables. It is from these figures, usually, that others are derived. The first column (A) in Table 1 shows for example the area (in thousands of sq. km.) of each of the regions, the fourth column (D) the number of urban dwellers (in thousands), and so on. The sets of absolute figures in Table 1 have been selected from many possible sets representing different variables, both to give an idea of the kind of data available and to present data of relevance to the text in this book and particularly to the studies that follow.

From the data in Table 1 it is possible to compare the size and number of people in the nineteen different regions, but a comparison by regions (still reading down the columns) of say electricity output is confused by the fact that there are many more people in some regions than in others. On the whole one would therefore expect the larger regions to have a better chance of producing or containing more of a given item than the smaller ones. Thus, to take as an example regions 18 and 19, Belorussia and Moldavia, in 1963 the former produced 5·5 times more electricity than the latter. In fact, however, Belorussia has nearly three times as many people as Moldavia and therefore obviously would be expected to need more. For purposes of comparison it may be better to express the amount of electricity produced not in absolute terms, as in Table 1, but in output per inhabitant (*per caput*) as in Table 2.

Table 2 shows some of the sets of absolute figures in Table 1 (capital letters are used to identify variables) together with some extra sets, expressed in terms of amount per person (or per so many people) or per unit of area. The influence of the regional differences in number of inhabitants or in territorial extent has thus been eliminated. The electricity figures in Table 2 still give Belorussia a higher index than Moldavia but the difference is less than in Table 1 now that the difference in total population between the two Republics has been allowed for. Table 2 reveals, for example, that even in *per caput* terms there are very great differences in *output* of electricity (column I) among the regions. Consumption *per caput* may of course be more uniform, since electricity is transmitted across regional boundaries.

In Table 2, it is possible to compare the data in two or more columns. Thus a comparison of electricity output per inhabitant (column I) with number of persons engaged in industry per 1,000 inhabitants (column R), suggests that, as would be expected, the more highly industrialized regions (*employment* in manufacturing being the criterion here) tend also to have a large consumption of electricity per inhabitant. Compare 3,100 (output of electricity *per caput*) and 146 (persons employed in manufacturing per thousand of the total population) for region 11 (Donets–Dnepr) with only

300 and 43·2 for region 19 (Moldavia). A correlation between the two variables can be detected visually, the assumption being that if electricity output and manufacturing were *not* connected, there would be no reason to expect a region with high figures in one column to have high figures in the other. A comparison, for example, of milk production (column G) and electricity production (in *per caput* terms) does not suggest any correlation (nor can one immediately think of a reason why there should be one). On the other hand, a comparison of urbanization (column D, urban dwellers as percentage of total population in each region) with electricity output again suggests a positive correlation.

It is legitimate to compare the *per caput* and other data in Table 2 for the different variables unless one is dependent on another. But it is more convenient, if only a rough assessment is desired as a preliminary probe before further investigation, simply to rank the nineteen regions according to their indices. This is done in Table 3 for the data in Tables 1 and 2, and for additional data. Lack of space in Tables 1 and 2 made it impossible to present all the original data for the rankings in Table 3, but the sources are noted in Appendix 3. Certain interesting data available only for 1961 have been included. As there have been some changes in the regions between 1961 and 1963, very precise comparisons are not therefore possible between some of the columns.

It is easier to compare the columns of data in Table 3 than those in 2 now that they have been simplified and ranked 1 to 19. A comparison of electricity output and employment in manufacturing, both ranked high to low (1 being the highest, 19 the lowest) shows that where one has a high ranking the other tends to do so (compare North-west, rankings 6 and 1; Centre, rankings 8 and 2; Volga–Vyatka, rankings 10 and 5; C. Blackearth, rankings 15 and 14, and so on). Obviously, if there were complete agreement in ranking, then the pairs of numbers for the two columns would match throughout. On the other hand, if the numbers 1 to 19 were drawn randomly (say by counters taken in turn out of a hat) and as they came out, placed alongside the electricity ranking figures, there would be near agreement in some cases but little agreement in others, while no correlation would be expected in total.

The numbers 1 to 19 can be arranged in two columns side by side to give complete agreement (a complete positive correlation) or complete disagreement (1 against 19, 2 against 18, and so on) only in one way each (positive and negative). If drawn randomly they could arrange themselves in very many possible different ways. The probability that they would arrange themselves by chance in the same order in both columns is in this case (with nineteen regions) only one time out of nineteen factorial times. Nineteen factorial – 19 (!) in brief – which is $19 \times 18 \times 17 \ldots \times 1$, is about 120×10^{15}. What is more important, the probability that the electricity and manufacturing figures would agree even to the extent that they do is very small, though not as remote by any means as 1 in 120×10^{15} times.

Space does not allow a fuller consideration of the statistical background to the kind of correlation envisaged here. By using a fairly simple formula[1] it is possible to work out an index of correlation (agreement) between the numbers in any pair of columns in Table 3. Strictly speaking this should be done by following the procedure of testing a hypothesis (for example, that there is or is not some relationship between the distribution of cropland and rainfall in the U.S.S.R.). Instead of finding the degree of correlation between a particular pair of variables, however, it is possible to find the degree of correlation between every pair, thus achieving what might be called a blanket correlation. This is laborious manually but can be done quickly with the help of an electronic computer, and has been done with the twenty-five variables and nineteen regions of the U.S.S.R. in Table 3. The results are displayed in the matrix (Table 4) in an abbreviated form on account of lack of space. For clarity, the variables have been numbered 1 to 25. These numbers represent the letters (or pairs of letters) used in Tables 1 to 3, and the conversion from letter to number is shown along the top of the matrix in Table 4. The numbers 1 to 25 both along the top of the matrix and down the side refer to the variables, not to the regions. Each index of correlation can

1. The formula, Spearman Rank Correlation Coefficient is: $r = 1 - \dfrac{6\Sigma \mathrm{d}^2}{n^3 - n}$; r is the correlation coefficient, n is the number of things ranked (in this case nineteen regions) and d is the difference in ranking between each pair of numbers in the columns. Σ (the sum of) means here 'sum (add) all the d^2'. This method of working out correlations has been used here because it is more easy to understand than the more precise product – moment method, which takes into account intervals between values, not just ranking.

fall somewhere between + 1·00 and − 1·00, which represent respectively complete agreement (complete positive correlation) and complete disagreement (complete negative correlation). In this table the 0 preceding the decimal point and the point itself have been omitted and the correlation is positive unless in italics, when it is negative. Thus a correlation of 0·691 would be written 69 in the matrix, one of − 0·632 would be *63*.

The degree of correlation increases from 0 to + 1 or to − 1, but since low correlation coefficients can be achieved when the numbers 1 to 19 (or any other range) are placed side by side in a random order, confidence levels are needed. In this case (with nineteen regions) the 95 per cent confidence level is about ± 0·4 and the 99 per cent confidence level is about ± 0·56. These mean that the probability of getting an index so far from 0 is only $\frac{1}{20}$ and $\frac{1}{100}$ respectively. In Table 4 only correlation coefficients further from 0 than ± 0·5 have been shown. If filled in completely there would be 25 × 25 indices. The correlation indices shown are strong enough to suggest that there is some connexion in area between the variables concerned. Note that the lower left half of the matrix would be a mirror image of the upper right half actually shown.

The data in Table 4 may be interpreted and used further in various ways. Here they are presented to bear out in a more precise way some of the conclusions drawn in the text about spatial relationships, and to point towards possible further lines of investigation. The matrix may be used as follows: to find, for example, the coefficient of correlation between electricity production (variable 17) and employment in industry (variable 20) find where row 17 and column 20 intersect. The figure 73 means that there is a correlation of + 0·73 (to two places of decimals), a fairly high correlation given that n (the number of regions) = 19. The very or fairly strong correlation between urbanization (variable 4) and electricity (17, 18), manufacturing (20), doctors (22) and higher educational establishments (23) is gratifying because it bears out what one suspected. The correlation between proportion of Russians (variable 7) and investment *per caput* during 1959–63 (16) gives food for thought. The correlation between population growth 1939–64 and increasing distance from Moscow (variables 5 and 24) is stronger than that between population growth 1959–64 and increasing distance from Moscow (6 and 24) suggesting a slackening in recent years of the eastward movement of population, a trend obviously worth closer investigation. Even the absence of correlation or a low index of correlation (such low indices are now shown in the matrix) may be of interest.

The reader is invited to look more closely at Tables 3 and 4. In doing so he should bear in mind several points. Firstly, a strong correlation of course arises by chance from time to time. Secondly, a correlation between two distributions not obviously connected may be revealed in the matrix. There may in fact be an indirect connexion between them. Thirdly, the correlation indices are true only for the U.S.S.R. as a whole, not for any part of it, and would differ somewhat even for the U.S.S.R. as a whole if different compartments had been used to collect the data. In conclusion, it must be pointed out that this blanket correlation is regarded by some statisticians with a little apprehension, since some of the rules of the game, as it were, are overlooked. In spite of this, in the view of the author such correlation indices are an improvement on the intuitive correlations proposed by geographers from a visual study of distributions, especially when, with the help of further techniques, the multiple relationship of several or many variables is assessed.

II. REGIONAL SHAREOUT OF PRODUCTION

The absolute figures for the nineteen regions, presented in Table 1, can be modified in another way to give a general idea of the extent to which the regions of the U.S.S.R. are deficient in or have surpluses of different items. The first step is to convert the absolute figures for each region in Table 1 to percentages of the national total. This has been done in Table 5, but the conversion has been expressed in per *mil* terms (i.e. the Soviet total = 1,000 units in each case) rather than in per *cent* terms, in order to give a reasonable degree of precision without introducing a decimal point. It is therefore possible in Table 5 to see at a glance what proportion of the national total each region has (looking down columns) and also, by looking along the rows, to see in which ways each region is strong and weak. Looking across row 1 (the North-west) it can be seen that this region is strong in timber production, having 247 per *mil* (or 24·7 per cent) of the national total. In contrast, the North-west is obviously weak in grain production, with only 9 per *mil* of the national total.

By taking a further step, it is possible to obtain an even more striking view of the balance or lack of balance in the various regions. If each region were balanced and self-sufficient, then each should have roughly as much of the national total of every item as it does of population. For example the North-west (row 1), with 51 per *mil* of the total population, should have an index near 51 in every other column. Clearly it does not. Its share of national meat production is only about half its share of population. Its electricity output is about the same as population. An index can be obtained giving an idea of the position, favourable or otherwise, of each region in relation to each item. The procedure is to measure the share of population against the share of each other item in turn. The calculation is worked out thus:

$$\frac{\text{per } mil \text{ of a particular item}}{\text{per } mil \text{ of population}} \times 100$$

The ratio of one to the other is multiplied by 100 to eliminate decimal points. The results are shown in Table 6. To illustrate the procedure in a particular instance, the grain index for the Centre (row 2) is:

$$\frac{55 \text{ (per } mil \text{ for grain)}}{115 \text{ (per } mil \text{ for population)}} \times 100 = 48$$

In Table 6, therefore, if a region has an index of 100 in any column other than population, it has or produces as much, in *per caput* terms, as the U.S.S.R. as a whole. In other words, Table 6 shows a *per caput* index, like Table 2, but in a way that makes comparison easier. The fact, however, that the index for a particular item in a given region exceeds 100 does not necessarily mean that this region has a surplus that goes to other regions. On the other hand, if its index is considerably above 100, then there is good reason to assume some surplus. In the North-west, for example, the index of 485 (timber) suggests a large surplus, while by the same line of argument, an index of 18 (grain) suggests a considerable deficit. Thus the data in this table can be used to supplement the incomplete information available in Soviet publications about the inter-regional movement of goods in the country.

Table 6 is also of interest in other ways, two of which are outlined here. Firstly, if all or most of the indices for a region are some way below 100, then it would appear to be generally deficient. Of course the items in which it is deficient should be examined one by one. From Table 6 it is obvious that both Belorussia (18) and Moldavia (19) are generally deficient. In contrast, West Siberia (8) has consistently high indices. Secondly, if the indices of a region fluctuate violently about 100, then the region is clearly badly balanced, with both large surpluses and large deficits. This occurs in Kazakhstan (17).

If more complete data were available it would be possible to sum the indices for each region (along the rows) and find the mean index for them all. This would be a way of arriving at an assessment of regional income expressed in *per caput* terms. This further step is not advisable with the figures in Table 6 because some are duplicated (e.g. electricity is a sub-set of all energy) while others (e.g. engineering) are not represented, and non-goods activities are not taken into account at all. A more complete picture of the regional shareout of productive activities could be compiled if a wide range of Soviet sources were combed for data, but there would still be figures lacking. The tables in this section therefore do no more than suggest what could be done.

III. SUMMARY

Figures 57 and 58 attempt to summarize concisely the main spatial problems facing Soviet planners. The compartments (regions) into which the country has been divided in Figure 57 do not of course end abruptly at the lines shown. There is usually a considerable area of transition. The U.S.S.R. has been divided first into 'empty' and 'occupied' parts. The empty part covers well over half of the total area of the country but has only a few million people. The occupied part varies greatly in density of population from one part to another, the western area being on the whole more densely populated.

Under present technological conditions empty U.S.S.R. offers little possibility for agriculture. On the other hand it contains great

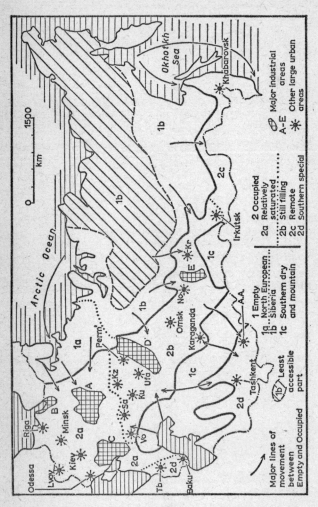

57. Summary map of the U.S.S.R.

Arctic Ocean

Okhotkh Sea

1500
0 km

Odessa
Lvov
Riga
Kiev
Minsk
2a
B
A
1a
Perm'
Kz
Sa
Ku Ufa
Vo
M
C
2a
Tb
Baku
2d
Omsk
2b
D
1b
No
E
Kr
1c
Karaganda
1c
A.A.
Tashkent
2d
Irkutsk
2c
1b
Khabarovsk

1 Empty
1a. North European
1b. Siberia
1c. Southern dry and mountain

2 Occupied
2a Relatively saturated
2b Still filling
2c Remote
2d Southern special

Major industrial areas
A-E
Other large urban areas

1b Least accessible part

Major lines of movement between Empty and Occupied

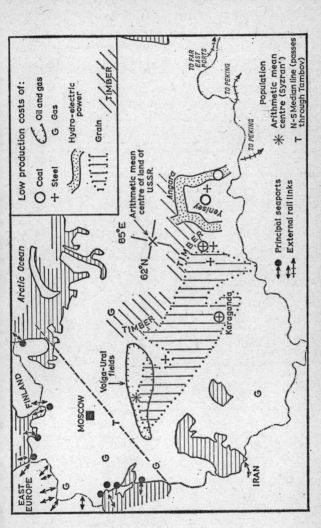

Low production costs of:

○ Coal   ☁ Oil and gas

+ Steel   G Gas

Hydro-electric power

Grain

TIMBER

Arithmetic mean centre of land of U.S.S.R.

85°E

62°N

Angara

Yenisey

Arithmetic mean centre (Syzran')

Population

N-S Median line (passes through Tambov)

● Principal seaports

External rail links

TO FAIR EAST PORTS

TO PEKING

TO PEKING

Arctic Ocean

FINLAND

EAST EUROPE

MOSCOW

Volga-Ural fields

TIMBER

TIMBER

Karaganda

G

G

G

G

IRAN

58. Summary map of the U.S.S.R. – western part.

reserves of minerals and timber. There is little manufacturing since population is nowhere large enough to generate large local markets. Without these, to offset the disadvantages of remoteness, new factories established to serve all or a large part of the national market would be unfavourably located. Much of the population is engaged in processing activities. The more remote part of region 1b can more easily send its minerals and timber to places in Asiatic U.S.S.R. In contrast to 1a and 1b, region 1c is mainly situated *between* two occupied areas, not on the periphery of one, but it sends the minerals it produces and processes mainly to region 2b rather than to region 2d. The general direction of movement of these is indicated by arrows on the map.

Occupied U.S.S.R. has been divided into four areas, two of which contain major industrial concentrations and all of which contain towns or clusters of towns large enough (with over about half a million people) to generate industrial growth. The five major industrial regions suggested (A–E on Figure 57) are:

A	Moscow and associated centres	D	Ural
B	Leningrad area	E	Kuzbass
C	Donets–Dnepr		

The four subdivisions of the occupied part of the U.S.S.R. (2a–2d) contrast in various ways. 2a contains major industrial concentrations as well as some good farmland, but production costs in manufacturing tend to be high, resources for industry are lacking, and much of the land is only of moderate quality and is farmed badly. 2b has a larger amount of farmland per inhabitant than 2a, though much of it is marginal in character. It has greater resources and lower production costs in industry. 2c is not without resources, but its remoteness has been a drawback. 2d lacks agricultural land, but the quality of its irrigated land is good. Industrial development is still limited in region 2d in general but energy and mineral resources are good in the part to the east of the Caspian.

While all the regions have their problems, Soviet planners are inevitably most concerned about regions 2a and 2b since these contain about four fifths of the total population of the country. Basically, the problem is to decide whether to try to move many people from region 2a into 2b (and later into 2c and 1b), or to move the resources, in processed or finished form, into 2a (and eventually even farther west to the COMECON partners in Central Europe). To move the bulk of the population east into 2b and beyond would be a major long-term operation. It would cut the U.S.S.R. off even more from access to the seas, and hence to other parts of the world by cheap sea transport. To move the resources westwards requires greatly improved transport facilities. The new pipeline system, the electrification of railways and the proposed all-Union electricity grid may be seen as means of making the necessary improvements. A compromise is of course possible. At all events, it can be said conclusively that in the mid 1960s most of the population of the Soviet Union is not where the resources are.

	A	B*	C	D*	E†	F†	G†	H†	I†	J†	K†	L†
	Area	Population (thousands)	Density of population	Urban population (thousands)	Sown land	Meat	Milk	Timber	Electricity	Cement	Cotton Textiles	Doctors (thousands)
1 North-west	1,663	11,519	7	8,139	31	270	2,653	90·8	21·7	3,256	222	38·4
2 Central	485	26,407	54	17,383	145	848	6,569	31·1	37·4	6,114	4,906	80·0
3 Volga–Vyatka	263	8,292	32	3,841	76	314	2,342	32·5	10·9	961	111	13·8
4 C. Blackearth	168	7,982	48	2,602	112	576	3,198	1·1	6·6	2,543	5	12·1
5 Volga	680	17,324	25	8,839	290	929	5,209	12·1	47·9	7,024	110	35·8
6 N. Caucasus	355	13,018	39	6,083	162	773	3,537	4·3	13·4	2,874	32	29·0
7 Ural	2,116	16,309	8	10,533	193	663	4,238	68·8	66·4	7,556	15	29·7
8 W. Siberia	992	10,822	11	6,247	186	645	3,921	20·9	31·8	3,186	147	20·4
9 E. Siberia	4,123	7,084	2	4,066	82	308	1,700	53·4	30·5	2,250	81	12·5
10 Far East	6,216	5,278	1	3,780	25	144	917	22·9	7·4	1,692	9	13·2
11 Donets–Dnepr	221	19,082	87	12,915	145	906	4,955	0·8	59·0‡	6,570	16	42·3
12 South-west	269	19,960	63	6,615	131	1,154	6,352	10·2	13·0‡	3,449	39	41·0
13 South	111	5,594	50	2,965	68	357	1,905	0·0	6·5‡	269	98	17·3
14 Baltic	189	7,049	37	3,806	51	498	4,237	9·3	8·7	1,978	196	17·7
15 Transcaucasia	186	10,866	58	5,328	25	219	1,241	1·3	16·1	2,840	261	30·2
16 C. Asia	1,279	16,459	13	6,106	58	352	1,646	0·2	12·4	3,321	341	26·9
17 Kazakhstan	2,715	11,511	4	5,313	326	665	2,834	1·9	14·9	3,425	20	18·9
18 Belorussia	208	8,455	41	3,146	60	430	3,210	7·5	5·5	1,266	7	16·3
19 Moldavia	34	3,242	97	819	19	144	584	0·2	1·0	445	2	5·3
U.S.S.R.	22,402	226,253	10	118,531	2,185	10,195	61,248	369·6	412·4	61,018	6,619	·005

MEASURES

A Thousands of sq. km.   E Thousands of sq. km.   H *Drevesina* in millions of cubic metres   J Thousands of tons   SOURCES:

C Persons per sq. km.   F, G Thousands of tons.   I Thousands of millions of kwh.   K Millions of metres   see Appendix 3.

*Population at January 1964   †Figures for 1963.

‡Based on 1963 total for whole of Ukraine, assuming that the same proportion contributed by each area in 1963 as in 1961.

TABLE 2. Selected *per caput* and per unit of area data. Letters in this table refer also to Table 1

		A	D	M	E	N	F	G	O	P	I	Q	J	L	R	S
		Area	Urban population	Population change 1939–64	Sown area / total area	Sown area / population	Meat	Milk	Kolkhoz income	Investment	Electricity	Electricity consumed in industry	Cement	Doctors	Persons employed in industry	Higher education
1	North-west	144	71	103	2	27	23	230	863	900	1,890	63·7	282	334	180·5	200
2	Centre	18	66	99	30	55	32	250	784	780	1,420	65·4	232	306	174	238
3	Volga-Vyatka	32	46	95	29	92	38	280	598	490	1,320	69·4	116	167	127·5	141
4	C. Blackearth	21	33	87	67	140	72	400	848	430	830	59·6	318	152	70·5	69
5	Volga	39	51	112	43	167	54	301	1,187	760	2,770	67·9	405	207	81·5	95
6	N. Caucasus	27	47	126	46	124	60	272	1,548	570	1,030	57·0	221	223	115	121
7	Ural	129	65	144	9	118	41	260	1,148	780	4,070	83·0	464	182	139	86
8	W. Siberia	92	58	136	19	172	60	364	1,078	870	2,940	73·9	294	189	113·4	118
9	E. Siberia	581	57	164	2	105	43	240	1,637	1,080	4,300	61·4	318	177	116	91
10	Far East	1,180	72	177	0·4	47	27	174	2,098	1,210	1,400	56·6	321	250	122	109
11	Donets–Dnepr	12	68	120	66	76	47	259	1,098	740	3,100	80·4	344	222	146	117
12	South-west	13	33	101	49	66	58	319	660	330	650	48·7	173	206	63·5	90
13	South	20	53	115	61	122	64	341	1,437	650	1,170	48·9	48	310	81	134
14	Baltic	27	54	121	27	68	71	600	989	590	1,230	59·1	281	251	111	112
15	Transcaucasia	17	49	135	13	23	20	114	582	470	1,480	70·6	261	278	65	117
16	C. Asia	78	37	155	4·5	35	21	100	1,792	410	760	52·7	202	164	43·6	111
17	Kazakhstan	236	46	192	12	283	58	420	1,835	940	1,290	47·6	298	165	56	79
18	Belorussia	25	37	95	29	71	51	380	620	410	650	53·4	150	193	72	79
19	Moldavia	10	25	132	56	59	44	180	925	300	300	37·0	137	164	43·2	71
	U.S.S.R.	99	52	119	10	96	45	270	995	670	1,820	67·2	270	222	105	118

KEY TO TABLE ABOVE

A Sq. km. per 1,000 inhabitants

D Urban population as a percentage of total population in 1964

M Population change 1939–64; 1939=100, 1964 expressed as percentage of this

E Sown area as a percentage of total land area in 1963

N Hectares of sown area per 100 inhabitants in 1963

F Meat production in kg. per inhabitant in 1963

G Milk production in kg. per inhabitant in 1963

O Collective farm income in roubles per collective farm family in 1963

P Investment in roubles per inhabitant during 1959–63

I Output of electricity in kwh. per inhabitant in 1963

Q Percentage of total electricity production consumed in industry in 1963

J Output of cement in kg. per inhabitant in 1963

L Doctors per 100,000 inhabitants in 1963

R Persons employed in industry per 1,000 inhabitants in 1961

S Students receiving higher education per 10,000 inhabitants in 1961

TABLE 3. Data ranked

	area	Population 1964	Area/Population	Urban 1964	Population change 1939-64	Population change 1959-64	Percentage Russians 1959	Temperature	Precipitation	Percentage forest 1961*	Growth of sown area 1961*	Sown area/population 1963	Meat 1963	Milk 1963	Kolkhoz incomes 1963	Investment 1959-63	Electricity production 1963	Percentage of electricity consumed in industry 1962	Industrial growth-rate 1958-63*	Employment in manufacturing 1961*	Cement 1963	Doctors 1963	Higher education 1961*	Distance from Moscow	Distance from centre of area
	A	B	C	D	M	T	U	V	W	X	Y	N	F	G	Z	P	I	AA	BB	R	J	L	S	CC	DD
1 North-west	5	8	4	2	14	4	4	13	12	2	18	18	16	14	13	4	6	8	18	2	9	1	2	4	6
2 Centre	9	1	15	4	18	1	1	12	7	5	15	15	15	12	15	6	8	7	19	1	12	3	1	1	9
3 Volga-Vyatka	12	13	9	13	19	2	3	15	8	3	13	13	9	9	18	13	10	5	15	5	18	15	3	2	5
4 C. Blackearth	17	14	13	18	17	3	2	9	11	14	4	4	14	8	14	10	5	10	1	14	6	19	19	3	11
5 Volga	8	4	8	10	9	6	6	7	16	12	6	3	8	10	5	8	14	6	9	8	13	5	12	6	8
6 N. Caucasus	10	7	11	12	5	10	10	17	6	13	3	5	10	17	12	5	4	12	12.5	11	7	9	5	12	12
7 Ural	4	6	5	5	13	8	8	16	13	7	5	2	13	5	8	12	2	4	9	4	3	8	15	13	3
8 W. Siberia	7	11	6	6	11	9	9	18	15	1	2	8	5	13	10	2	1	9	12.5	7	8	12	6	18	1
9 E. Siberia	2	15	2	3	5	7	7	19	17	6	8	2	12	16	4	1	9	13	10	6	5	14	13	16	2
10 Far East	1	18	1	7	7	7	7	18	10	4	16	8	17	11	2	9	3	16	5.5	9	4	6	11	19	10
11 Donets-Dnepr	13	2	18	1	10	12	12	8	2	17	12	6	7	6	1	11	17	15	8	16	15	10	8	9	13
12 South-west	11	17	2	17	16	18	18	8	5	16	13	9	3	7	9	18	13	12	12.5	12	19	14	8	7	17
13 South	18	10	17	9	12	15	15	5	14	19	15	10	6	7	6	10	16	11	5.5	10	10	4	10	8	17
14 Baltic	15	16	10	11	3	13	13	11	5	10	9	12	1	18	11	14	7	4	16	15	14	7	9	14	18
15 Transcaucasia	16	5	16	15	16	16	16	2	2	17	10	17	19	19	19	17	16	15	16	18	14	16	7	16	14
16 C. Asia	6	10	7	7	4	14	14	1	3	18	17	11	18	19	1	4	15	18	2	17	7	17	11	5	16
17 Kazakhstan	3	5	3	15	2	11	11	14	18	1	1	1	9	2	17	3	16	14	3.5	18	16	10	17	4	7
18 Belorussia	14	12	12	16	15	17	17	10	18	8	14	14	11	4	12	11	18	19	2	13	17	16	16	11	15
19 Moldavia	19	19	19	8	6	4	19	9	4	15	19	12	13	15	16	16	17	19	19	19	17	18	18	19	19
Number of variable†	1	2	3	4	5	6	7	8	9	10	11	12	13	14	15	16	17	18	19	20	21	22	23	24	25

* Data for somewhat earlier period; sizes ...

Table 4 Correlation matrix

Column key:

Code	No.	Variable
A	1	Area
B	2	Population
C	3	Density
D	4	Percentage urban
M	5	Population increase 1939–64
T	6	Population increase 1959–64
U	7	Percentage Russians
V	8	Temperature
W	9	Precipitation
X	10	Forest
Y	11	Growth of sown area 1913–61
N	12	Sown area/population
F	13	Meat
G	14	Milk
Z	15	Kolkhoz Incomes
P	16	Investment
I	17	Electricity production
AA	18	Percentage of electricity used in industry
BB	19	Industrial growth-rate
R	20	Employment in manufacturing
J	21	Cement
L	22	Doctors
S	23	Higher education
CC	24	Distance from Moscow
DD	25	Distance from centre of area

Correlation matrix:

	1	2	3	4	5	6	7	8	9	10	11	12	13	14	15	16	17	18	19	20	21	22	23	24	25
1		85	50	55				62			70				58	73	52				55			50	78
2																									
3				50				68			72				58										79
4																80	78	57		84	53	62	58		
5						76					55				72									93	
6							50		51						62					52			71		
7								55								55	51	55		70					66
8										71	53					71	52			55					67
9													56												61
10																				62					
11												55			65	55					53			52	70
12													73	63					61						
13														85					60						
14																			58						
15																51								64	
16																		75	63	62					65
17																		80		73	71				64
18																				70	52				
19																							59		
20																							59		
21																									51
22																							66		
23																									
24																									
25																									

TABLE 5. Regional data per *mil* of national total

		A	B	D	E	EE	F	G	H	FF	I	GG	J	HH	L	P	T
		Area	Population	Urban population	Sown land	Grain	Meat	Milk	Timber	Energy	Electricity	Steel	Cement	Cotton textiles	Doctors	Investment	Population growth
1	North-west	75	51	69	14	9	27	43	247	60	52	56	53	33	76	67	10
2	Centre	22	115	147	66	55	83	107	85	30	91	27	100	743	160	136	− 2
3	Volga-Vyatka	12	37	32	35	37	31	38	88	8	27	11	16	17	28	27	− 12
4	C. Blackearth	8	36	22	51	42	57	52	2	1	16	11	42	20	24	23	− 33
5	Volga	30	77	75	133	146	91	85	32	271	117	22	115	16	71	87	52
6	N. Caucasus	16	58	51	74	73	76	58	11	72	33	16	47	5	58	49	75
7	Ural	95	72	89	88	102	65	69	187	59	162	318	124	2	59	85	141
8	W. Siberia	44	48	53	85	93	63	64	56	83	77	83	52	22	41	62	83
9	E. Siberia	185	31	34	38	45	30	28	145	20	74	6	37	12	25	51	65
10	Far East	279	23	32	11	8	14	15	61	17	18	4	28	1	26	42	64
11	Donets–Dnepr	10	85	109	66	55	89	81	2	209	144	407	108	2	84	93	88
12	South-west	12	88	56	60	49	113	104	27	32	32	0	57	6	82	44	8
13	South	5	25	25	31	27	35	31	0	1	16	0	4	15	35	24	20
14	Baltic	9	31	32	23	16	49	69	25	9	21	2	32	30	35	30	34
15	Transcaucasia	8	48	45	12	11	21	20	3	50	39	26	47	39	60	34	80
16	C. Asia	57	73	51	27	18	35	27	2	32	30	4	54	52	54	45	163
17	Kazakhstan	122	51	45	149	186	65	46	5	43	36	5	56	3	38	72	155
18	Belorussia	9	37	26	28	21	42	53	20	3	13	5	21	1	33	23	− 13
19	Moldavia	2	14	7	9	7	14	10	2	0	2	0	7	0	11	6	22

See under Tables 1 and 2 for further information about the variables.

L

TABLE 6. Localization indices. Derived from per *mil* figures in Table 5

	A	B	D	E	EE	F	G	H	FF	I	GG	J	HH	L	P	T
	Area	Population	Urban	Sown	Grain	Meat	Milk	Timber	Energy	Electricity	Steel	Cement	Cotton textiles	Doctors	Investment	Population growth
1 North-west	147	100	135	27	18	53	84	485	118	102	110	104	65	149	131	20
2 Centre	19	100	128	57	48	72	93	74	26	79	23	87	645	130	118	—
3 Volga–Vyatka	32	100	86	95	100	84	103	238	22	73	30	43	46	76	73	—
4 C. Blackearth	22	100	61	141	117	158	144	6	3	44	31	117	3	67	64	68
5 Volga	39	100	97	173	190	118	110	42	352	152	29	149	21	92	113	129
6 N. Caucasus	28	100	88	127	126	131	100	19	124	57	28	81	9	100	85	196
7 Ural	132	100	124	122	142	90	96	260	82	225	442	172	3	82	118	173
8 W. Siberia	92	100	110	177	194	131	133	117	173	161	173	108	46	85	129	210
9 E. Siberia	597	100	110	123	145	97	90	468	65	238	194	120	39	81	165	278
10 Far East	1,213	100	139	48	35	61	65	27	74	78	17	122	4	113	183	104
11 Donets–Dnepr	12	100	128	78	65	105	95	2	246	169	479	127	2	99	109	9
12 South-west	14	100	64	68	56	128	118	31	36	36	0	65	7	93	48	80
13 South	20	100	100	124	108	140	124	0	4	64	0	16	60	140	96	110
14 Baltic	29	100	103	74	52	158	223	81	29	68	6	103	97	113	97	110
15 Transcaucasia	17	100	94	25	23	44	42	6	104	81	54	98	81	125	71	167
16 C. Asia	78	100	70	37	25	48	37	10	44	41	5	74	71	74	62	224
17 Kazakhstan	240	100	88	292	365	127	90	10	84	71	10	110	6	75	141	304
18 Belorussia	24	100	70	76	57	113	143	54	8	35	5	57	3	89	62	—
19 Moldavia	14	100	50	64	50	100	71	14	0	14	0	50	0	78	43	157
U.S.S.R.	100	100	100	100	100	100	100	100	100	100	100	100	100	100	100	100

APPENDIX 1

TRANSLITERATION[1]

Apart from certain well-known places (e.g. Caucasus for Kavkaz) and cumbersome names (e.g. Azerbaijan for Azerbaydzhanskaya S.S.R.), place-names have been transliterated from Russian using the following equivalents:

Russian letter	English version	Notes on pronunciation and transliteration
А а	A	As *ar* in *car*.
Б б	B	
В в	V	
Г г	G	
Д д	D	
Е е	YE	When initial letter in word, or following another vowel, hard sign or soft sign, as *Ye* in *Yes*. In all other cases, as *ay* in *say*.
Ё ё	E	Not differentiated from E in transliteration.
Ж ж	ZH	Almost as *s* in *pleasure*.
З з	Z	
И и	I	As *ee* in *fleet*.
Й й	Y	As *i* in *bit*.
К к	K	
Л л	L	
М м	M	
Н н	N	
О о	O	Almost as *ore* in *more*.
П п	P	
Р р	R	Always rolled in Russian.
С с	S	
Т т	T	
У у	U	As *oo* in *boot*.
Ф ф	F	
Х х	KH	As *ch* in Scottish *loch*.
Ц ц	TS	As *ts* in *bits*.
Ч ч	CH	As *ch* in *church*.
Ш ш	SH	As *sh* in *ash*.

1 Based on 'Notes on Transliteration' in *A Geography of the U.S.S.R.* by J. P. Cole and F. C. German, Butterworth, 1961.

Russian letter	English version	Notes on pronunciation and transliteration
Щ щ	SHCH	As *shch* in *Ashchurch*.
Ъ ъ	"	(hard sign). Not pronounced.
Ы ы	Y	No English sound resembles this. The sound may be approached by attempting to pronounce *ee* in *feet* and *oo* in *boot* simultaneously.
Ь ь	'	(soft sign). Not pronounced.
Э э	E	As *e* in *egg*.
Ю ю	YU	As *you* in *youth*.
Я я	YA	As *ya* in *yard*.

English equivalents have been used for:

1. Most of the fifteen Soviet Socialist Republics, e.g. Ukraine for Ukraina, Georgia for Gruzia.

2. The following well-known place-names:

English	*Russian*
Archangel	Arkhangel'sk
Caucasus	Kavkaz
Crimea	Krym
Gorky	Gor'kiy
Kiev	Kiyev
Lvov	L'vov
Moscow	Moskva
Siberia	Sibir'

Note: Central Asia should more precisely be translated Srednyaya Aziya (Middle Asia).

APPENDIX 2

SELECTED PLACE-NAMES WHICH HAVE BEEN CHANGED
SINCE THE SECOND WORLD WAR

From	To	Location
Akmolinsk	Tselinograd	Kazakhstan
Chkalov	Orenburg	Ural
Chistyakovo	Torez	Ukraine
Koenigsburg	Kaliningrad	R.S.F.S.R.
Memel	Klaypeda	Lithuania
Molotov	Perm'	Ural
Molotovsk	Severodvinsk	North-west
Osipenko	Berdyansk	Ukraine
Proskurov	Khmel'nitskiy	Ukraine
Shcherbakov	Rybinsk	Centre
Stalinabad	Dushanbe	Tadjikistan
Stalingrad	Volgograd	Volga
Stalino	Donetsk	Ukraine
Stalinogorsk	Novomoskovsk	Centre
Stalinsk	Novokuznetsk	West Siberia
Stavropol'	Tol'yatti	Volga
Voroshilov	Ussuriysk	Far East
Voroshilovgrad	Lugansk	Ukraine

APPENDIX 3

SOURCES OF DATA IN TABLES 1–6, CHAPTER 12

Source	Title
I	*Narodnoye khozyaystvo SSSR v 1963 godu*, Moscow, 1965.
II	*Narodnoye khozyaystvo RSFSR v 1963 godu*, Moscow, 1965.
III	*Narodnoye khozyaystvo SSSR v 1961 godu*, Moscow, 1962.
IV	*Narodnoye khozyaystvo SSSR v 1959 godu*, Moscow, 1960.
V	*Atlas sel'skogo khozyaystva SSSR*, Moscow, 1960.

TABLE 1

A: I, p. 12
B: I, p. 12
C: Derived from A, B
D: I, pp. 15–17, II, pp. 12–14

E: I, pp. 254–5
F: I, p. 315
G: I, p. 316
H: I, pp. 174–5

I: I, p. 158, II p. 114
J: I, p. 181
K: I, p. 190
L: I, p. 629

TABLE 2

A: I, p. 12
D: I, pp. 15–17
M: I, p. 12
E: I, pp. 254–5
N: I, pp. 254–5

F: I, p. 315
G: I, p. 316
O: I, p. 347
P: I, p. 448
I: I, p. 158

Q: I, p. 59
J: I, p. 181
L: I, p. 629
R: III, p. 133
S: III, p. 135

TABLES 3 and 4
As for Tables 1 and/or 2 except:

T: I, p. 12
U: IV, pp. 16–20, and other references
V: V
W: V

X: I, p. 175
Y: I, pp. 254–5
Z: I, p. 347
AA: I, p. 59

BB: I, p. 116, II, pp. 82–3
CC: Measured in atlas
DD: Measured in atlas

TABLES 5 and 6
As for Tables 1, 2 or 3 except:

EE: I, p. 256

FF, GG: Compiled from various data

HH: I, p. 190

APPENDIX 4

SELECTED SITES OF NEW DEVELOPMENTS IN THE U.S.S.R.
(See Figure 59)

Fe	iron ore	Mt	other metals
HEP	hydro-electricity	En	energy
Mf	manufacturing	V	other, various

Map a: Western U.S.S.R.

1	Bol'she–Tokmaksk	Fe	15 Salavat	En
2	Cherepovets	Mf	16 Sarbayskoye	Fe
3	Dashava	En	17 Severodvinsk	Mf
4	Gay	Mt	18 Shebelinka	En
5	Izobil'noye	En	19 Slantsy	En
6	Kachkanar	Fe	20 Sokolovskoye	Fe
7	Kirovabad	Mf	21 Starobin	V
8	Komev	HEP	22 Stavropol'	En
9	Kursk Magnetic Anomaly	Fe	23 Stavropol' (now Tol'yatti)	Mf
10	Lisakovskoye	Fe	24 Sumgait	Mf
11	Mozyr	Mf	25 Volgodonsk	V
12	Nevinnomyssk	Mf	26 Volzhskiy	Mf
13	Polotsk	En	27 Zhodino	Mf
14	Rudnyy	Mf		

Map b: Central U.S.S.R.

1	Abakan	V	19 Korshunovskoye	Fe
2	Abalakova	Mf	20 Krasnoyarsk	V
3	Achinsk	En	21 Maklakovo	Mf
4	Angarsk	En	22 Novokuznetsk (ZAPSIB)	Mf
5	Arkalyk	Mf	23 Pavlodar	Mt
6	Atasu	Fe	24 Rudnogorskoye	Fe
7	Baykal	Mf	25 Sayan	HEP
8	Berezovo	En	26 Semipalatinsk	Mf
9	Bratsk	HEP, V	27 Sotnik	Mf
10	Divnogorsk	HEP	28 Tashtagol'skoye	Fe
11	Dzhezkazgan	Mt	29 Tayshet	Mfq
12	Ekibastuz	En	30 Temirtau	Mf
13	Inya	Fe	31 Tselinograd	Mf
14	Itat	En		

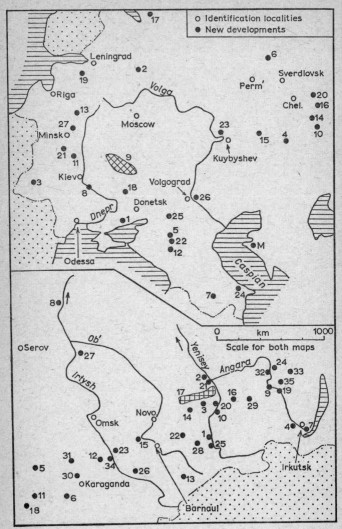

59. Names of selected places connected with recent economic developments.

SELECTED REFERENCES

I. WORKS IN ENGLISH

(a) General non-geographical

Crankshaw, E., *Khrushchev's Russia*, Penguin Books, 1959.

Nove, A., *The Soviet Economy*, Allen and Unwin, 1961.

Problems of Communism, bi-monthly periodical issued by the U.S. Information Agency, 1776 Pennsylvania Avenue N.W., Washington 25, D.C.

Sturley, D. M., *A Short History of Russia*, Longmans, 1964.

(b) General geographical

Cole, J. P., and German, F. C., *A Geography of the U.S.S.R.*, Butterworth, 1961.

Cressey, G. B., *Soviet Potentials. A Geographic Appraisal*, Syracuse U.P., 1962.

East, W. G., *The Soviet Union*, Princeton, Van Nostrand, 1963.

French, R. A., *U.S.S.R. and Eastern Europe*, Oxford University Press, 1965.

Hooson, D. J. M., *A New Soviet Heartland?*, Princeton, Van Nostrand, 1964.

Lydolph, P. E., *Geography of the U.S.S.R.*, Wiley, 1964.

Mellor, R. E. H., *Geography of the U.S.S.R.*, Macmillan, 1964.

Oxford Economic Atlas, the U.S.S.R. and Eastern Europe, Oxford University Press, 1956 and later editions.

(c) Comecon and East Europe

Kaser, M., *Comecon, Integration Problems of the Planned Economies*, Oxford University Press, 1965.

Ionescu, G., *The Break-up of the Soviet Empire in Eastern Europe*, Penguin Books, 1965.

Osborne, R. E. H., *East-Central Europe*, Chatto and Windus, to be published 1967.

(d) Selected journal references

Demko, G., 'Trends in Soviet Geography', *Survey*, No. 55, April 1965, pp. 163–70.

French, R. A., 'The Reclamation of Swamp in pre-Revolutionary Russia', *Transactions and Papers of the Institute of British Geographers*, 1964, Publication No. 34, pp. 175–88.

Hooson, D. J. M., 'The Middle Volga – an Emerging Focal Region in the Soviet Union', *Geographical Journal*, Vol. CXXVI, Part 2, June 1960, pp. 180–90.

Hooson, D. J. M., 'Methodological Clashes in Moscow', *Annals of the Association of American Geographers*, Vol. 52, No. 4, December 1962, pp. 469–75.

(e) *'Soviet Geography, Review and Translation'*

The non-Russian speaking reader who wishes to go more deeply into the geography of the U.S.S.R. is advised to locate and go through appropriate articles in *Soviet Geography, Review and Translation*, a monthly (except July and August) journal published by the American Geographical Society, Broadway at 156th Street, New York, N.Y., U.S.A. Each number of this journal contains several important papers by Soviet geographers, translated from Russian, as well as notes on new developments in the Soviet Union. The contents of each number are clearly displayed at the beginning. Below are some examples of papers from the journal on important or controversial topics discussed in this book.

Gerasimov, I. P., 'Natural resources of the Soviet Union, Their Study and Utilization' (October 1964).

Vendrov, S. L., and others, 'The Problem of Transformation and Utilization of the Water Resources of the Volga River and the Caspian Sea' (September 1964).

Pokshishevskiy, V. V., and others, 'On Basic Migration Patterns [in U.S.S.R.]' (December 1964).

Davidovich, V. G., 'Urban Agglomerations in the U.S.S.R.' (November 1964).

Yegorova, V. V., 'The Economic Effectiveness of the Construction of Pioneering Railroads in Newly Developed Areas' (April 1964).

Symposium on the Economic Geography of the U.S.S.R. Various papers on regionalization (November 1964).

Saushkin, Yu. G., and others, 'An Approach to the Economic-Geographic Modeling of Regional Territorial Production Complexes' (December 1964).

Probst, A. Ye., 'Calculation of the Economic Effect of Regional Productive Specialization' (February 1964).

Zhakov, S. O., 'The Long-term Transformation of Nature and Changes in the Atmospheric Moisture Supply of the European Part of the U.S.S.R.' (March 1964).

Budtolayev, N. M., and others, 'Problems of Economic Development of the West and East of the Soviet Union' (January 1964).

Blazhko, N. I., 'The System of Urban Places of the Donets Territorial–Production Complex' (February 1964).

Adamchuk, V. A., 'The Problem of Creating a Kazakhstan Metallurgical Base' (June 1964).

Feygin, L. Ya., 'Problems of Improving Inter-regional Productive Relationships of the Central Asian Economic Region' (June 1964).

Probst, A. Ye., 'Further Productive Specialization of the Central Asian Region' (June 1964).

Geller, S. Yu., and others, 'The Transformation of Nature and Development of the Natural Resources of Arid Areas' (September 1964).

Various papers on Siberia – transportation, water-management, dust storms (May 1964).

Sochava, V. B., 'Geographical Problems of Development of the Tayga [Northern Forest]' (September 1964).

Various papers on Socialist [= Communist] countries (January 1965).

The following are condensed references for 1960–63:

Physical and resources: May 1960 (climates of U.S.S.R.); January 1962 (surface water resources, transforming nature); December 1962 (water resources); May 1963 (Poles'ye).

Transportation: April 1960 (sea transport); June 1961 (rail); November 1961 (Volgobalt); September 1963 (general); November 1963 (C. Asia and N.E.U.S.S.R.).

Population: March 1962 (various articles on urban population); April 1962; January 1963 (migration).

Regionalization and planning: April 1963 (various); June 1960; April 1961 (models); October 1961; January 1962; November 1962; January 1963.

Agriculture: December 1960; February 1963 (physical and agriculture); May 1963 (virgin lands kray); November 1963 (various articles on organization).

Industry: March 1960 (engineering); November 1961 (steel in Kazakhstan); January 1962 (location); May 1963 (Kursk).

Major projects: September 1961 and January 1962 (Caspian Sea); May 1962; June 1963 (Arctic rivers diversion).

II. WORKS IN RUSSIAN

(a) *The following have been referred to frequently during the writing of this book*

Narodnoye khozyaystvo SSSR and *Narodnoye khozyaystvo RSFSR* (Statistical Yearbooks), particularly the volumes for 1961 and 1963.

Vedishchev, A. I., *Problemy razmeshcheniya proizvoditel'nykh sil SSSR*, Moscow, 1963.

Atlas SSSR, Glavnoye upravleniye geodezii i kartografii Ministerstva geologii i okhrany nedr SSSR, Moscow, 1962.

Pravda, daily newspaper, organ of the Central Committee of the Soviet Communist Party.

(b) *Other selected references*

Atlas sel'skogo khozyaystva SSSR, Moscow, 1960.

Lavrishchev, A. N., *Ekonomicheskaya geografiya SSSR*, Moscow, 1965.

Shuvalov, E. L., *Ekonomicheskaya geografiya SSSR*, Moscow, 1965.

'Ekonomicheskiye svyazi i transport', *Voprosy Geografii*, N.61, Geografgiz, Moscow, 1963.

Atlas tselinnogo kraya, Moscow, 1964.

Bol'shoy sovetskiy atlas mira, First volume, Part 2, Moscow, 1937.

Atlas istorii SSSR dlya sredney shkoly, in three parts, Moscow, various editions.

INDEX

Italics — reference in map or diagram
Bold print = important reference

APPLIED GEOGRAPHY

L. DUDLEY STAMP

Geography, literally 'writing about the earth', still means to far too many of us, influenced by school-day memories, the wearisome descriptions of countries in which lists of capes, bays, mountains, rivers, towns, and products play a major part. But its real interest is to describe and reflect the complex, underlying causes – the physical build and the natural resources, the sequence of human occupation and social organization – which have built the world we know, and will change and develop it in years to come. To know and understand these causes and their certain or probable effects is vital in all planning for the future, and this is the field of applied geography. In this book, a pioneer effort in its field, the principles of geographical survey and analysis are applied to the problems of Britain today.

THE FACE OF THE EARTH

G. H. DURY

The young natural science of geomorphology – the study of the form of the ground – is much less forbidding than its name. It is developing fast, and already promises to achieve some independence both of geology and of physical geography. In this book a professional geomorphologist tells how this field of knowledge is advancing, examines some of the hotly-disputed problems which have to be solved, and discusses the processes by which construction and erosion affect the physical landscape. Among the topics receiving attention are the weakening of rocks by weathering, their removal by the forces of erosion, the cyclic development of the land-surface, the evolution of river-systems, the effects of volcanic action and of glaciers, and the surface forms of deserts.

In choosing his examples, the author has been able to select freely from the results of his own field work. There are 102 diagrams in the text and 48 pages of plates.

A DICTIONARY OF GEOGRAPHY

W. G. MOORE

A Dictionary of Geography – now revised and enlarged – describes and explains such commonly met terms as the Trough of Low Pressure (from the weather forecast), a Mackerel Sky, a Tornado, the Spring Tides, and hundreds of others. But there are also sections on such stranger phenomena as the Willy-willy of Australia, the Doctor of West Africa, the Plum Rains of Japan, the Volcanic Bomb, the Anti-Trades, the Bad Lands, and the Celestial Equator.

Because Geography is largely a synthetic subject, the items of the Dictionary are derived from many sciences, including geology, meteorology, climatology, astronomy, physics, anthropology, biology. Even the most abstruse terms, however, are of the kind that the student is likely to meet in the course of his reading – terms which the author of geographical works employs but often has no space to define. The dictionary may thus help to clarify and systematize the reader's knowledge.

THE MAKING OF MODERN RUSSIA

LIONEL KOCHAN

'This is a history of Russia from the earliest times up to the outbreak of the Second World War. However, in keeping with his choice of title, Mr Kochan has concentrated on the modern period, devoting about as many pages to the eighty years following the Emancipation of the Serfs in 1861 as to the preceding 800-odd years. ... The result is a straightforward account of a complicated story. A successful balance has been held between such conflicting themes as foreign policy, foreign influences and native intellectual trends.

... His book could be a valuable introduction to the general reader in search of guidance ... a commendable book' – *Sunday Times*

'He handles his material with skill and sympathy. I cannot think of a better short book for acquainting the general reader with the broad outlines of Russian history. I hope many will read it' – Edward Crankshaw in the *Observer*

'Gives proper weight to economic, geographical, and cultural, as well as political and military factors, and which, while giving long-term trends their place, manages very often to convey a sense of real events happening to real people' – Wright Miller in the *Guardian*

'It reads easily, it is the ideal book for the general reader' – *The Economist*

THE GEOGRAPHY OF AFRICAN AFFAIRS

PAUL FORDHAM

The African continent, with its estimated population of 150 million inhabitants living south of the Sahara, measures over 5,000 miles from north to south, and is 2,000 miles wide at the level of the Congo river. Africa thus possesses the rare advantage of sufficient space for economic expansion and development. Technically, however, it lags far behind the rest of the world, owing largely to the physical environment and to the isolation of the individual nations.

In *The Geography of African Affairs* Paul Fordham has tried to 'select from the whole mass of geographical facts about Africa south of the Sahara such information as seems important for the understanding of current political problems.' His book, which includes a number of explanatory maps and tables, provides a clear general survey of Africa, its resources and problems' followed by detailed studies of each different region. The information it contains is essential to a proper understanding of a continent which has been attracting more and more interest in recent years.

Another Pelican by John Cole

GEOGRAPHY OF WORLD AFFAIRS

Day after day more and more places are mentioned in the newspapers, on the radio, and on television. It may be possible to follow world affairs and world problems without knowing anything about Queen Maud Land or Okinawa, Rwanda and Burundi or Surinam, but few people have more than a vague impression even of such important places as Formosa, Turkey, or Venezuela. The main purpose of this book is to help the reader who is not a specialist in geography to find his way about the world and to provide him with facts about the location, population, size, and activities of the more important countries in it. Most of the material in this book is geographical in nature, but many questions cannot be considered, even from a purely geographical viewpoint, without reference to history, politics and economics.